PROCEEDINGS OF THE TWELFTH SYMPOSIUM IN
APPLIED MATHEMATICS

Held in New York City
April 14–15, 1960

Sponsored by

AMERICAN MATHEMATICAL SOCIETY
ASSOCIATION FOR SYMBOLIC LOGIC
LINGUISTIC SOCIETY OF AMERICA

ROMAN JAKOBSON
Editor

PROCEEDINGS OF
SYMPOSIA IN APPLIED MATHEMATICS
VOLUME XII

STRUCTURE OF LANGUAGE

AND ITS

MATHEMATICAL ASPECTS

AMERICAN MATHEMATICAL SOCIETY

190 HOPE STREET, PROVIDENCE, RHODE ISLAND

1961

Second Printing, 1964

Cosponsored by
THE INSTITUTE FOR DEFENSE ANALYSES
under Contract Nonr 2631(00)
with the Office of Naval Research
and under Subcontract IDA 2631(00)-6

CONTENTS

INTRODUCTION

The Symposium on the Structure of Language and its Mathematical Aspects arose through the fortunate initiative of the American Mathematical Society which fully realized that the attention of linguists, logicians and mathematicians has become focused upon problems of mutual interest.

The need for an ever closer contact between linguistics and mathematics was clearly understood at the threshold of our century by the two great anticipators of the modern structural analysis of language—Baudouin de Courtenay, and Ferdinand de Saussure. As early as 1894, Saussure noted: "Les quantités du language et leurs rapports son régulièrement exprimables dans *leur nature fondamentale*, par des formules mathématiques," and somewhat later, discussing the problem of simplest expression for linguistic concepts, he stated: "L'expression simple sera algébrique ou elle ne sera pas." Finally, in 1911, while working on his last course in general linguistics, Saussured pointed out that this science appeared to him as a system of geometry: "On aboutit à des théorèmes qu'il faut démontrer."

Attacking, since the seventies, the crucial questions of the relation between continuity and discreteness in language, Baudouin de Courtenay attempted to utilize in the study of language some of the basic notions of contemporaneous mathematics, and in his historical survey of linguistics, published in 1909, he expressed his conviction that this scholarship would become ever closer to the exact sciences. Upon the model of mathematics it would on the one hand, deploy "ever more quantitative thought" and on the other, develop "new methods of deductive thought." In particular, "just as mathematics converts all the infinities to denumerable sets amenable to analytic thought," Baudouin expected somewhat similar results for linguistics "from improved qualitative analysis."

While Baudouin referred to the mathematical model for the analysis of language, at about the same time, before the 4th International Congress of Mathematicians in 1909, E. Borel discussed the antinomy of the denumerable infinities and appealed to the fundamental role of language in mathematical operations, "car les prétendus systèmes entièrement logiques reposent toujours sur le postulat de l'existence de la langue vulgaire; ce langage commun à des millions d'hommes, et avec lequel ils s'entendent à peu près entre eux, nous est donné comme un fait, qui impliquerait un grand nombre de cercles vicieux, s'il fallait le créer *ex nihilo*." The linguistic inference therefrom became Bloomfield's thesis according to which "mathematics is merely the best that *language* can do" (1933). If "mathematics, the ideal use of language," is a mere superstructure over the common language, the interrelation between this superstructure and its basis must be of primary interest for mathematicians and linguists alike.

Both the theoretician of language and the investigator of languages in their single stages or in evolution, equally as the workers in the rapidly developing branches of applied linguistics, are attracted by the manifold mathematical disciplines: mathematical logic, in particular, the theory of recursive functions and automata; the topological, algebraic and quantitative facets of mathematics; the theory of communication and probabilistic models. One cannot but agree with the mathematician J. Hadamard, who in 1943 acknowledged the progress of the structural trend in the science of language by declaring linguistics to be a bridge between mathematics and humanities.

Roman Jakobson

LOGIC AS A SOURCE OF SYNTACTICAL INSIGHTS

BY

W. V. QUINE

Mathematicians expedite their special business by deviating from ordinary language. Each such departure is prompted by specific considerations of utility for the mathematical venture afoot. Such reforms may be expected to reflect light on the ordinary language from which they depart, and the light reflected is all the brighter for the narrowly utilitarian character of the reforms. For in each case some special function which had hitherto been only incidentally and inconspiciously performed by a construction in ordinary language now stands boldly forth as the sole and express function of an artificial notation. As if by caricature, inconspicuous functions of common idioms are thus isolated and made conspicuous.

Thus consider the mathematician's use of parentheses to indicate grouping. Once this systematic device is in the forefront of our minds, we gain clearer insight into the purpose or survival value of certain related devices of ordinary language. We come to appreciate, for instance, that the pair of particles 'either-or' is not just a redundant elaboration of the simple 'or', but that the 'either' does the useful work of a left-hand parenthesis marking the beginning of the compound whose connective is 'or'. It is the 'either' that enables us verbally to resolve the ambiguity of 'p and q or r'. It enables us to draw the distinction between 'either p and q or r' and 'p and either q or r'—precisely the distinction which would be shown with parentheses as '(p and q) or r' versus 'p and (q or r)'. The analogous purpose is served by the particle 'both' in connection with 'and'; thus '(p or q) and r' and 'p or (q and r)' come out as 'both p or q and r' and 'p or both q and r'. This insight into the syntactical function of 'either' and 'both' could, of course, perfectly well have been vouchsafed us even if we had had no acquaintance with the method of parentheses; but they are likelier insights for the parenthesis-minded. Here, then, is a first crude instance of how the artificialities of mathematical notation may be expected to encourage syntactical insights into ordinary language.

For more persuasive examples, we do well to turn to mathematical logic. This branch of mathematics is especially rich in artifices that reflect light on the ordinary language from which they depart. My example of 'either-or' and 'both-and', indeed, was already drawn from logic; but there are also deeper examples to be drawn from that domain. Whereas most of the linguistic departures in mathematical developments other than logic have little to do with the very central devices of language, the departures in mathematical logic are as central as can be.

One distinction, obscure in ordinary English, that is brought into sharp relief by modern logical notation is the distinction of scopes of indefinite singular terms. Thus take the indefinite singular term 'every poem'. If I say 'I do not know every poem', am I to be construed as saying of every poem that I do not know it, or am I to be construed merely as denying the sentence 'I know every poem'? In the one case the scope of the indefinite singular term 'every poem' is the whole sentence 'I do not know every poem'. In the other case the scope is 'I know every poem', a subordinate sentence which the 'not' then denies.

Most of you are familiar with the modern logical notation which reduces indefinite singular terms and pronouns to so-called quantifiers and variables. It resolves questions of scope vividly and unambiguously. Ordinary language often resolves them too, but so unobtrusively that without benefit of the vivid rendering in modern logic one is unlikely to appreciate either the problem or the work which the locutions of ordinary language perform in resolving it. Once we have clearly appreciated the question of scope in the light of logical notation, we can return to ordinary language and see, as never before, what had been happening all along. What we find is an interplay of the apparent synonyms 'any' and 'every', as connoting wide and narrow scope respectively.

Let us return to our example. 'I do not know every poem' is definitely understood as confining the indefinite singular term 'every poem' to the narrower scope 'I know every poem', and then applying the 'not' to this subordinate sentence. The rule, implicit in usage but never brought to explicit attention until modern logic intervened, is that 'every' always calls for the narrowest available scope. 'Any' is subject to the contrary rule; it calls for the wider of two available scopes. Thus when we say 'I do not know any poem' the scope of the indefinite singular term 'any poem' is the whole sentence including the 'not'.

It is illuminating in this connection to compare 'I am ignorant of every poem'. This is equivalent, not to 'I do not know every poem', but to 'I do not know any poem', just because the scope is in this case the whole sentence, merely for lack of any shorter; the 'i-' of 'ignorant', unlike 'not', happens to be inseparable, so that the scope of 'every' in 'I am ignorant of every poem' has to be the whole sentence.

The contrast between 'any' and 'every', in point of scope, holds not only in connection with negatives but generally. Thus compare 'If John knows any poem, he knows 'The Raven'' and 'If John knows every poem, he knows 'The Raven''. The scope of 'any poem' is the whole conditional; the scope of 'every poem' is only the antecedent of the conditional. The one conditional says of each poem that if John knows it he knows 'The Raven'; the other conditional says only that John knows 'The Raven' if he knows them all.

We could have wondered alternately why English tolerates both of the apparent synonyms 'any' and 'every', and why they so often fail to be interchangeable. Chaos reduces to order once we gain a clear understanding of the scope of indefinite singular terms, through the regimented notation of mathematical logic. Retrospectively we appreciate that the difference in function between 'any' and 'every' is simply a matter of wide and narrow scope.

Questions of scope arise also apart from indefinite singular terms. Thus consider the phrase 'big European butterfly'; are we to take it as applying to all European butterflies that are big for European butterflies, or only to European butterflies that are big for butterflies? It is instructive to contrast with this example the formally similar one 'square black box', where the question of scope is irrelevant. The reason why the one example raises a question of scope and the other does not is that 'big' figures as a syncategorematic adjective, like 'poor' in 'poor sport' or 'mere' in 'mere child', while 'square' figures as a categorematic adjective. The keynote of the categorematic use is that a square so-and-so is simply anything that is square and a so-and-so; a mere child, in contrast, is not mere and a child, nor is a big butterfly simply big, absolutely, and a butterfly. This contrast is purely an affair of ordinary English, yet it is one that would have been less readily appreciated without the insights afforded by logical regimentation. In this case the notational departure of logic which may be expected to have fostered the relevant insight is a notation which resolves 'is a square so-and-so' into something like 'is square and is a so-and-so'; this susceptibility to resolution is what distinguishes the categorematic use of adjectives from the syncategorematic.

The resolution of linguistic compounds into their immediate constituents is another linguistic enterprise where modern logic can contribute occasional insights. Thus take 'the lady I saw you with'. Do we have here a singular term 'the lady' governed by a relative clause 'I saw you with', or do we have a general term 'lady I saw you with' governed by an article 'the'? The latter is definitely the preferable analysis, for it justifies the definiteness of the article by first incorporating all available determinants of uniqueness into the general term to which the article is applied. This insight would have been less likely without benefit of the theoretical study, in modern logic, of singular descriptions.

A modification of this example reveals, next, a curious anomaly. Let us paraphrase the example to read 'the lady such that I saw you with her'. By the preceding analysis, this phrase resolves into 'the' and a general term 'lady such that I saw you with her'. But then what, within this general term, is the grammatical antecedent of the final 'her'? Evidently 'lady'; and the anomaly is the occurrence of a general term as antecedent of a pronoun. What intuitively sustains the use of the whole construction, surely, is the feeling rather that 'her' refers back to the singular term 'the lady'; yet this way of dividing the construction violates our previous point, that the article 'the' should be taken to govern a maximum description in the interests of uniqueness. Let me leave this quandary unresolved, remarking merely that it owes its very existence to insights from the side of modern logic.

Another insight which logic encourages is that pronouns are best classed with definite singular terms such as 'Henry', 'the man', and the like, rather than with indefinite singular terms such as 'a man' or 'every man'. The pronoun 'he', indeed, is roughly interchangeable with 'the man'; not with 'a man'. To say 'I saw a man and you saw him', for instance, is by no means equivalent to saying 'I saw a man and you saw a man'; the one implies identity and the other does not. To say 'I saw a man and you saw him' is equivalent rather to saying 'I saw a man and you saw the man'. Note the subtle contrast: in the sentence 'I saw a man and you saw him' the grammatical antecedent of 'him' is 'a man' but the appropriate substitute for 'him' is 'the man'. Pronouns do not stand for their grammatical antecedents; they may have indefinite

singular terms as antecedents but they can be supplanted only by definite
singular terms. And such they are.

This point about pronouns is clear enough, once enunciated, without appeal
to subtleties of mathematical logic. Still, the regimented notation of logic is
what is likeliest to suggest the point, because of the striking way in which
that notation analyzes the work of pronouns and other singular terms, definite
and indefinite.

And logic enables us to drive the point further. What our example revealed
was only that the pronoun may have an indefinite singular term as antecedent,
and can be supplanted only by a definite singular term. But modern developments in logic enable us to say further that in principle the pronoun is
never needed with other than an indefinite singular term as antecedent, and
that definite singular terms other than pronouns are needed not at all. We
can systematically so paraphrase our sentences that the only definite singular
terms to survive are variables used pronominally in apposition with indefinite
singular terms, like the variable 'x' in 'Every region x contains a region
smaller than x'. Such a reduction theorem can be of linguistic interest as
affording a new perspective on the function of pronouns.

Let us next examine the basic role of pronouns according to this view. A
typical sentence whose pronouns have indefinite singular terms as antecedents
is this: 'Some whom none dislike do not appreciate themselves'. Now notice
that the pronouns here are simply combinatorial devices for abstracting complex general terms from sentential clauses. An alternative device that would
do the work of 'whom', in the complex general term 'whom some dislike', is
the passive participial ending: thus 'disliked'. Similarly the complex general
term 'whom none dislike' amounts to 'undisliked'. Again an alternative
device that would do the work of the pronoun 'themselves', in the complex
general term 'appreciate themselves', is the prefix 'self'-: thus 'self-appre-
ciators'. The whole sentence becomes 'There are undisliked non-self-appreciators'. No singular term remains, definite or indefinite, not even a pronoun.

The pronoun, in what may be viewed as its basic role, is thus seen as a
device similar in purpose to the passive endings and the reflexive prefix. Its
advantage over these latter lies merely in its flexibility, which spares us the
trouble of such painstaking constructions as 'undisliked non-self-appreciators'.

I have brought out this point in an ordinary verbal example. The point
comes, however, from mathematical logic, and it is there that the general
proof exists. It is there proved that variables, which are the pronouns of
logic, can in principle be dispensed with in favor of a few suitable chosen
operators comparable to our passive ending and reflexive prefix [1]. One way
of accomplishing this is due to Schönfinkel [2], whose ideas have been further
developed by Curry under the name of combinatory logic [3]. What may be
seen as a drawback of that particular approach is that it imports an excessively strong body of mathematical theory, tantamount to higher set theory;
but this is unnecessary. The half-dozen operators that I have in mind are,
unlike Schönfinkel's, definable at the level of the elementary logic of predicates
or quantifiers. And note finally that the point of them is not that they are
handier than variables or pronouns, but that they suffice, however clumsily,

to do the same job. To know this is to understand better than before just what the peculiar job of pronouns is.

REFERENCES

1. W. V. Quine, *Variables explained away*, Proc. Amer. Philos. Soc. vol. 104 (1960) pp. 343–347.

2. Moses Schönfinkel, *Ueber die Bausteine der mathematischen Logik*, Math. Ann. vol. 92 (1924) pp. 305–316.

3. H. B. Curry and Robert Feys, *Combinatory Logic*, vol. 1, Amsterdam, North-Holland Publishing Co., 1958.

HARVARD UNIVERSITY,
  CAMBRIDGE, MASSACHUSETTS

ON THE NOTION "RULE OF GRAMMAR"[1]

BY

NOAM CHOMSKY

1. General desiderata for grammatical theory. The traditional aim of a grammar is to specify the class of properly formed sentences and to assign to each what we may call a "structural description," that is, an account of the units of which the sentence is composed, the manner of their combination, the formal relations of the sentence to other sentences, and so on. If we hope to go beyond traditional grammar in some significant way, it is essential to give a precise formulation of the notion "structural description of a sentence," and a precise account of the manner in which structural descriptions are assigned to sentences by "grammatical rules." The rules contained in a traditional grammar are of widely diversified kinds, and there is no clear indication of what is to be the exact nature of a structural description. Modern linguistics has devoted a great deal of attention to clarifying the latter question, but has not considered with any seriousness the notion "grammatical rule." Inattention to the process by which structural descriptions are generated and assigned to sentences leaves a serious gap in linguistic theory, however, and leaves open to serious doubt particular decisions about the inventory of elements in actual descriptive studies, since clearly such choices should not be independent of the complexity of the system of rules by which the structural description of each sentence is specified. In any event, it seems that a really insightful formulation of linguistic theory will have to begin by a determination of the kinds of permitted grammatical rules, and an exact specification of their form and the manner in which they impose structural descriptions on each of an infinite set of grammatical sentences.

By a "grammar of the language L" I will mean a device of some sort (that is, a set of rules) that provides, at least, a complete specification of an infinite set of grammatical sentences of L and their structural descriptions. In addition to making precise the notion "structural description," the theory of grammar should meet requirements of the following kind. It should make available:

(1) (a) a class of possible grammars $G_1, G_2, \cdots$,

(b) a class of possible sentences $s_1, s_2, \cdots$,

(c) a function f such that $f(i,j)$ is the set of structural descriptions of the sentence s_i that are provided by the grammar G_j,

(d) a function $m(i)$ which evaluates G_i,

(e) a function g such that $g(i, n)$ is the description of a finite automaton that takes sentences of (b) as input and gives structural descriptions assigned to these sentences by G_i (i.e., various, perhaps all members of $f(i, j)$) as

[1] This work was supported in part by the U.S. Army (Signal Corps), the U.S. Air Force (Office of Scientific Research, Air Research and Development Command), and the U.S. Navy (Office of Naval Research). It was also supported in part by the National Science Foundation. I am indebted to Morris Halle for several important suggestions.

6

output, where n is a parameter determining the capacity of the automaton.

(a) is the requirement that the general theory of language must provide a schema and notation for grammatical description, a precise formulation of the notion "grammatical rule."

(b) can be met by incorporating a fixed phonetic alphabet, for example, Jakobson's theory of distinctive features, as a part of linguistic theory.

(c) simply asserts that it must be possible to determine what a grammar states about particular sentences without exercise of intuition. $f(i,j)$ should contain more than one structural description only if the sentence s_i is ambiguous—that is, this is a reasonable empirical condition, one of many, on the grammar of a language.

(d) amounts to a demand for justification of grammars. That is, m may be a measure of complexity that leads to choice among alternative proposed grammars that are compatible with given data.[2] It is quite evident that if there is to be any hope of meeting (c) and (d) in any significant manner, the specification in (a) and (b) of the available descriptive apparatus will have to be extremely narrow and limiting. To put it differently, only a fairly rigid and special set of assumptions about the nature of linguistic universals will make it possible to justify particular grammars in any general way.

(e) is a requirement of a different sort. A grammar, in the sense described above, is essentially a theory of the sentences of a language; it specifies this set (or generates it, to use a technical term which has become familiar in this connection)[3] and assigns to each generated sentence a structural description. It is not, however, a model of the speaker or hearer. It neither synthesizes particular sentences, as does the speaker, nor does it recognize the structure of presented sentences, as does the hearer. It is quite neutral as between speaker and hearer in this respect. (1e) would take us one step closer to a theory of the actual use of language. We can attempt to construct g in such a way that $g(i,n)$ will be a reasonable model for the production (or recognition) of sentences by the speaker (or hearer) who has internalized the grammar G_i and who has a memory capacity determined by the value of n. Notice that although the grammar G_i mastered by the user of a language is of course finite, it is not to be expected (and, in the case of natural languages, it is not in fact true) that a finite automaton can be constructed which will be able to accept (or generate) all and only the sentences generated by G_i, or which will be able to "understand" just these sentences (i.e., give the structural descriptions assigned to these sentences by G_i as outputs, when these sentences, but not others, are provided as inputs). This is no stranger than the fact that someone who has learned the rules of multiplication perfectly (perhaps without being able to state them) may be unable to calculate $3{,}872 \times 18{,}694$ in his head, although the rules that he has mastered uniquely

[2] For some discussion of the question of evaluation of grammars, see my *Syntactic structures*, The Hague, 1957, Chapter 6, and *A transformational approach to syntax*, Proceedings of the 1958 University of Texas Symposium on Syntax (to be published), §10; and Morris Halle, *On the role of simplicity in linguistic descriptions*, this volume.

[3] See, e.g., Post, *Recursively enumerable sets of positive integers and their decision problems*, Bull. Amer. Math. Soc. vol. 50 (1944) pp. 284–316.

determine the answer. We need only require of a reasonable procedure g that as n increases, the device $g(i, n)$ be capable of understanding, in the appropriate sense, more and more of the sentences generated by G_i (just as a reasonable model for the person who has learned arithmetic should have the property that as its memory aids and available time increase, more and more calculations should be correctly performed). It would be absurd to require of the grammars of (1a) that their output be the kinds of sets of strings, or sets of structural descriptions, that can be handled by strictly finite automata, just as it would be absurd to require (whether for the purposes of mathematical or psychological researches) that the rules of arithmetic be formulated so as to reflect precisely the ability of a human to perform calculations correctly in his head. Such a requirement would have neither theoretical nor practical motivation.

Among the rules of a grammar there are some that play a part in the generation of an infinite set of strings, each of which is an essentially orthographic representation of some grammatical sentence. These we will call "syntactic rules"; the final result of applying only these, we will call a "terminal string." Other rules, called "morphophonemic," convert a terminal string into the phonetic description of an utterance, i.e., into one of the s_i's of (1b). The morphophonemic component of the grammar I will not further discuss here.[4]

Part of the structural description of a terminal string t will be a bracketing of t into phrases categorized into particular types. Call this element of the structural description a Phrase-marker (P-marker) of t. A P-marker can be represented as a labelled tree with the symbol S (standing for "sentence") labelling the root, symbols of t labelling the endpoints, and phrase types (e.g., Noun Phrase (NP), Verb Phrase (VP), Noun (N), etc.) as labels of other nodes. In studying syntactic theory, we assume as a known empirical condition, a partial specification of P-markers of many sentences in many languages, and we ask how a linguistic theory of the type (1) above can be constructed so that given a corpus, grammars chosen by the evaluation procedure m will provide P-markers that meet the given empirical conditions of adequacy.

2. Constituent structure grammars.

A grammar is based on a certain vocabulary of symbols used for the representation of utterances and their parts, and including, in particular, the "a priori"[5] phonetic alphabet provided by linguistic theory in accordance with requirement (1b), above. Suppose that a grammar contains, in addition, a designated "initial" symbol S and a designated "boundary" symbol ‡. A particularly simple assumption about the form of grammars ((1a), above) would be that each rule be an instruction of the form "rewrite φ as ψ" (symbolically, $\varphi \rightarrow \psi$), where φ and ψ are strings of symbols. Given such a grammar, we say that σ' *follows from* σ if $\sigma = \cdots \varphi \cdots$ and $\sigma' = \cdots \psi \cdots$, (that is, if σ' results from substitution of ψ for a certain occurrence of φ in σ), where $\varphi \rightarrow \psi$ is a rule of the

[4] See Morris Halle, *Sound pattern of Russian*, The Hague, 1959, for a detailed study of the structure of this component of a grammar.

[5] From the standpoint of a particular grammar, that is.

grammar. We say that a sequence of strings $\sigma_1, \cdots, \sigma_n$ is a φ-*derivation* if $\varphi = \sigma_1$ and for each i, σ_{i+1} follows from σ_i. A φ-derivation is *terminated* if its final line contains no substring χ such that $\chi \rightarrow \omega$ is a rule. In particular, we will be interested in terminated $\#S\#$-derivations; that is, terminated derivations that begin with the string $\#S\#$.[6]

Suppose that each syntactic rule $\varphi \rightarrow \psi$ meets the additional condition that there is a single symbol A and a non-null string ω such that $\varphi = \chi_1 A \chi_2$ and $\psi = \chi_1 \omega \chi_2$. This rule thus asserts that A can be rewritten ω (i.e., ω is of type A) when in the context $\chi_1 - \chi_2$, where χ_1 or χ_2 may, of course, be null. A set of rules meeting this condition[7] I will call a *constituent structure grammar*. If in each rule $\varphi \rightarrow \psi$, φ is a single symbol, the grammar (and each rule) will be called *context-free*; otherwise, *context-restricted*.[8] In the case of a constituent structure grammar, it is a simple matter to construct the procedure f required by (1c), above, that specifies the P-markers of the terminal strings. It is also not difficult to give a fairly reasonable specification of m of condition (1d).[9]

For the remainder of this section we consider only context-free constituent structure grammars.

We say that φ *dominates* ψ ($\varphi \Rightarrow \psi$) if there is a derivation $\sigma_1, \cdots, \sigma_n$ such that $\sigma_1 = \varphi$ and $\sigma_n = \psi$ (i.e., if ψ is a step of a φ-derivation). In terms of "self-dominance," each non-terminal symbol A will be of one or more of four important types: (i) A is non-recursive if for no non-null φ, ψ is it the case

---

[6] For a more careful account of such systems, and a study of some of their properties, see my *On certain formal properties of grammars*, Information and Control vol. 2 (1959).

[7] And, in fact, certain others which must be added to guarantee uniqueness of the associated P-marker. These do not affect anything discussed here. We need not require that the morphophonemic rules meet these conditions, since structural description on this level does not involve subdivision into further phrases.

[8] Immediate constituent analysis as developed within linguistics, particularly in the form given to this theory by Z. S. Harris, *Methods in structural linguistics*, Chicago, 1951, Chapter 16, suggests a form of grammar close to what is here called "context-free constituent structure grammar." Another approach based on rather similar ideas originates in Leśniewski's theory of semantical categories, and has been modified for linguistic purposes recently by Bar-Hillel, *A quasi-arithmetical notation for syntactic description*, Language vol. 29 (1953) and Lambek, *The mathematics of sentence structure*, Amer. Math. Monthly vol. 65 (1958) and *On the calculus of syntactic types*, this volume. The equivalence of context-free constituent structure grammars, categorial grammars in the sense of Bar-Hillel, and categorial grammars in the narrower sense of Ajdukiewicz, *Die syntaktische Konnexität*, Studia Philosophica vol. 1 (1935) is proven in *On categorial and phrase structure grammars* by Bar-Hillel, Gaifman and Shamir, forthcoming in the Bull Res. Council Israel (where two theories that specify form of grammar are called "equivalent" if any language that can be represented by a grammar permitted by one theory can be represented by a grammar permitted by the other). Context-restricted constituent structure grammars have greater generative capacity (*On certain formal properties of grammars*, Theorem 4, p. 147), and context-restricted rules are unavoidable, in practice, in grammatical description, whatever the theoretical possibilities may turn out eventually to be.

[9] See my *Logical structure of linguistic theory*, 1955 (microfilm at Massachusetts Institute of Technology Libraries), Chapter 3.

that $A \Rightarrow \varphi A \psi$; (ii) A is left-recursive if there is a non-null φ such that $A \Rightarrow A\varphi$; (iii) A is right-recursive if there is a non-null φ such that $A \Rightarrow \varphi A$; (iv) A is self-embedding if there are non-null φ, ψ such that $A \Rightarrow \varphi A \psi$. If a grammar contains left-recursive symbols, it will generate P-markers that branch indefinitely far to the left, as in (2i); if it contains right-recursive symbols, it will generate configurations like that of (2ii); if it contains self-embedding symbols, it will generate such configurations as (2iii), and will, in the interesting cases, contain nested dependencies of arbitrary depth in the resulting terminal strings.

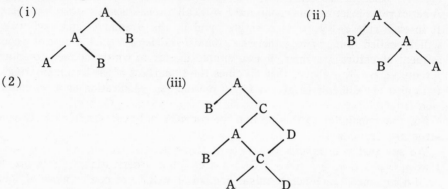

(i)

(ii)

(2)   (iii)

Nesting of dependencies is common in natural languages.[10] Consequently, if

[10] For examples in English, which can easily be multiplied, see my *Syntactic structures*, Chapter 3. Both left- and right-recursive symbols have also been found in P-markers of every language so far studied from this point of view. In some (e.g., English), right-recursive structures are much more abundant; in others, the opposite appears to be the case. (E.g., Japanese. cf. Bloch, *Studies in colloquial Japanese.* II: *Syntax*, Language vol. 22 (1946), reprinted in Joos, ed., *Readings in linguistics*. Sentence 24 of the analyzed text (p. 182 in *RiL*), for example, contains an embedded phrase with the following structure:

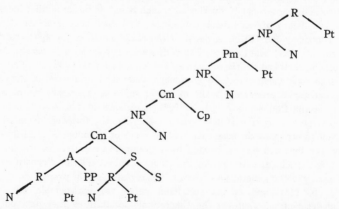

I am indebted to Karl V. Teeter for this reference.) Though no language has yet been found to lack of any of the types (i)–(iv), it should be emphasized that study of questions of this sort has barely begun.

they have constituent structure grammars at all, such grammars must contain many self-embedded symbols.

Suppose that Q is a P-marker. We say that $B = (a_1, \cdots, a_k)$ is a *branch* of Q, where each a_i is a node, if a_1 is the root and a_i is connected to a_{i+1}, for each $i < k$. Each node is labelled by some symbol. We say that $a_i \equiv a_j$ if the same symbol labels both a_i and a_j.

Suppose that B_1, B_2 and B_3 are three distinct branches of Q, where

(3) (i) $B_1 = (a_1, \cdots, a_{j+k})$,

    (ii) $B_2 = (a_1, \cdots, a_j, b_1, \cdots, b_r)$,

    (iii) $B_3 = (a_1, \cdots, a_j, c_1, \cdots, c_s)$ $(j, k, r, s \geq 1)$,

    (iv) $a_{j+k} \equiv a_j \not\equiv a_{j+i}$ $(1 \leq i < k)$,

    (v) b_r is to the left of a_{j+k} and c_s to the right of a_{j+k} in Q

(in the the obvious sense, which, to be made precise, requires labelling of lines as well as nodes in Q). In this case, we say that a_j is a *self-embedding node* in B_1. We now define the *degree* of Q as the largest integer n such that there is a branch $B = (a_1, \cdots, a_k)$ and a sequence of integers $(b_1, \cdots, b_n)$, $1 \leq b_i < b_{i+1} \leq k$ such that each a_{b_i} is self-embedding in B and for each i, j, $a_{b_i} \equiv a_{b_j}$.

In other words, the degree of a P-marker is the maximum number of times that some constituent is successively self-embedded—the maximal depth of self-embedding in this P-marker. In (2iii), for example, the degree would be 2.

In terms of these notions, we can turn to (1e), that is, the question how a constituent structure grammar is related in generative capacity to a finite automaton,[11] that is, a device that presumably has the capacity of the speaker

for both A v C

---

[11] Or finite Markov source in the sense of Shannon, cf. his *Mathematical theory of communication*, Urbana, 1949. A finite automaton is a device with a finite number of states $S_0, \cdots, S_q$ and a finite vocabulary $a_0, \cdots, a_m$, and its behavior can be represented by a finite set of rules (i, j, k), where such a triple indicates that when in state S_i the device can switch to state S_k emitting transition symbol a_j (equivalently, on reading the input symbol a_j). Where S_0 is a designated initial state, we can define a produced string as the sequence of transition symbols given as output (equivalently, the sequence of symbols accepted as input) when the device switches from S_0 to a first return to S_0. We can think of a_0 as the identity element in the output (input) alphabet. A set of sentences produced (accepted) by such a device is what Kleene has called a "regular event" (cf. his *Representation of events in nerve nets and finite automata*, Automata Studies, Princeton, Princeton University Press, 1956, for study of such devices from a point of view close to that adopted here; see also Chomsky and Miller, *Finite state languages*, Inf. and Control vol. 1 (1958); Rabin and Scott, *Finite automata and their decision problems*, IBM J. Res. Develop. vol. 3 (1959)). Whether we regard such a device as producing or recognizing a sentence is inconsequential; it is merely a matter of how we decide to read the notation that defines it.

The assumption that sentences are produced or recognized by a device of this sort tells us almost nothing about the method of processing. E.g., a finite automaton as a recognizing device may store a long (though bounded) sequence of symbols which it then processes from right to left, from center out, or whatever; it may process a string as it receives its symbols in left-to-right (temporal) order; it may do both, in some complex way. In the case of sentence recognition by humans, it is clear that storage of large units must often precede final processing—that is, it is easy to find examples of sentences, or hearer with fixed (in particular, without any) supplementary aids, and that somehow produces or accepts sentences. It is easy to show that

(4) a set of sentences cannot be represented by a finite automaton (i.e., is not a regular event)[11] just in case all of its constituent structure grammars contain self-embedding symbols.[12]

We can also establish a closely related, but considerably more interesting result that can, slightly oversimplified,[13] be stated as follows:

(5) There is a mechanical procedure g such that where G_i is a constituent structure grammar,[13] $g(i, n)$ is the description of a finite automaton which, given a string s as input, will give as output all P-markers of degree $<n$ assigned to s by G_i.

To put the main point simply, (5) provides a program for a general purpose computer such that when the rules of a constituent structure grammar G are put in the memory, and the size of memory is fixed, the device will "understand" any sentence generated by G that does not contain too much nesting of constituents of a single type. This device, is, furthermore, optimal. That is, it follows from (4) that the construction g cannot essentially be improved upon. If a grammar G generates P-markers of arbitrary degree, there will not, in general, exist a finite device that will accept (produce) just the sentences of the language specified by G. Therefore the procedure g gives the best possible way of meeting requirement (1e), in the case of the linguistic theory that limits grammars to context-free constituent structure grammars.[13] $g(i, n)$ fails only where success is in principle unattainable.

---

early parts of which cannot be interpreted until later parts are received.

In general, it is important to guard against the temptation to assume that the finite automaton (Markov source) model somehow implies left-to-right (temporal) processing of actual sentences, either in production or recognition. It is, of course, not surprising that an abstract system of such an unstructured type as that described above is so unilluminating (being compatible with so many specific alternatives) as a model for actual behavior.

[12] For a simple proof of this, see Chomsky, *A note on phrase structure grammars*, Inf. and Control vol. 2 (1959). An earlier proof, following from (5), below, is in *On certain formal properties of grammars*, where the proof of (5) appears.

[13] The oversimplification is that in Chomsky, *op. cit.*, (5) is shown to hold only for a certain class K of constituent structure grammars limited (in order to simplify the proof of (5)) to those that have the lexicon (i.e., the rules that give terminal symbols) totally separated from grammatical rules, and that permit only binary constituent breaks (with a few other restrictions)–thus, K is limited to grammars of the type that linguists usually consider as typical representatives of the results of Immediate Constituent analysis. However, it is also shown there that the class K is comprehensive enough to contain a grammar for each language for which there exists a context-free constituent structure grammar at all. Furthermore, it is quite easy to broaden the class K for which (5) holds to include grammars with rules of many other kinds, and it can probably be extended to include all context-free grammars. (5), as stated here, involves a trivial modification of what is actually proven in Chomsky, *op. cit.* (and, in fact, involves also a slight modification of the notion finite automaton, to provide for a specific sort of output). To the construction given there, a small number of rules would have to be added to permit $g(i, n)$ to actually draw the P-markers of the sentences that it "understands."

N. B.
automaton as
model for
the speaker -
hearer

We may think of the automaton $g(i, n)$ as being, indifferently,[14] a model for the speaker or hearer who knows and uses the grammar G_i but has a finite memory that determines the permitted degree of self-embedding n. Of course, if the memory restriction is relaxed by allowing more time or computational aids, the bound n increases. Such a speaker or hearer, we would predict, should be unable to "process" a sentence just in case it contains too much self-embedding, but should be able to understand or produce sentences with left- and right-recursive P-markers of great complexity, or even with nesting of distinct constituents. This is the only prediction that follows from the assumption of finiteness of memory, and it seems to be fairly well borne out by the facts.[15]

m P

Since there has been a good deal of confusion about the matters discussed above, I would like to reemphasize same basic points. From the fact that memory is finite, the fact that a sentence is heard or spoken from "left-to-right" (i.e., through time), or the fact that the rules of a generative grammar (to be sharply distinguished from a model of the speaker or hearer) may be partially ordered, nothing whatsoever can be concluded about left- and right-branching in P-markers. All of these facts are perfectly compatible with left- or right-branching, extended arbitrarily far. Only self-embedding is incompatible with finiteness of memory.

Suppose, however, that we make the additional hypothesis (A) that the speaker produces the P-marker of a sentence "from top down" (that is, that he invariably selects grammatical constructions before he selects the words that he will use, etc.). From this it follows immediately that left-branching

---

[14] See footnote 11. It should be reemphasized that $g(i, n)$ as it stands is by no means a realistic model of the speaker or hearer who has mastered the grammar G_i, but at most, a first step towards such a model.

[15] Yngve has suggested (*A model and a hypothesis for language structure*, forthcoming) that a grammar may contain devices that partially overcome the limitation on memory by allowing reformulation of sentences. This is an important observation. It appears that many of the singulary grammatical transformations of the type described below are purely "stylistic" in the sense that they do not significantly change content, and have only the effect of converting a string to an equivalent one with less self-embedding. Thus there is a transformation which converts "that he left was unfortunate" (which embeds the sentence "he left") to "it was unfortunate that he left," which is right-branching rather than self-embedding; and there is a transformation that converts "the cover that the book that John has has" to "John's book's cover," which is left-branching rather than selfembedding.

To complete the picture, however, we should note certain transformations that have, in general, the effect of *increasing* the complexity of the sentence that they reformulate, e.g., the transformation that converts "I saw the old man" to "it was the old man whom I saw," "I gave the book to the old man" to "it was to the old man that I gave the book," etc.

It should also be noted that the concept of structural complexity that Yngve proposes differs from that stated above. In his formulation, left-branching and self-embedding contribute equally to what he calls "depth" (i.e., to structural complexity). That is, in his sense of "depth" there are P-markers of arbitrarily great depth that *can* be recognized (equivalently, produced) by a strictly finite automation such as $g(i, n)$ of (5) (with n fixed).

cannot be tolerated, beyond a certain limit.[16] By quite similar reasoning from the additional hypothesis (B) that the hearer produces a P-marker (i.e., constructs a structural description of a heard sentence) strictly "from bottom up," it would follow that right-branching trees should not be tolerated beyond a certain point, though left-branching should offer no problem. Of these twin hypotheses, (A) seems to me to have neither any particular plausibility, nor any empirical support, while (B) seems not totally implausible.[17] From (B) we would predict that a hearer will tend to group left-branching units of a complex sentence (as, e.g., in "many more than half of the rather obviously much too easily solved problems") as units quite readily, but that he would tend to treat right-branching units (as, e.g., "the book that was on the table that was near the door that was newlypainted," etc.) as successive and disjointed, rather than integrated segments, on first hearing.[18]

Whatever the facts may turn out to be when proper empirical study of this question is carried out, it is important to remember that neither (A) nor (B) is supported by the fact that unaided speakers (or hearers) cannot produce (or understand) sentences with too much self-embedding. This fact, and this alone, follows from the assumption of finiteness of memory (which no one, surely, has ever questioned). The automaton $g(i, n)$ guaranteed by (5) essentially traces through the P-marker in a systematic manner, avoiding both the restriction against left-and right-branching, while preserving finiteness of memory. Similarly, other sorts of evidence that might be thought, on superficial examination, to support one or the other of (A) or (B), must also be regarded with caution. Thus it has often been observed that there is a tendency to avoid

---

[16] It is the assumption (A), rather than those stated in the preceding paragraph, that is the basis for the model proposed by Yngve, *op. cit.*

[17] It is, however, by no means as obviously true as it may appear at first glance. There are, I believe, much more promising approaches to a theory of the listener. Cf., in particular, Halle and Stevens, *Analysis by synthesis*, forthcoming in Information and Control; Halle, *Review of Sbornik po mašinnomu perevodu*, Language vol. 36 (1960); MacKay, *Mindlike behavior in artefacts*, British J. Philos. Sci. vol. 2 (1951); Bruner, *Neural mechanisms in perception*, The brain and human behavior, Solomon, Cobb and Penfield, editors, p. 122f.; and, more generally, the many discussions of the effect of set and expectancy in perception, which are quite relevant to these suggestions. The attempt to develop a reasonable account of the speaker has, I believe, been hampered by the prevalent and utterly mistaken view that a generative grammar in itself provides or is related in some obvious way to a model for the speaker.

It seems to me very likely that attempts to construct a model for the speaker or hearer are quite premature at this point, since we can hardly claim to have an adequate characterization of the form of the grammars that provide the devices that are employed, in some way, in the production and understanding of speech.

[18] This seems not unlikely. Thus in the right-branching case (as, e.g., in "The house that Jack built," and similar examples), the reader would, I think, tend to place the intonation break before the "that," in each clause, contrary to the immediate constituent analysis, a fact which may suggest that these right-branching structures are indeed more difficult to recognize.

a discontinuity when the intervening element is long or complex.[19] Thus such a sentence as (a) "I called the man who read the book that was on the table that was near the door up" (with the discontinuous verb "call up") is extremely awkward, and would always be replaced by (b) "I called up the man····." If, accepting the hypothesis (A), above, we measure "depth" in the manner suggested by Yngve, then the depth of (b) will be either the same as that of (a)[20] or less by one than that of (a).[21] In either case, however, the awkwardness of (a) can scarcely be attributed to depth, in this sense, since the depth of (a) is under any calculation less than that of such perfectly natural sentences as "quite a large majority of the students here are hard-working," and so on. Careful scrutiny of such cases seems to lead to the conclusion that the tendency to avoid discontinuities is independent of at least any simple consideration involving left-branching, self-embedding, or right-branching.

3. Transformational grammars. This discussion has so far been based on the assumption that the correct set of P-markers can be generated in a natural and formally well-motivated way by a constituent structure grammar. There are strong reasons to believe that this is not the case, however. Immediate constituent analysis has been sharply and, I think, correctly criticized as in general imposing too much structure on sentences.[22] Consider, for example, such a sentence as

(6) Why has John always been such an easy fellow to please?

The whole is a sentence; the last several words constitute a noun phrase; the words can be assigned to categories. But there is little motivation for assigning phrase structure beyond this. The same is true of the sentence "I-brought-it-in-yesterday-from the garage-after dinner," and many others. In all such cases, immediate constituent analysis is not really to the point, and a constituent structure grammar would be most unrevealing. The extreme example of this difficulty is the case of true coordination, e.g., "the man was old, tired, tall ..., but friendly." The only correct P-marker would assign no internal structure at all within the sequence of coordinated items. But a constituent structure grammar can accommodate this possibility only with an infinite number of rules; that is, it must necessarily impose further structure, in quite an arbitrary way. Examples such as this are important as a reminder

---

[19] In some as yet undefined sense, cf., e.g., my *Syntactic structures*, p. 77n. The question is apparently not trivial. Thus such sentences as "I called the man you saw up" seem to me less natural than "I called almost all of the men from Boston up", and, in general, embedding of a short sentence (hence, self-embedding) seems less natural than embedding of a fairly long phrase. It is by no means obvious that grammatical or intonational considerations will be sufficient to account for relative naturalness in such cases.

[20] If the analysis of the construction Article-Noun-Relative clause is (Article (Noun-Relative Clause)).

[21] If the analysis accepted is (Article-Noun-Relative Clause) or ((Article-Noun) Relative Clause).

[22] See, e.g., Sledd, *A short introduction to English grammar*, Chicago, 1959.

that to achieve adequacy, a linguistic theory must provide grammars for every desired infinite set of P-markers, not only for every interesting infinite set of sentences (natural language). This requirement the theory of constituent structure cannot possibly meet.

The basic reason why the theory of grammar sketched above cannot be accepted, however, lies in its failure, in practice, to make possible the construction of simple and revealing grammars. An attempt to demonstrate this would go well beyond the bounds of this paper. I do not see, however, how this fact can be doubted by anyone who makes a serious attempt to apply such a theory as this in detail to a natural language.

A great many of the difficulties[23] that confront a constituent structure grammar seem to be overcome if we revise the schema for grammatical description (i.e., (1a), above) in the following way. We limit the rewriting rules $\varphi \to \psi$ discussed above to a sequence of rules, used to generate a finite number of derivations of terminal strings, to each of which we associate, as before, a labelled tree representing constituent structure. In this way we generate only those terminal strings that underlie the simplest sentences. These strings, however, embody all or most of the selectional restrictions on choice of elements. We now add to the grammar a set of operations of the type that have been called by Harris[24] "grammatical transformations." Each of these is a mapping of P-markers onto P-markers. The

[23] For an indication of some of these, see my *Logical structure of linguistic theory*, Chapters 7 and 8, and *Syntactic structures*, Chapter 6.

[24] In his work on analysis of extended discourse (*Discourse analysis*, Language vol. 26 (1952), and *Discourse analysis: a sample text*, ibid.), Harris brought to light the important fact that large areas of traditional grammar that had been quite overlooked in modern linguistics could be given a unified treatment in terms of some notion of grammatical transformation. In his *Cooccurrence and transformation in linguistic structure*, Language vol. 31 (1957) he developed a notion of grammatical transformation (with applications in English) as, essentially, a relation holding between two sequences of morpheme classes which can be partially paired, class by class, so that the same choice of morphemes can occur in paired clases. D. Worth has applied this notion to the study of Russian inflection in his *Transform analysis of Russian instrumental constructions*, Word vol. 14 (1950). The approach that I will describe here bears little formal resemblance to this conception, although it was suggested by Harris' observation noted above. It is based on the account of grammatical transformations given in the references of footnotes 2 and 9, and my *Three models for the description of language*, I. R. E. Transactions on Information Theory vol. IT-2 (1956). For a study of large segments of English grammar in essentially these terms, going well beyond what is contained in the references just cited, see R.B. Lees, *A grammar of English nominalizations*, Baltimore, 1960 (supplement to International Journal of American Linguistics). This book also contains some material on Turkish and German. Further material on German is presented in J.R. Applegate, *Structure of the German noun phrase*, in preparation. This descriptive work on English has been extended in important ways in papers by Lees, *Adjectival constructions in English*, forthcoming in Language; Lees and Klima, *Rules for English pronominalization*, forthcoming; and Klima, *Negation in English*, forthcoming. Klima has presented material on Russian in his review of *Bezličnye predloženija v sovremennom Russkom jazyke* by Galkina-Fedoruk (Int. Jour. of Slavic Ling. and Poetics vol. 5 (1961)). Within essentially the same theoretical framework there is also a very detailed

recursive property of the grammar is now attributed entirely to these trans-formations. I will now briefly describe how the schema for grammatical description can be extended to accommodate operations of the required kind, and how these operations impose P-markers on the terminal strings formed by their application to already generated P-markers (i.e., how the function f of (1c), above, must be revised in accordance with this extension of the form of grammars.[25]

The motivation for adding tranformational rules to a grammar is quite clear. There are certain sentences (in fact, simple declarative active sentences with no complex noun or verb phrases—or, to be more precise, the terminal strings underlying these) that can be generated by a constituent structure grammar in quite a natural way. There are others (e.g., passives, questions, sentences with discontinuous phrases and complex phrases that embed sentence trans-forms, etc.) that cannot be generated in an economic and natural way by a constituent structure grammar, but that are systematically related to sentences of simpler structure. Transformations that are constructed to express this relation can thus materially simplify the grammar, when used to generate more complex sentences and their structural descriptions from already generated simpler ones.

The problem is to construct a general and abstract notion of grammatical transformation which will incorporate and facilitate the expression of just those formal relations between sentences that have a significant function in language.[26] It is clear, first of all, that application of a transformation to a string requires knowledge of the constituent structure of this string. Thus the question transformation has the effect of preposing a certain element of the main verbal phrase of a declarative sentence. Applied to (7) it yields (8) but not (9):

(7) The man who was here was old.
(8) Was the man who was here old?
(9) Was the man who here was old?

That is, we must know that the second, not the first occurrence of "was" is to be preposed, and this requires that the constituent structure be available.

study of an American Indian language by G. H. Matthews (*A grammar of Hidatsa*, forthcoming; cf., also, his *Ergative relation in Hidatsa*, Quart. Prog. Rep. of Res. Lab. of Electronics, January, 1960) and (in preparation) grammars of several Philippine languages by R. Stockwell and several of his students.

[25] In fact, the notion "structural description of a sentence s" must itself be extended to include along with the P-marker of s and of the strings underlying s transformational-ly, an object which we might call a T-marker that represents the transformational history of s. I will not go into this matter here, however.

[26] Just as in the case of P-markers (see above, p. 8), we must assume, for the purpose of constructing a significant concept, some advance knowledge of empirical conditions that the notion "grammatical transformation" must meet. Thus we assume that a reasonable notion of grammatical transformation must lead to the conclusion that "John saw Bill" and "Bill was seen by John" are related quite differently than "John saw Bill" and "Bill saw John," and so on. I do not see what conceivable alternative there is to this approach, in the case of transformation or any other linguistic concept, nor does this seem to me to be in any way objectionable.

Similarly, we want the passive transformation to apply to "the man saw the boy" to produce "the boy was seen by the man," but not to "the man saw the boy leave" to form, say, "the boy leave was seen by the man." Thus we must know what substrings of each sentence are Noun Phrase, Auxiliary, and Verb. A transformation cannot simply be an operation defined on terminal strings, or morpheme class sequences with no further structure.

It would also defeat the ends of transformational analysis to regard transformations as higher level rewriting rules that apply to undeveloped phrase designations, i.e., in the case of the passive, as a rule

(10) NP_1 Auxiliary Verb $NP_2 \rightarrow NP_2$ Auxiliary be Verb en by NP_1

or something of this sort. Such a rule would be of the type discussed in §2, but would not meet the additional condition imposed on constituent structure rules (that is, the condition that only a single symbol be rewritten—cf. §2) that makes construction of the P-marker possible in the manner presupposed above.[27] A sufficient argument against this is that transformations, so formulated, would not provide a method for simplifying the grammar where selectional restrictions on choice of elements appear. Thus among active sentences we find

(11) (a) the fact that the case was dismissed doesn't surprise me,
      (b) Congress enacted a new law,
      (c) the men consider John a dictator,[28]
      (d) John felt remorse,

and so on, but not the sequences formed by interchange of subject and object in such cases. In the corresponding passives the selectional relations are obviously preserved, appearing now in a different arrangement. If the passive transformation were to apply as a "rewriting rule," at a stage of derivation preceding the application of the context-restricted rewriting rules that provide the selectional restrictions on the choice of subject, verb, object (as would be the case, e.g., if (10) were taken as the formulation of this rule), an entirely independent set of context-restricted rules would have to be given to determine the corresponding subject, verb, agent selection in the passive. One of the

---

[27] That is, a grammar would now be simply a set of rules $\varphi \rightarrow \psi$, where φ and ψ are strings of symbols. It would be, in other words, a system of a well-studied kind called technically a "semi-Thue system" (cf., e.g., Davis, *Computability and unsolvability*, New York, 1958, Chapter 6). Linguistic theory would, essentially, reduce to the assertion that a grammar is an arbitrary Turing machine, in this highly unstructured formulation. This is the most general (and consequently, least interesting) possible formulation of grammatical theory. The apparent gain in flexibility that results from thus dropping all constraints on the form of grammars is quite illusory, however, since it merely shifts the problem of specifying the formal features that make natural language distinctive, among arbitrary effectively specifiable (recursively enumerable) sets, from the characterization of (1a), above (where this problem properly belongs) to the characterization of (1c, d). The revision of transformational theory criticized here is (if I understand him correctly) essentially that suggested implicitly by Householder *On linguistic primes*, Word vol. 15 (1959) p. 233f., and *review of Hockett', A course in modern linguistics* in Language vol. 35 (1959) pp. 506–507, 517.

[28] More properly, we should have here the underlying terminal string "the men – consider a dictator – John," itself, of course, a transform of simpler strings.

virtues of a transformational grammar is that it provides a means of avoiding this pointless duplication of selectional rules. But this advantage is lost if we apply the transformation before the selection of particular elements.[29] The same is true of most transformational rules.

It therefore seems to me evident that a transformational rule must apply to a full P-marker. Since transformational rules must reapply to transforms, it follows that the result of applying a transformation must again be a P-marker, the *derived* P-marker of the terminal string resulting from the tranformation. A grammatical transformation, then, is a mapping of P-markers into P-markers.

We can formulate such a notion of "grammatical transformation" in the following way. Suppose that Q is a P-marker of the terminal string t, and that t can be subdivided into successive segments $t_1, \cdots, t_n$ in such a way that each t_i is traceable, in Q, to a node labelled A_i. We say, in such a case, that

(12) t is *analyzable* as $(t_1, \cdots, t_n; A_1, \cdots, A_n)$ with respect to Q.

In the simplest case, a transformation T will be specified in part by a sequence of symbols $(A_1, \cdots, A_n)$ that defines its domain by the following rule:

(13)   a string t with P-marker Q is in the domain of T if t is analyzable as $(t_1, \cdots, t_n; A_1, \cdots, A_n)$ with respect to Q.

In this case, we will call $(t_1, \cdots, t_n)$ a *proper analysis* of t with respect to Q, T, and we will call $(A_1, \cdots, A_n)$ the *structure index* of T.

To complete the specification of the transformation T, we describe the effect that T has on the terms of the proper analysis of the string to which it applies. Thus T may have the effect of deleting or permuting certain terms, of substituting one for another, of adding a constant string in a fixed place, and so on. Suppose that we associate with a transformation T an underlying *elementary transformation* T_{el} which is a formal operation of some sort on n terms, where the structure index of T is of length n. Let

(14) $T_{el}(i; t_1 \cdots, t_n) = \sigma_i$ ~~with respect to.~~

where $(t_1, \cdots, t_n)$ is the proper analysis of t (wrt) Q, T, and T_{el} underlies T. Then the string resulting from application of the transformation T to the string t with P-marker Q is

(15) $T(t, Q) = \sigma_1 \cdots \sigma_n$.

Obviously, we do not want any arbitrary mapping of the sort just described to qualify as a grammatical transformation. Thus we would not want to permit in a grammar a transformation that associates such pairs as:

(16) (i)   John saw the boy – I'll leave tomorrow,

    (ii)   John saw the man – why don't you try again,

    (iii)   John saw the girl – China is industrializing rapidly,

and so on,[30] but only such rules as express genuine structural relations between

---

[29] For each particular case, some ad hoc adjustment or principle can be employed to cope with the problem. But a general alternative to the transformational approach to this matter has not yet been suggested.

[30] More correctly, the theory of transformations must be designed so that a relation of this sort could only be expressed by a sequence of transformations. Notice that a program such as (1), above, will collapse completely unless the choice of available

sentence forms, as, e.g., active-passive, declarative-interrogative, declarative-nominalized sentence, and so on. We can avoid this by an additional and quite natural requirement on elementary transformations that can be formulated loosely as follows:

(17) If T_{el} is an elementary transformation, then for all integers i, n and strings $x_1, \cdots, x_n, y_1, \cdots, y_n$, it must be the case that $T_{el}(i; x_1, \cdots, x_n)$ is formed from $T_{el}(i; y_1, \cdots, y_n)$ by replacing y_i in the latter by x_i, for each $i \leq n$.

In other words, the effect of an elementary transformation is independent of the particular choice of strings to which it applies.

This requirement has the effect of ruling out the possibility of applying transformations to strings of actually occurring words (or morphemes). Thus no single elementary transformation meeting (17) can have the effect of replacing (18a, b) by (19a, b), respectively:

(18) (a) John will try,
      (b) John tried,
(19) (a) will John try,
      (b) did John try,

though this is clearly the effect of the simple question-transformation. The elementary transformation that we need in this case is that which converts $x_1 - x_2 - x_3$ to $x_2 - x_1 - x_3$, that is, the transformation T_{el} defined as follows, for arbitrary strings x_1, x_2, x_3:

(20) $T_{el}(1; x_1, x_2, x_3) = x_2$; $T_{el}(2; x_1, x_2, x_3) = x_1$; $T_{el}(3; x_1, x_2, x_3) = x_3$.

But if this is to yield (19b), it will be necessary to apply it not to (18b) but rather to a hypothetical form

(21) John past try,

parallel in structure to (18a), that underlies (18b). In general, we cannot require that terminal strings be related in any very simple way to actual sentences. The obligatory mappings (transformational and morphophonemic) that specify the physical shape may reorder, add or delete elements, and so on.[31]

The notion of transformation just described must be generalized in several directions, for empirical adequacy. First, we must allow transformations that apply to pairs of P-markers. Thus the terminal string underlying the

---

transformations is strictly limited. The wider the class of permitted transformations, the more difficult it becomes to meet requirement (1d) in a significant way. Cf. the remark on page 7 concerning (1c, d), and footnote 26.

For a more adequate and precise formulation of (17), below, see my *Three models for the description of language*, p. 122, (44)–(46).

[31] Only on the level of words is the relation between sequence of elements in a representing string and actual time sequence in speech in general order-preserving. We cannot expect to meet this condition on the level of morphemes, phonemes, or any of the even more abstract syntactic levels.

It is important to note that in the case just discussed there are several quite independent reasons for setting up the same abstract underlying strings. Note also that the effect of the question transformation is to convert (18a) to (19a) and (21) to "past John try," which is converted to (19b) by an obligatory transformation of considerable generality that introduces "do" as a bearer of an unaffixed affix.

sentence (22) is constructed transformationally from the already formed strings underlying (23a, b) (with their respective P-markers):

(22) his owning property surprised me,

(23) (a) it surprised me,

(b) he owns property.

We can provide for this possibility by allowing all strings

(24) $\#S\#\#S\# \cdots \#S\#$

to head derivations in the underlying constituent structure grammar, instead of just $\#S\#$, as above (or in several equivalent, and equally simple ways). We then allow such structure indices as

(25) $(\#, NP, V, NP, \#, \#, NP, V, NP, \#)$

thus providing for (22) and similar cases (this necessitates a simple modification of (13) which I will not describe here).

We must also extend the manner in which the domain of a transformation and the proper analysis of the transformed string is specified. First, there is no need to require that the terms of a structure index be single symbols. Secondly, we can allow the specification of a transformation to be given by a finite set of structure indices. More generally, we can specify the domain of a transformation simply by a structural condition based on the predicate "analyzable" (cf. (12) above). In terms of this notion, we can define identity of terminal strings, and can allow for terms of the structure index to be unspecified. By this extension, which I will not describe here, we can provide an explicit and precise basis for the informal descriptions of transformations that have appeared in the linguistic literature.[32]

A grammatical transformation, then, is determined by a structural condition stated in terms of the predicate "analyzable" and an elementary transformation.[33] It was remarked above, however, that a transformation must produce not merely strings, but derived P-markers. It remains, then, to show how constituent structure is assigned to the terminal string formed by a transformation. It seems that the best way to do this is by a set of rules that form part of general linguistic theory, rather than by an additional clause appended to the specification of each individual transformation. Precise statement of these rules would require an analysis of fundamental notions going well beyond the informal account sketched above, or for that matter, the more precise versions of it that have appeared previously. Nevertheless, certain features of a general solution to this problem seem fairly clear. We can, first of all,

---

[32] In particular, the transformational aspects of syntax described in the references cited in footnotes 2, 9, and 24.

[33] What we actually specify in this way is not merely "grammatical transformation" in extension (i.e., a class of pairs of P-markers), but "transformational rule." That is, different such specifications may lead to the same transformation, in extension, in a particular language. In general, we are interested not so much in the extension of the notions "grammar" (i.e., a sequence $\sigma_1, \sigma_2, \cdots$ of elements of the class given in (1b)), "transformation," etc., but in the particular manner in which these devices are specified. The study of grammatical transformations, in extension, will become interesting only when it becomes possible to extend to transformational grammars studies of the kind carried out for constituent structure grammars in the references cited in footnote 12.

assign each transformation to one of a small number of classes, depending on the underlying elementary transformation on which it is based. For each such class we can state a general rule that assigns to the transform a derived Phrase-marker, the form of which depends, in a fixed way, on the Phrase-markers of the underlying terminal strings. A few examples will illustrate the kinds of principles that seem to be necessary.

Generalized transformations that produce a string from a pair of underlying strings (e.g., (22)–(23) above) appear to be the basic recursive devices in the grammar. That is, there is apparently a bound on the number of singulary transformations that can apply in sequence. Most generalized transformations are based on elementary tranformations that substitute a transformed version of the second of the pair of underlying terminal strings[34] for some term of the proper analysis of the first of this pair.[35] In such a case, one general principle seems sufficient to determine the derived constituent structure of the transform. Suppose that the transformation replaces the symbol a of σ_1 (the matrix sentence) by σ_2 (the constituent sentence). The P-marker of the result is simply the former P-marker of σ_1 with a replaced by the P-marker of σ_2.[36]

It appears that all other generalized transformations are "attachment transformations" that take a term α of the proper analysis, with the term β of the structure index that most remotely dominates it (and all intermediate parts of the P-marker that are dominated by β and that dominate α), and attaches it (with, perhaps, a constant string) to some other term of the proper analysis. In this way, we form for example, "John is old and sad" with the P-marker (26) from "John is old," "John is sad," by a transformation with the structure index (NP, is, A, ##, NP, is, A).[37]

(26)

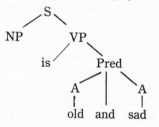

<hr />

[34] In the terminology suggested by Lees, *A grammar of English nominalizations*, the "constituent string." It is, for several reasons, convenient to analyze an operation such as (22)–(23) into two transformations, one which converts (23b) into "his owning property" which is substituted, by the second transformation, for "it" of (23a). It is the second of these that we are discussing now.

[35] In Lees' terminology, the "matrix string."

[36] The same notion can obviously be extended to singulary substitution transformations.

[37] In addition, the structural condition associated with the transformation will specify that the first term of the proper analysis must be identical with the fourth. Clearly this is a special case of a much more general conjunction transformation (or family of transformations). I have oversimplified the description in several respects.

Again, we can extend this notion immediately to cover singulary attachment transformations.

Many of the singulary transformations are permutations of terms of the proper analysis. For example, one transformation converts (27a) to (27b):

(27) (a)

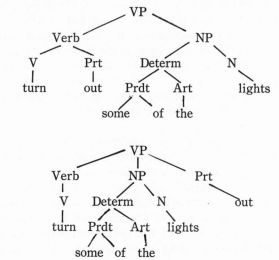

(b)

The general principle of derived constituent structure in this case is simply that the minimal change is made in the P-marker of the underlying string, consistent with the requirement that the resulting P-marker again be representable in tree form. The transformation that gives "turn some of the lights out" is based on an elementary transformation that permutes the second and third terms of a three-termed proper analysis; it has the structure index (V, Prt, NP). (27) illustrates a characteristic effect of permutations, namely, that they tend to reduce the amount of structure associated with the terminal string to which they apply. Thus while (27a) represents the kind of purely binary structure regarded as paradigmatic in most linguistic theories, in (27b) there is one less binary split and one new ternary division; and Prt is no longer dominated by Verb. Although binary divisions are characteristic of the simple structural descriptions generated by the constituent structure grammar, they are much more rarely found in P-markers associated with actual sentences. A transformational approach to syntactic description thus allows us to express the element of truth contained in the familiar theories of immediate constituent analysis, with their emphasis on binary splitting, without at the same time committing us to the arbitrary assignment of superfluous structure required by such theories. Furthermore, by continued use of attachment and permutation transformations, in the manner illustrated above, we can generate classes of P-markers that cannot in principle be generated by constituent structure grammars (in particular, those associated with coordinate constructions) thus permitting us to overcome the intrinsic inadequacy of constituent structure grammars noted at the outset of this section.

Finally, certain singulary transformation simply add constant strings at a designated place in the proper analysis, and others simply delete certain terms of the proper analysis. The former are treated just like attachment transformations. In the case of deletion, we delete nodes that dominate no terminal string, and leave the P-marker otherwise unchanged. It is possible to restrict the application of deletion transformations in a rather severe way, apparently. In particular, it seems that it may be possible to place a limit both on the number of deletions that can apply in the derivation of a string, and the length of the string that is deleted. The restrictions on applicability of deletion transformations play a fundamental role in determining what kinds of language (infinite set of strings) can be generated, in principle, by transformational grammars.

A transformational grammar, then, consists of a finite sequence of context-restricted rewriting rules $\varphi \rightarrow \psi$ and a finite number of transformations of the type just described, together with a statement of the restrictions on the order of application of these transformations. The result of a transformation is in general available for further transformation, so that an indefinite number of P-markers, of quite varied kinds, can be generated by repeated application of transformations. At each stage, a P-marker representable as a labelled tree is associated with the terminal string so far derived. Thus we have sketched the outlines of a theory that meets requirements (1a, c). There is a fairly substantial accumulation of evidence suggesting that it may be possible to meet empirical conditions of the kind mentioned at the end of §1 in widely different languages,[38] so that the search for a relatively straightforward technique of evaluation (1d) can be pressed with some hope for success. The question of requirement (1e), however, and, in fact, almost all questions concerning generative capacity of transformational grammars and realistic models for the speaker or hearer who uses such a grammar, remain completely open and, in fact, can scarcely be posed without further clarification of the concepts involved.

MASSACHUSETTS INSTITUTE OF TECHNOLOGY,
   CAMBRIDGE, MASSACHUSETTS

---

[38] See the references cited in footnote 24.

SOME ISSUES IN THE THEORY OF GRAMMAR

BY

HILARY PUTNAM

Introduction. Although this symposium is devoted to problems in the field of mathematical linguistics (a peculiar field, in that some of its leading experts doubt its existence), in my paper I am not going to attempt to prove any theorems or state any results. Rather, I shall take advantage of my privilege as a philosopher and devote myself to a survey of work done by others in the area and to a discussion of issues raised by linguists concerning the work done in this area. There are, in addition to the difficult technical problems, whose existence everyone acknowledges, also very serious conceptual difficulties, as is shown by the fact that Chomsky's book *Syntactic structures*, which is regarded by some as a foundation-stone for this kind of activity, has been described by no less an authority than Roman Jakobson as an *argumentum a contrario*[1] showing the impossibility of the whole enterprise.

What I want to do first is to provide, so to speak, a conceptual setting for the kind of work that Chomsky is doing. I believe that the conceptual setting I will provide is one that will be acceptable to Chomsky himself—but this, of course, is not vital. The interpretations of a scientific theory most acceptable to the scientist himself may often be the least tenable ones, and so we shall worry about finding an interpretation or conceptual setting, for the theory of grammars which seems to us to be correct, not necessarily one which some particular linguist will ratify.

In particular, I propose to connect the theory of grammars with a program in linguistics initiated by Paul Ziff and presented by him in his forthcoming book, *Semantic analysis*. Ziff is concerned of course not only, or even primarily, with questions of grammar, but with questions of meaning. Even if most linguists, however, are not yet primarily or very deeply concerned with semantical questions, it seems to me fairly obvious that at some not very distant date, linguistics must begin to deal with these questions much more extensively than it is doing today, and that programs in grammar are to be judged to some extent at least, by the way in which they fit into reasonable programs for linguistic investigation as a whole—that means, in the long run, into programs for investigating not only grammatical but also semantical aspects of natural languages.

I. On understanding deviant utterances. The main concept with which Ziff works is the concept of a *deviant* sentence (or, as he prefers to say, "deviant utterance"). By a deviant sentence, he means any sentence which deviates from any linguistic regularity whatsoever, where by a linguistic regularity we may understand either an inductively certifiable generalization concerning the observable behavior of informants, or a projection introduced

---

[1] In *Boas' view of grammatical meaning*, American Anthropologist vol. 61 (1959) pp. 139–145.

by the linguist for reasons of systematic simplicity, that is to say an idealization of some sort. I shall assume here that some degree of idealization is
inevitable in linguistic work, and I shall also assume that the question of how
much idealization is legitimate is one that has no general answer. What one
has to answer in a specific case is whether the idealizations made by a particular linguist in a particular context were or were not too severe.

Now, the regularities from which a deviant sentence deviates may be sometimes gramatical regularities or sometimes semantical regularities. The sentence
"She goed home." we would all presumably classify as deviant, and presumably
there would be no hesitation in classifying the deviation as a deviation at
the level of grammar. The sentence "The star by which seafarers normally
steer is graceful." is also deviant, but at a more subtle level. What is deviant
about this sentence is that the word "graceful" ordinarily has to do with form
and motion, and a star does not have form or motion. This kind of deviation
is obviously at the level of semantics.

Two things should be noticed at once: First, some linguists believe that
they can do without any notion of linguistic deviation, but this is a mistake.
If one recognizes linguistic regularities at all, then one must recognize actual
or possible deviations from those regularities. Now then, a grammar of a
language is nothing but a statement of certain supposed linguistic regularities.
Anyone who writes a grammar of any natural language is therefore automatically classifying certain sentences as non-deviant, and by implication, certain
others as deviant. Secondly, some linguists claim that any sentence, which
could under any circumstances, no matter how far-fetched, be "passed" by an
informant, is non-deviant. This may be a nice theoretical position, although
I shall argue against it in a moment; but it should be observed, that even if
it were the correct theoretical position, it is a position that no linguist actually
conforms to in practice. I am quite sure that the very linguists who claim that
any sentence that an informant might conceivably use is non-deviant, will in
writing a grammar of any language whatsoever automatically rule out, by implication at least, many sentences that informants might employ. For example,
Joseph Applegate once reported to me an amusing conversation with another
linguist who had somewhat rashly claimed that an English speaker would
under no circumstances understand a sentence in which the verb "sneezed"
was used as a transitive verb. Within a very few minutes in the same conversation he had succeeded in tricking the other linguist into herself using
the somewhat "exotic" sentence: "Pepper doesn't sneeze me." Now then,
this is extremely amusing, and it does establish a point: Namely, that no
matter how deviant a sentence may be it is extremely unwise to say that there
are no circumstances under which a speaker of the language might produce
or a hearer of the language might construe it. But this example should not
be taken as making the quite different point that the sentence "Pepper does
not sneeze me." is non-deviant. I shall argue this below. For the moment
I only make the weaker claim that even if a linguist when arguing linguistic
theory claims that, for instance, "Pepper does not sneeze me." is non-deviant;
when *writing* a grammar of English, he is very likely to inadvertently contradict his own philosophy of linguistics by ruling out this very sentence.

He may not rule it out explicitly by calling it ungrammatical; in fact, he may not use the term "ungrammatical" at all. But that does not matter. If he gives rules for producing grammatical sentences of English and these rules have the feature that they would never produce the sentence just mentioned, then we may obviously say that he has ruled out the sentence just mentioned by implication. It is clear, in fact, that the only way in which one could avoid ruling out any sentences of the form exhibited by "Pepper does not sneeze me." as deviant, would be by writing a grammar of English in which every verb was allowed to be used as a transitive verb. And even if one did that, it wouldn't help! For presumably, unless the grammar is the one-sentence grammar which says "Any finite sequence of English words is a sentence.", then there must be *some* finite sequences of English words which, by implication at least, are ruled out as deviant and I will here and now guarantee to find situations under which informants would produce some of these sentences and hearers would understand some of them. In short, if someone says, "Why isn't this a reasonable program for linguistic theory: to write a grammar of, say, English which predicts all and only those sentences which English speakers might conceivably use or English hearers might conceivably understand?", the answer is two-fold. First, that a grammar in this sense would not resemble any grammar ever written by any linguist (and I include linguists who claim that the program just alluded to is *their* program) and secondly, that the program would either be trivial or impossible of execution. It would be trivial of execution if one took the standpoint that for any finite sequence of English words not exceeding a certain length there are some circumstances under which that sequence might be employed; then one gets the one-sentence grammar alluded to before. In fact, one can write a single one-sentence grammar for all natural languages at once on this view! If one, however, interprets more narrowly the notion of a sentence that an English speaker might use or an English hearer might understand, then, I think two things are going to happen: namely, some degree of arbitrariness is going to creep in (e.g., one linguist will count "Pepper does not sneeze me." as a sentence that an English speaker might use, and another will reject it), and secondly, arbitrariness or no arbitrariness, no one will succeed in carrying out the task. This prediction is not as daring as it might seem, for it takes only a moment's reflection to see that the program we have just been criticizing is the program of doing wholly without idealizations in linguistic theory; and no science, whether it be a life science or a physical science, has ever managed to take a single step without the very liberal use of idealizations. Even those linguists, and they are fortunately few, who have an exaggerated confidence in the powers of such statistical techniques as multiple-factor analysis, forget that multiple-factor analysis is itself one of the most ingenious idealizations ever introduced into the empirical sciences.

Let me assume, then, that our objective is going to be to set down some system of linguistic regularities characterizing some aspects of a particular natural language, and that we are going to be willing, indeed eager to idealize and "oversimplify" to some extent. To put it another way, we will be worried about the criticism that someone has produced a better description of the same

language than we have, but not worried about the criticism that our description is not ideal in the impossible sense of conforming exactly to the exact
behavior of every hearer and speaker.

There are now two questions which face us corresponding to the two classes
we have distinguished: deviant and non-deviant. These are, what to say
about the non-deviant sentences, and what to say about the deviant sentences.
The former problem is the problem of showing how the non-deviant sentences
are built up, what their composition is, how their meaning is determined by
their composition, *et cetera*. This is the problem which, at the grammatical
level, occupies Chomsky in his *Syntactic structures*, and which occupies Ziff
at the semantical level in *Semantic analysis*.

Important and seemingly insuperable as this problem is, I wish to neglect
it here and to focus attention on a different problem, namely the problem of
what to say about the deviant sentences. One thing we might do, of course,
is to say nothing about them. We might take the standpoint that to call a
sentence deviant is to say "Let's forget about it. Linguistic theory does not
have to deal with this." But if this were our standpoint then I would be
inclined to sympathize with all the linguists who dislike such notions as
"deviant", "ungrammatical", and so forth. Shutting one's eyes to the very
empirical facts one is supposed to be trying to account for is not good scientific
practice; and this is presumably what the people who make the unrealistic
proposal that we should count every sentence ever heard as non-deviant, have
in mind. Indeed, as Ziff repeatedly emphasizes, since a great deal of the discourse most commonly used and especially the discourse of greatest conceptual
importance, discourse of innovators in every field—in science, in politics, in
moral life, in philosophy—consists of deviant sentences, to reject the problem
of accounting for the use and the understanding of deviant sentences is to
reject one of the most interesting problems in linguistics. Thus, Ziff proposes as a program for linguistics, not merely to provide a description of the
non-deviant sentences of a language, but to go on, using that description as
a base, and to try to account for the various kinds of deviancy in terms of
meaning, function, structure, and so forth. This program is only stated as
a program in *Semantic analysis*, which focuses attention mainly on non-deviant
sentences; however, Ziff, since the completion of *Semantic analysis*, has been
working extensively on a theory of the way in which we understand deviant
utterances.

The details of this theory need not concern us here, but I will give one or
two very simple examples in order to illustrate what is meant by accounting
for the way in which we understand deviant sentences, and to show the role
played by the notion of a deviant sentence in the account. The first example
is the Dylan Thomas line, "A grief ago I saw him there." Clearly, "grief"
is being used figuratively here. But what exactly does it mean to say that
a word is being used figuratively? A plausible account might be along somewhat the following lines: The hearer, on hearing the sentence, "A grief ago
I saw him there.", immediately recognizes that the sentence he has just heard
is deviant. He then proceeds to find a similar sentence which is non-deviant
from which the given sentence may be, in some sense or other, derived. One

such sentence would be, "A moment ago I saw him there."; another would be, "A year ago I saw him there."; another would be, "An age ago I saw him there."; and so forth. Notice that the substitution of a single word for the word "grief" is capable of turning the sentence, "A grief ago I saw him there." into a non-deviant sentence; and notice, moreover, that all the words that we have so far substituted in order to regularize this sentence have this semantical feature in common: that they are measures of time. This accords with the natural, informal explanation of the line: namely, "Grief is being used as if it were a measure of time." Notice what we have done here: Although we call the sentence, "A grief ago I saw him there." a deviant sentence, this does not mean that it is in any sense a bad sentence, or that Dylan Thomas ought not to have used it. The term "deviant" is obviously a technical term which has an explanatory, and not a valuational, function. Calling the sentence deviant is also not to say that it is a freak, that it is something that transcends all possibility of linguistic explanation. On the contrary, calling it deviant is an essential part of the explanation.

"But then," the reader may object, "if you are going to recognize this sentence as a "good" sentence, if you are going to try to account for it, why call it deviant at all? Why not just modify your grammar so that the word "grief" can occur in any position in which a measure of time can occur?" This proposal, however, leads us right back to the blind alley of rejecting all idealizations. A more reasonable proposal is this: We first rather stringently, perhaps over-stringently rule out all but certain privileged uses of the word "grief" as deviant. We then frame a definition of the word "grief" which covers the remaining non-deviant uses. Notice that this is possible precisely because we have been so stringent in what we are willing to accept as non-deviant uses. The lenient standpoint which counts all possible uses on a par has as one of its many disadvantages that it makes the framing of ordinary dictionary definitions either impossible or untestable. The framing of an adequate dictionary definition of the word "grief" is impossible if the definition is supposed to account for all uses of the word "grief", and all uses count as equally good. Try to think of a definition of the word "grief" that would be reasonable in a dictionary and that would fit the use of "grief" both as a mood or feeling and as "a measure of time." On the other hand, if we retain the usual dictionary definitions and also count all uses on a par, but simply say that a definition need not agree with the uses of the word of which the definition is a definition—then it becomes wholly unclear what the function of a definition is, or how one definition might be said to be correct and another might be said to be incorrect. All of these matters have been taken up at much more length in the book by Ziff I have mentioned, and I will not discuss them further here.

Moreover, it will be noticed that the program of first accounting for the regularities which are represented by a distinguished set of non-deviant uses, and then trying to account for a much wider set of deviant uses by regarding these as in some sense derived from the non-deviant uses, fits the ancient and intuitive distinction between literal and figurative uses of a word.

Finally, and this is the most important point, notice that the recommendation that we draw no distinction between the use of "grief" in the sentence, "A grief ago I saw him there.", and the sentence, "She was in a state of grief." —while it sounds ever so much more lenient and non-discriminatory than the Ziffian approach—in fact, gives one not the slightest hint of a procedure for explaining the Dylan Thomas line in question. On the other hand, the discriminatory procedure of beginning with the idea that the sentence is deviant actually gives us a method not of rejecting the sentence but of understanding it. Namely, we have the procedure (this, of course, is a procedure only for a very simple class of deviant sentences) of trying to find a non-deviant sentence from which the deviant sentence in question may be derived by a one-word substitution and then of seeing the meaning associated with the whole class of relevant one-word substitutions. This was the technique we used above, and, of course, this particular sentence is a very good one for this particular technique.

Classifying a sentence as deviant can often be the most useful first step in analyzing it in terms of what it deviates from, and how and why. Following Fodor[2], we might go further and, for example, introduce the notion of standard deviations from standardness, uniform mechanisms for producing and understanding whole classes of deviant sentences, e.g., irony.

In the present connection, I should like to take up an argument of Jakobson's against Chomsky's work. Jakobson contends[3] that certain sentences that are ruled out by Chomsky's description of English, for example, "Ideas are green.", are perfectly regular, non-deviant sentences. His view is that the sentence, "Ideas are green." is simply a false sentence. Now then, one should never call a sentence ungrammatical or even deviant at a semantical level if the only thing wrong with it is that it happens to be false. But I think that there is something decidedly wrong with the view that such sentences as "Ideas are green.", or "Virtue swims.", are *merely* "false".

I don't want to go into this issue at length, simply because it has been discussed for so many years by so many philosophers; but let me, as it were, allude to some of the results of the philosophic debate. In the first place, philosophers have found it useful to distinguish between a sentence-type or sentence on the one hand, and the various acts that could be performed with sentences of that type on the other, e.g., statement-making. As soon as one draws this distinction one is inclined to be unhappy with the notion of a *false sentence*. If a sentence had the feature that every token of the type could be used to make one and only one statement, and that statement had a clear truth-value—if it was always truth or always falsity—then one might understand the locution "This sentence is false." as short for "The statement that one would be making, if one employed a token of this type in order to make a statement, would be false." But the fact is that there are very few, perhaps no, sentences in English which can be used to make one and only one statement.

Moreover, I think the sentence "Ideas are green." is clearly *not* such a sentence. If one uttered the sentence "Ideas are green." one would probably

(which raises lots of questions about the theory of truth)

---

[2] In *Some uses of "use"*, Princeton Doctoral Dissertation, 1960.
[3] Op. cit., pp. 144–145.

be taken not to be making a statement at all, but to be doing something else —for instance, telling a joke, interrupting a conversation, *et cetera*. Try it and see! Linguists and philosophers are too prone *not* to make such simple experiments as this one. But I am quite serious. Try to use the sentence "Ideas are green." to make a statement, and see what reaction you get from your hearers. You may, in your own opinion, succeed in using the sentence "Ideas are green." to make a statement, but I doubt whether you will be taken as having made a statement by the people who listen to you. Giggles, rather than dissent, are likely to be the reaction you will face; and giggles, be it remembered, are the normal reaction when it is believed that someone, when uttering a sentence in a statement-making tone of voice has not made a statement and has not really in fact intended to make a statement.

But suppose we grant that, in some far-fetched circumstances perhaps, the sentence "Ideas are green." might be employed to make a statement. Jakobson says that the statement would be a false one—but how does he know? Presumably he thinks that there is only one statement that the sentence "Ideas are green." could plausibly be used to make, and that the statement is clearly false; but I would think, and many philosophers would agree with me that a) there is no statement that the sentence "Ideas are green." could plausibly be used to make, and b) there are a number of statements that the sentence "Ideas are green." could implausibly be use to make, and, of the latter, some are probably true and some are probably false.

Note that it would do no good to say in an authoritative tone of voice that when one says the sentence "Ideas are green." is false, one is assuming of course, that the sentence "Ideas are green." is being used to make one particular statement, namely the statement *that ideas are green*. For saying, with no contextual clue to help the hearer out, "When I say 'ideas are green', I *mean* ideas are green", is not saying what you mean at all. If someone says, "Well just consider the context of philosophic discussion. Suppose one asserted as an abstract truth, 'Ideas are green' he would have made a false statement, wouldn't he?" My position is that he wouldn't have made any statement that I understand at all.

But I don't wish to rest my case on the sentence-statement distinction just alluded to. Let me assume for the sake of argument that Jakobson is right; that there is, considered in the abstract, such a statement as the statement that ideas are green, and that this statement is clearly false. Does it follow that when we reject the sentence "Ideas are green." as deviant, we are rejecting it *merely* because it's "false"? Not at all! For suppose that my necktie is not green and consider the two sentences "Ideas are green." and "My necktie is green." Both are "false", but it is quite clear that the two sentences must be "false" in different ways. Traditional philosophers distinguished the two kinds of "falsity" as *a priori* falsity and *a posteriori* falsity. That is, "My necktie is green." is contingently false; on the other hand, the "statement" "Ideas are green." must, if it has a truth value at all, be *a priori* false. This distinction is, however, all we need to justify calling the sentence "Ideas are green." a deviant sentence, for as soon as we have the distinction between *a priori* and contingent falsity, we can ask, "What is the characteristic

of the nouns N, such that 'N's are green.' is not *a priori* false or nonsense?"
The characteristic would presumably be that these are the so-called concrete
nouns. This might be rendered by saying that the phrase "are green" "takes"
a concrete subject; and saying that the sentence "Ideas are green." deviates
from a linguistic regularity by employing with the phrase "are green" a subject that the phrase does not "take".

weak

Thus the sentences "Ideas are green.", "Virtue swims.", "Golf plays John.",
and so forth deviate from statable linguistic regularities, at least at the level
of semantics. Moreover, this is so independently of whether one regards
them as "false" or not. Showing that they are deviant may involve methodological problems; but these problems (of justifying a description of a language)
arise even at the level of grammar.

II. The line between grammar and semantics. So far, the only
question we have considered is the question whether a sentence is deviant or
non-deviant. Given that a sentence is deviant, we have not raised the further
question whether it should be called grammatical or ungrammatical. But this
question can no longer be postponed; for the job of a grammar is not to rule
out all deviant sentences—e.g., a grammar should not rule out the sentence
"The star by which seafarers normally steer is graceful."—but to rule out
only those deviant sentences whose deviancy is in some sense grammatical
deviancy. But how are we to tell whether a given case of deviancy is grammatical or semantical?

A position that I have heard linguists put forward is that there are two
sharply different kinds of deviancy, grammatical deviancy and semantical
deviancy, and that very little is grammatically deviant. That is to say, most
of the sentences we have been calling deviant are deviant, but deviant for
reasons that should be called semantical and not grammatical.

A few examples may make the dispute clear. These linguists would for
example reject the category "animate noun" as a permissible grammatical
category, although they would of course admit it as a potential semantical
category. Now, suppose a Frenchman says, referring to a table, "She is red,"
or, to put more of the context into the sentence itself, suppose he says,
"George gave me a table and I saw at once that she was red and had four
legs." Chomsky would say that this sentence is ungrammatical because the
pronoun "she" does not agree with the inanimate noun "table". These linguists,
on the other hand, would maintain that the sentence in question is grammatical, simply because they have no basis for calling it ungrammatical. One
wonders how they would deal with such languages as German and French,
where questions of gender have long been regarded as grammatical questions:
Would they proceed the same way, or would they have one policy for English
and another for French, and if so, on what basis? Their position, as I gather
it, is that it is only features that are arbitrary, that have nothing to do with
meaning, that are properly called grammatical. However, I agree with
Jakobson and with Boas, that there do not appear to be any arbitrary features
in a language in the sense indicated. For example, if one says that it is
arbitrary that we say "She is here." and not "Is she here.", the obvious

answer is that while it may be arbitrary in some absolute sense, in the context of English it is not arbitrary; we use one when we want to make a statement and the other when we want to ask a question. Notice that if we agree that the categories "abstract" and "concrete" should be prohibited in grammar, then on exactly the same grounds we should prohibit "masculine" and "feminine" on the one hand, and "indicative" and "interrogative" on the other.

There is, of course, an absolute sense which one has a vague feeling for but which one has difficulty putting into words, in which one is tempted to say that word-order in English *is* arbitrary; that is to say, the conventions determining *which* word-order is declarative and which is interrogative could conceivably have been reversed without, as far as we can see, impairing the functional efficiency of the language. The trouble is that in this absolute sense, if it can be made sense of at all, semantical features are just as arbitrary as syntactical ones. Any word might, after all, have meant something different from what it does mean.

Without prolonging this dispute any further, let us just say this: that adding a category to our grammar has mainly the function of enabling us to state more regularities. If these regularities seem to pertain to a very small class of sentences we will in general be unhappy at calling them grammatical regularities; if they pertain to a great many sentences, or to the use of important morpheme classes, e.g., the pronouns or the articles, then it will seem more conventional to call them grammatical regularities. On this view, exactly where we should draw the line between semantics and grammar is a matter of convenience, and not a genuine theoretical question at all.

III. Independence of meaning. An issue that we can hardly bypass, if only because it has generated so much controversy, is the issue between those who assert and those who deny that grammar can be done "independently of meaning". Among American linguists, Zellig Harris was the first I know of to emphasize this claim. On the other hand, Jakobson claims in the article alluded to above that Chomsky's monograph is a "magnificent *argumentum a contrario*" on this very point, and speaks optimistically of a pending "hierarchy of grammatical meanings".

As a preliminary to taking a look at this vexed question, let me consider a somewhat parallel (if irrelevant-sounding) question: "Can one discover a man's occupation without seeing him at work?" The answer is obviously "yes"—one can, for example, put the question "What do you do for a living?" But even if this is ruled out as "cheating", the answer is not necessarily "no". Sherlock Holmes, as we all know, could discover an enormous number of things about someone—not just his occupation—from the most irrelevant seeming clues. So the proper answer to the above question is (roughly): "It depends on how good a detective you are".

Coming to language: it is apparent that the question: "Can one discover the phonemes (morphemes, form-classes, etc.) of a language without learning the language (learning the meaning of any form, learning that any two forms are synonymous)?" is quite parallel to the occupation question, and it seems evident (to me, at least) that the immediate answer is the same: "It depends on how good a detective you are."

Thus, some linguists apparently maintain (at least when they are arguing this question) that one cannot discover the phonemes of a language without learning the meanings of the forms in that language (or at least learning that certain pairs are pairs of non-synonymous expressions). I am sure that these very same linguists, however, would not be surprised (provided the statement were not connected with this "controversy") to hear that some linguist had inferred the phonemes of a language X from the way the X-speaker spoke English (*a fortiori*, without learning X). One would, of course, regard this as an amazing "*tour de force*", but not as impossible in principle. But if someone could conceivably do this as a *tour de force*, why might he not do it repeatedly, and even train graduate students in the art. (Cf. the accomplishments of Pike in establishing rapid comprehension of portions of an alien language. These would count as an individual *tour de force*—except that Pike has repeated the "TRICK" on many occasions, and has taught it to some of his students.) Finally, why might one not even "mechanize" such a trick, by reducing it to say a standardized test of some kind that could be administered by a properly trained clerk (or a machine)?

Again, if there is nothing inconceivable in the idea of someone's inferring the phonemes of a language from the way the speaker of that language speaks a different language, why might not a list of nonsense syllables take the place of the different language? I am not saying that any of these procedures is practicable today or will ever be practicable, but only that no issue of principle is involved. Every linguist believes that phonemics have an "obligatory" character, and that the phonemics of one's native language influence the way one speaks (in the overwhelming majority of cases) even when one is speaking a different language, reciting (or making up) nonsense syllables, etc. But then how on earth could it be impossible in principle to discover the phonemes of an alien language except in one way?

Viewed in this light, Harris' methods do not appear so surprising. Harris discovers the phonemes of a language in roughly the following way: the linguist recites a sequence of expressions, e.g. "cat, cat, cad, cab, cab, cad", and the informant describes what he heard. If the informant says: "you said A twice and then B and then C twice and then B" (where A, B, C in the above example would be cat, cad, cab as pronounced by the informant, or approximations thereto) then one would conclude (tentatively, of course!) that b, c, t were allophones of different phonemes in the alien tongue. On the other hand, if the informant says: "you said A three times and then B twice and then A again" (where A is cad or cat or something intermediate, and B is cab) then one would be pretty sure that b, d were allophones of different phonemes and d, t were allophones of the same phoneme in the alien language. (Harris would normally use expressions in the alien language itself in this test, but the test might conceivably "work" with nonsense syllables, in which case one would have the possibility envisaged in the preceding paragraphs.)

Coming to morpheme boundaries, Harris again uses "structural" methods, instead of relying on such notions as "shortest meaningful unit". I will not describe these methods in detail, but they depend roughly on the counting of "exclusions"—that is, sounds that cannot occur immediately after certain initial segments of sentences, e.g., all sounds except "t" are excluded after the initial segment "Isn't that a daguerreo-". These exclusions are exclusions "going from left to right". Similarly one can count exclusions "going from right to left"—that is, sounds that cannot occur immediately before certain terminal segments of sentences (e.g., "h" is excluded immediately before "-ing". Then (Harris finds) morpheme boundaries can be identified as local minima in the number of exclusions which are minima counting both from left to right and from right to left. This test not only does not "depend on meaning", but seems more successful than any test that *does* "depend on meaning" that I know of.

But why should all of this evoke argument among linguists? I don't mean, why should Harris' methods in particular evoke argument (anybody's methods naturally evoke argument, in any science)—perhaps these particular methods don't work; I mean, why should there be argument that methods of this kind *can't* work in principle? Why couldn't there be a linguistic counter-part of Sherlock Holmes?

I suppose what is bothering Harris' opponents is this: the notions "phoneme" and "morpheme" have been conventionally defined in terms of semantical notions; hence any method of discovering what the phonemes/morphemes of a language are must utilize semantical information. But this is a non-sequitur! (Just as it would be a non-sequitur to conclude from the definition of "occupation" as the way a man makes his living, that one cannot *discover* a man's occupation unless he is engaged in working.) Language is doubtless learned when its various parts are performing their various semantical functions; but once one has learned the segmentation of one's language into parts, one may "give away" this segmentation in other apparently irrelevant contexts, just as one may give away anything else one knows.

Of course, I should not like to give the impression that I believe Harris to have found a procedure whereby one cannot fail (in principle) to discover the phonemes or morphemes of a natural language. Harris and his opponents both seem to think that linguistics can provide uniform discovery procedures. I agree with Chomsky that whether one uses "semantical information" about a language or not, the objective of a uniform procedure for discovering the correct description is as utopian in linguistics as in any other natural science. And that is yet another reason for finding the pseudo-issue of "independence of meaning" not very interesting; it depends too fundamentally on the misconception that the task of linguistic theory is to eliminate the theorist altogether, not just to provide him with useful tools (tests, procedures, etc.).

IV. The autonomy of grammar. An issue closely related to the one discussed in the preceding section is this: Is it possible to define the fundamental concepts of grammar, e.g., "morpheme" "phoneme" in non-semantical terms? Although this issue *is* closely related to the one discussed in the preceding section, it is important to realize that two distinct issues are involved. In the preceding section we were discussing the feasibility of discovery procedures in linguistics which do not require any semantical

information, as input. In this section we are discussing the way in which
certain fundamental concepts in linguistics should be defined. Unfortunately,
a great deal of confusion seems to be rife in linguistic circles as to the
difference between these two issues.

Chomsky seems inclined to the view that the fundamental concepts of
structural linguistics can be defined without employing any semantical notions,
and this is perhaps what he means when he speaks of the autonomy of grammar. On the other hand, it should be realized that even if Chomsky is wrong,
his work cannot possibly be taken as an *argumentum a contrario* against the
thesis of the autonomy of grammar, simply because Chomsky does not, in
fact, define the fundamental concepts of structural linguistics at all. He takes
them as primitive or undefined notions in his entire work. Indeed, it is just
this that makes Jakobson's attack on Chomsky so puzzling. Many of Jakobson's criticisms are to the effect that certain sentences are being ruled out
by Chomsky as ungrammatical merely because they are false or somehow
absurd on the basis of their meaning. But this would seem to indicate, not
that Chomsky is placing too little reliance on meaning but too much reliance
on meaning. If anything, the charge should then be that Chomsky's work
is an *argumentum a contrario* against the possibility of basing a grammar on
certain fundamental semantical notions, e.g., truth and falsity. Certainly it
is not an *argumentum a contrario* against the thesis that there exist non-
semantical discovery procedures in linguistics, because Chomsky refrains from
talking about discovery procedures at all, except to express a pessimism (which
I share) with respect to the possibility of finding useful uniform discovery
procedures, whether or not one uses semantical information; and, as just
remarked, Chomsky does not define the fundamental notions "phoneme",
"morpheme", "noun", "verb", etc. at all; rather, he models his grammar exclusively on a hypothetico-deductive system in which certain terms are taken
as "primitives". But Chomsky's work aside, we are left with the question
of just how, if at all, to define such notions as "phoneme" and "morpheme".

Before saying something about this question, however, let us first consider
what might be meant by the distinction between semantical and syntactical
notions, as applied to a natural language. I wish to suggest that we might
take the fundamental syntactical notion to be the notion of structural identity.
We might say that two sequences of phones in a natural language are
structurally identical if a speaker of the language counts them as the same
expression and otherwise structurally non-identical. Of course, this raises a
number of problems: It is not crystal clear what it means to say that a
speaker of a natural language counts two phone sequences as the same expression, apart from contexts in which we have available a bilingual informant
who is willing to make explicit metalinguistic statements, at least of a very
simple kind ("You said the same word twice!"), and a linguist who is willing
to rely on such explicit metalinguistic statements. If we ask for characterization of what it means to say that an informant counts two phone sequences
as the same, where the informant is a speaker of only one language x, and
the characterization is to be wholly behavioral, and not to refer to dispositions
to make certain kinds of explicit metalinguistic statements about x, then we

shall probably not be able at present to say very much. Moreover, even if we succeed in thinking of a number of things that we might call "symptoms" of the disposition to count two phone sequences as the same expression, it would still be a mistake to think that one could arrive at an explicit definition of this disposition in terms of such symptoms. I will not go into this last point any further, since to do so would take us afield into the familiar controversy pro and con operationalism. Instead I will just remark that here we are reminded that linguistics is after all a social science and that its fundamental concepts have the same kind of dispositional and human character as do the fundamental concepts of any other social science.

Another less serious problem that we must face is this: What if someone says that the relation of structural identity, as defined above, is a semantical notion and that therefore syntax, as the study of the properties of phone sequences that are invariant under this relation, is a branch of semantics? This problem is not serious because it is obviously purely verbal. Of course, one can "prove" that syntax is not autonomous by defining the terms "syntax" and "semantics" so that syntax becomes *by definition* a part of semantics. But no useful object is thereby gained. I would propose, guided admittedly by the usual practice in formal languages, to take as the fundamental notions of semantics the notions of truth and synonymy; and my thesis is that the relation of structural identity of expressions is more basic than the notions of semantics in two senses: the latter notions seem to presuppose the former notion; and the notion of structural identity is, I believe, not definable in terms of the semantical notions referred to.

Assuming that the notion of structural identity and non-identity is an acceptable one, however, we are part of the way to the notion of a phoneme. Namely, the notion of a contrasting pair may now be defined. Two structurally non-identical phone sequences A and A' are a contrasting pair, if A is identical with A' except that A' contains one occurrence of a phone P', where A has one occurrence of a phone P. In this case we shall also say that P and P' are verifiably non-equivalent phones. Now then, if the complementary relation, the relation of *not* being verifiably non-equivalent phones, were only an equivalence relation, we should have the full notion of a phoneme. Namely, the phonemes would be just the equivalence classes generated by this equivalence relation. Unfortunately, and this is what makes the notion of a phoneme a somewhat difficult one, although it is obviously based on the relation of not being verifiably non-equivalent phones, the relation which holds between two phones if and only if they are allophones of the same phoneme *is* to be an equivalence relation. What one does in practice is to seek the biggest relation which *is* an equivalence relation and whose complement includes the relation of verifiable non-equivalence alluded to above. But in general there is no unique such biggest relation, and thus there is some degree of arbitrariness in the classification of the phones of a language into separate phonemes. What this goes to show, however, is not that the notion of a phoneme is fundamentally a semantical one, but that it is to some extent a defective one; or to put it better, that it should be relativized not just to a language but to a particular description of a language.

To sum up: The classification of phones into phonemes is a somewhat artificial classification which is based on deliberately ignoring the fact that the complement of the verifiable non-equivalence relation is not an equivalence relation. But this classification, artificial though it may be, is by our lights a purely structural matter. Phonemics, then, is autonomous in Chomsky's sense. When we come to the notion of a morpheme, however, it is more difficult to know what to say. Speaking for myself, I should say that I have never seen a satisfactory definition of this concept in either semantical or non-semantical terms. Also, I am not satisfied with Chomsky's idea of taking the concept as primitive. The trouble with modeling linguistic theory on the notion of a hypothetico-deductive system is that the model does not seem a particularly reasonable one. A hypothetico-deductive system is a reasonable model for a physical theory in which one is inferring unobservable entities from observable entities. But I don't think that Chomsky wants to say that morphemes are inferred entities, and if he does want to say this, then *I* want to say that I find myself very unclear as to the alleged nature of these inferred entities and as to the nature of the supposed inference to their existence. Sometimes Chomsky writes as if he held both the view that a hypothetico-deductive system is a reasonable model for a physical theory and the view that the primitive terms in such a system need not be supposed to refer to anything. On this view, scientific theories are, so to speak, merely computational devices. I don't know whether I do Chomsky an injustice or not in ascribing this view to him. But I do know that I do not find it an acceptable philosophy of science for physics, and I should be extremely suspicious of the view that it was an acceptable philosophy of science for any one of the social sciences, including linguistics.

Another possible way out would be this: We might say that the morphemes of a language, relative to a particular grammar, are the shortest phone sequences which are assigned to phrase-structure categories in that grammar. Besides bringing in a host of new undefined terms, e.g., phrase-structure categories, this proposal would have the drawback of relativizing the notion of morpheme to a grammar. This relativization goes against the very deep-seated intuitive feeling that a language does have natural building blocks, no matter how difficult it may be to make this concept of the natural building-block precise, and that the morphemes are they.

Yet another proposal, which is extracted not so much from Chomsky's work as from discussions with Chomsky, might be to first relativize the notion of a morpheme to a grammar, in the way just proposed, and then to say that the "real" morphemes in a language are to be identified with the morphemes according to a simplest grammar of that language. This last proposal seems to have two objectionable features: First, that it is by no means clear that there is such a thing as a well-defined simplest grammar of a natural language, and secondly that if there is such a thing, then there may be two simplest grammars A and B which do not segment the language into building-blocks in the same way. If this last eventuality—the possibility of two non-isomorphic simplest descriptions of a natural language—is not really a possibility, then the reason it is not really a possibility must be that a natural language really has a set of fundamental building-blocks in some sense which has nothing to do with descriptions of that language. But then we should try to make that sense clear, and not go the long way around via talk about all possible theories and via employment of the catch-all term "simplicity".

I am not recommending that we abandon the concept "morpheme"; I think the vague characterization of the morphemes as the smallest units that belong to phrase-structure categories is enough to go on for the time being. On the other hand, further attempts to provide a foundation for the notion are clearly in order. To put it bluntly, I feel that there are a great many things here that are presently not *understood,* and that it will take more insight into language structure as a whole before we are able to say in precisely what sense a language has natural building-blocks.

V. The grammatical sentences of a language are a recursive set.

In this section I should like to present evidence of several kinds for the view that the grammatical sentences of a natural language, under a mild idealization, form a recursive set. The following facts seem to me to point in this direction: (1) The self-containedness of language. By the self-containedness of language, I mean the fact that speakers can presumably classify sentences as acceptable or unacceptable, deviant or non-deviant, *et cetra,* without reliance on extra-linguistic contexts. There are of course exceptions to this rule, but I am more impressed by the multiplicity of non-exceptions. I imagine, for example, that if I were on any number of occasions presented with a *list* of sentences and asked to say which ones I thought were grammatical and which ones I thought were ungrammatical, I would on each occasion and without any information on the supposed context of use of the individual sentence classify "Mary goed home" as an ungrammatical sentence, and "Mary went home" as a grammatical sentence. This act of classifying sentences as grammatical or ungrammatical seems to be one I can perform given no input except the sentences themselves. In short, it seems that in doing this job of classifying I am implicitly relying on something like an effective procedure.

In this connection, I am of course relying on certain very general hypotheses as to the character of the human brain. To be specific, I would suggest that there are many considerations which point to the idea that a Turing machine plus random elements is a reasonable model for the human brain. Now, although the idea that random elements are a part of the human brain is important in the life sciences in a great many contexts, the present context is one in which the role of the random elements should be left out, at least for purposes of idealization. Even if it is true, that given a list of sentences to classify as grammatical or ungrammatical, my behavior would be to a tiny extent random, e.g., one time in a hundred I might classify "Mary goed home" as grammatical instead of as ungrammatical, this is a fact which we wish to leave out in our idealization. In other words, we wish to pretend that the classifier, if he will classify a sentence as grammatical on one occasion, will classify it as grammatical on any occasion. With this idealization in force, it seems to me that we are in effect committed (at least if we have the over-all mechanistic view of the brain that I do) to viewing the classifier as simply a Turing machine.

Even if the classifier is a Turing machine, however, it does not follow that the set of grammatical sentences is recursive. This only follows if the classifier is a Turing machine without input; or more precisely, without input other than the individual sentence that he is classifying. That the individual sentence that he is classifying may be regarded as the sole relevant input, amounts, however, to saying just that if a sentence is counted as grammatical, then it will be counted as grammatical even if presented on a different occasion, and even if different sentences have been previously presented; and this seems, if not exactly true of actual classifiers, at least a reasonable idealization. This, of course, is just what I mean by the self-containedness of language.

(2) A second argument supporting the view that the classification of sentences as grammatical and nongrammatical is something effective or mechanical (and hence that the set of grammatical sentences is recursive, at least if we assume Church's thesis) is the usability of nonsense sentences. As Chomsky has pointed out, one can perfectly well ask a classifier to look through a list of nonsense sentences and to say which ones are grammatical and which ones are ungrammatical. Here again it seems to be very much the case that the relevant input is simply the sentence being classified and that, moreover, the features of the sentence being classified that are relevant are almost certainly purely structural. Jakobson has pointed out that so-called grammatical nonsense sentences can often be construed, but I feel that we may neglect this in the present context. Even if it is true that after some minutes of reflection I can succeed in construing the sentence "Colorless green ideas sleep furiously." I feel very certain that I do not tell that it is grammatical by first construing it in the manner suggested in Jakobson's paper.

(3) A third consideration supporting the view that the classification of sentences into grammatical and ungrammatical is a machine-like affair is the teachability of grammar and the relative independence of intelligence level of this skill. Even a person of very low-grade intelligence normally learns both to speak his particular dialect grammatically and to recognize deviations from grammaticalness. It is important, of course, in connection with this point, not to confuse the grammar of the particular dialect with "grammar" in the high-school sense, that is to say, the grammar of the prestige dialect. I am well aware that people belonging to lower-income groups often speak "ungrammatically" (that is to say, they speak their own dialect perfectly grammatically, but speaking their own dialect is what is usually called "speaking ungrammatically"). My point is that a moron whose parents happen to speak the prestige dialect may have serious vocabulary deficiencies but he rarely has grammar deficiencies. He too learns to speak the prestige dialect, and to feel that there is something wrong with sentences that deviate from the grammatical regularities of the prestige dialect, even if he does not have the extremely complicated skill (parsing) which is required to say what is wrong. But an ability of this kind, which can be acquired by practically anyone or which can be utilized by practically anyone independently of intelligence level, is almost certainly quasi-mechanical in character.

I am willing to grant that no one of the considerations cited above is by itself decisive; but it seems to me that the collection of these facts—the self-containedness of language, the usability of nonsense sentences, and the relative universality of grammar intuitions within a dialect group, taken together support the model of the classifier as a Turing machine who is processing each new sentence with which he is provided according to some mechanical program. To accept this idealization, however, is just to accept the following model of grammar: that the grammatical sentences under consideration are a recursive set.

Accepting this idealization makes it legitimate to seek recursive function-theoretic structures which could serve as models for grammars. In Chomsky's book *Syntactic structures* a number of such models are examined and found too narrow. In particular, a widely used model, phrase-structure grammar, is found by Chomsky to be over-restrictive since it rules out certain extremely convenient types of rules. For example, the following very simple rule, which would seem to be a legitimate kind of linguistic rule, is not a phrase-structure rule. If S_1 and S_2 are grammatical sentences, and S_1 differs from S_2 only in that x appears in S_1 where y appears in S_2, and x and y are constituents of the same type in S_1 and S_2, respectively, then S_3 is a sentence, where S_3 is the result of replacing x by x *and* y in S_1.

To make an analogy with formal languages, we may say that phrase-structure grammars employ rules that correspond to axiom schemata in, say, the propositional calculus. On the other hand, a transformational rule like the familiar rule that "any formula of the form $(x)A \supset A'$ is to be an axiom, provided A' is like A except for containing free y wherever A has free x" already goes beyond the bounds of phrase-structure grammar. And Chomsky is, in effect, proposing that structural grammars may legitimately use rules that are modeled on the last-cited rule, and not just on axiom schemata.

I find the examples that Chomsky gives of transformations in English extremely convincing. (I mean his examples of permissible kinds of linguistic rules. There may be empirical objections to certain of them as statements about English.) However, Chomsky's general characterization of a transformational grammar is much too wide. It is easy to show that any recursively enumerable set of sentences could be generated by a transformational grammar in Chomsky's sense. Since, however, the whole motive for seeking transformational grammars was to reflect the character of natural languages and since the fundamental insight, if it is an insight, on which transformational grammars are based is the insight that the set of sentences in a natural language is a recursive set, then transformational grammars should be characterized in such a way that this feature is "built in".

In short, I think Chomsky has convincingly set the problem for theory of grammars—namely, the problem of delimiting a class of transformational grammars which is wide enough to include all the grammars we will ever want to write as grammars of natural languages, but not so wide as to include any grammar for a non-recursive language (that is, for a language in which the set of grammatical sentences is not recursive). This problem appears, however, to be extremely difficult. In closing I shall make a few remarks about the direction in which one might seek for a solution.

VI. The problem of characterizing transformational grammars.

The transformations employed by Chomsky in *Syntactic structures* mostly have the property that the product is longer than the datum. (1) It might be possible, without altering the resultant set of "terminal strings" (grammatical sentences yielded by the grammar) to rewrite the grammar so as to use *only* rules with this property (let us call them "cut-free" rules). Then (as is easily verified) the set of terminal strings would always be recursive.

The above suggestion (1) seems unattractive, however, since using only cut-free rules, even if it can be done (and it is not known whether or not it can be) involves *complicating* the statement of the grammar, and the main argument for admitting "transformations" in the first place was the resultant simplification.

(2) One might impose two restrictions on all grammars for natural languages: (a) that not more than n_1 words may be deleted in a deletion-transformation; and (b) that not more than n_2 deletion-transformation may occur in the derivation of a terminal string, where n_1, n_2 are constants depending on the language. However, the second restriction seems *ad hoc* and unattractive. (The first restriction can usually be met in a natural way, e.g., by confining deletions to cases of the form "preposition + pronoun.") It seems to me that it would be quite natural and important to seek to prove a theorem of the form: *Whenever one can derive σ in L* (where σ is a variable over terminal strings and L is some language), *one can find a* derivation (of the same string σ) *which does not use more than n_2 deletions* (where n_2 may depend on L); but this is quite different from making a restriction on the number of deletions part of the definition of a derivation. However, there is no hope of proving a theorem of this kind for all L's which posses a transformational grammar, unless one first has a suitable definition of "transformational grammar." This, then, is a significant (and probably very difficult) open question: to define "transformational grammar" in a way which (i) wide enough for all linguistic purposes; (ii) free of "artificial" clauses like the one restricting the number of uses of deletion in a derivation; and (iii) such that a "cut-elimination" theorem will be forthcoming about all L's with a transformational grammar. Unfortunately, I have no idea how to solve this problem.

PRINCETON UNIVERSITY,
    PRINCETON, NEW JERSEY

CONGRAMMATICALITY, BATTERIES OF TRANSFORMATIONS AND GRAMMATICAL CATEGORIES

HENRY HIŻ

I am dealing here[1] with that branch of grammar which takes a body of sentences given empirically as its starting point, which compares sentences, which arranges them in grammatically connected sets and, by pointing out their similarities and differences arrives at structures of sentences and at smaller units into which sentences are analyzable. This procedure is manifestly the reverse of a constructive or generative path in grammar where one attempts to build up sentences from more elementary constituents.

Between some sentences of a language a specific grammatical relation holds which may be called congrammaticality. This can be illustrated by a pair of sentences of which one is a negation of the other or a pair where one sentence is a question to which the other is an answer. Congrammaticality is, roughly speaking, the relation of being sentences for similar reasons. This intuitively obvious relation is cumbersome to describe precisely, but it can be defined within the usual conceptual apparatus. Congrammaticality is a relation between sentences and not between abstract structures, like trees, even though abstract structures may be needed to define it. Just as the relation of successor occurs between natural numbers, but to define it one uses tools from set theory.

To define congrammaticality I make six assumptions.

(1) It is understood what a segment of a text is. In many examples that follow, segments will be continuous fragments of written texts, fragments that may be composed of half words but not of half letters. For other purposes one can take phonetic fragments of utterances as segments.

(2) Concatenation[2] of segments leads to new segments. Thus concatenation of two segments that actually occur in a language may lead to a segment that does not occur in the language. In English an initial $l \frown r$ does not occur though its two components do occur in other environments. The notion of a segment is therefore revealing about the language under study only in this: a segment is divisible into segments each of which occurs in the language; some segments are never parts of sentences.

(3) Conformity[3] is a relation between segments by virtue of which two segments are recognized as looking the same.

(4) The unspecific large quantifier 'there are many' is used in the way

---

[1] This paper was written while I was engaged in the Transformations and Discourse Analysis Project at the University of Pennsylvania. The project is sponsored by the National Science Foundation. All co-workers on the project contributed substantially to the ideas presented in this paper.

[2] About concatenation see [8, pp. 172–174] and [5, p. 217].

[3] The notion of conformity was first introduced into the study of (formal) languages in [6].

suitable for linguistics. To say, e.g., that in a large segmented text there are many segments, or discontinuous combinations of segments, satisfying a given condition means that a suitably large proportion of segments of the text, or of such combinations, satisfy the condition. To say 'there are many' is not the same as to say 'there are some' nor 'there are infinitely many.' The claim that there are many adjectives in Latin does not assert that they are infinitely numerous, but that the set of Latin adjective constitutes, say, 4 per cent of the total Latin vocabulary. The assertion that there are many Latin prepositions is false, because it is easy to list all the Latin prepositions.

(5) A list of specific segmental constants

$$C_1, C_2, \cdots, C_n$$

is presupposed. The choice of constants for the list is not unique for a given language, and grammars of the language may slightly differ due to different choices of constants. In practice every such list will contain most frequent "grammatical morphemes" and will resemble the list of chapter titles in a grammar primer. Prepositions, flexion suffixes and prefixes, articles, classifiers, conjunctions are typical constants useful as a basis for a grammar. It seems that grammars are often built by distinguishing some classes of segments with only a few members, each of the other classes containing very many members.

(6) Lastly, it is assumed that sentences are segments which are sharply distinguished from segments that are not sentences. Though in practice there may be hesitations about sentencehood of many segments, the grammatical considerations that follow are relative to a decision (possibly an arbitrary one) in each case.

As a technical device I shall use the concept of a sequence of symbols each of which is either a constant C_i from the assumed list or a numeral. A numeral is used here just as a place-holder. Two sequences may be such that the very comparison of them forces us to distinguish between some elements but does not require us to distinguish between some others; so that, two symbols in succession may be taken as if they were a single symbol. Thus in the pair of sequences

$$\langle 1, 2, 3 \rangle \quad \text{and} \quad \langle 3, 1, 2 \rangle$$

1 and 2 are not distinguished but 3 is.

A recursive definition of a distinguished symbol in a set of sequences says that:

(a) every constant is distinguished;

(b) if a sequence in the set is composed of one single symbol only, then the symbol is distinguished;

(c) every symbol that appears in two sequences of the set with different immediate neighbors is distinguished (more precisely this is composed of three conditions: (c') if there are sequences $X = \langle x_1, x_2, \cdots, x_k \rangle$, $Y = \langle y_1, y_2, \cdots, y_m \rangle$, $Z = \langle z_1, z_2, \cdots, z_p \rangle$ (Y and Z not necessarily different, but each different from X) and there are i, j, h (not necessarily different) such that x_i, y_j and z_h all conform to each other and x_{i+1} does not conform to y_{j+1} and x_{i-1} does not conform to z_{h-1} where $1 < i < k, 1 < j < m, 1 < h < p$, then x_i is distinguished; (c'') if there are X and Y as before and there is j $(1 < j < m)$ such that x_1 conforms to y_j and x_2 does not conform to y_{j+1}, then x_1 is distinguished; (c''') if there are X, Y, and j as before such that x_k conforms to y_j and x_{k-1} does not conform to y_{j-1}, then x_k is distinguished);

(d) if the immediate neighbors are distinguished, then the symbol is distinguished (this is composed again of three conditions on $X = \langle x_1, x_2, \cdots, x_k \rangle$ in the set: (d') if x_{i-1} and x_{i+1} $(1 < i < k)$ are distinguished, then x_i is distinguished; (d'') if x_2 is distinguished, then x_1 is distinguished; (d''') if x_{k-1} is distinguished, then x_k is distinguished);

(e) if a symbol conforms to a distinguished symbol, it is distinguished.

If in a (finite) set of sequences every symbol is distinguished and the set of numerals occrring in one is the same as the set of numerals occurring in any other sequence, then the sequences of the set are called related. Thus if sequences are related, they differ at most by constants, permutations, or repetitions.

Here are a few examples of sets of related sequences.

(1) $\langle 1 \rangle$, $\langle 1 \rangle$;
(2) $\langle 1, C \rangle$, $\langle 1, C \rangle$;
(3) $\langle 1, 2, 3, 4, 5 \rangle$, $\langle 5, 1, 2, 3, 4, 3, 1 \rangle$;
(4) $\langle 1, 2, 3, 1 \rangle$, $\langle 3, 2, 2, 3, 1 \rangle$;
(5) $\langle 3, 1, 2, 4 \rangle$, $\langle 3, 1, 2, 3, 4 \rangle$, $\langle 2, 3, 4, 1 \rangle$;
(6) $\langle 1, 2, 3, 4 \rangle$, $\langle 1, 2, 4, 3 \rangle$, $\langle 3, 2, 4, 1 \rangle$.

About sets of related sequences one can prove the following theorem.

If, in a set of related sequences, **a, d** occurs and **b, e** occurs, then the set of sequences resulting from replacing **a** by **b, c** and **e** by **c, d** is also a set of related sequences.

The theory of related sequences, besides its applications to linguistic analysis, may be of interest in itself. Sequences considered here resemble the kind of graphs Goodman and Pownall[4] consider. An obvious, but not easy, generalization may be to sets of n-dimensional matrices; another one to infinite sequences.

If in a set of related sequences one replaces numerals by linguist segments uniformly (conforming segments for conforming numerals) and one obtains a sentence in place of each sequence of the set, then these sentences are locally congrammatical. "Locally" here means "irrespectively of the rest of the language."

For instance

(1) The pill hits the window

and

(2) The wind hits the pillow

are locally congrammatical. They are obtained from the pair of related sequences $\langle 1, 2, 3, 4, 5 \rangle$ and $\langle 1, 4, 3, 2, 5 \rangle$ by replacements: *the* for 1, *pill* for 2, *hits the* for 3, *wind* for 4, *ow* for 5.

If we pay due respect to the rest of the language we define a set of sentences to be congrammatical when they are locally congrammatical and for each

---

4 See [3] and [7].

segment used in replacing numerals of the related sequences there are many
and varying segments which could have been used instead.

(1) and (2) are congrammatical only locally but not globally.

Instead of *the* in the sentences (1) and (2) one could use *a, my, a hard* and
many others, but instead of *pill* one can use only either a very few words
like *bill* or segments always ending on one of those few words—not satisfying
the requirement of variety of segments which one could use.

Note that the requirement that a numeral of the sequence be replaceable
by many and varying segments preserving sentencehood in each case is to be
understood in such a way that one changes replacements for a single numeral
holding all the other segments the same. Otherwise nearly all the sentences
of a language may prove to be congrammatical.

The same pair of sequences, $\langle 1, 2, 3, 4, 5 \rangle$ and $\langle 1, 4, 3, 2, 5 \rangle$ has many replacements that are globally congrammatical, e.g.

(3) Almost all young, vigorous, healthy boys know how to swim

(4) Almost all healthy, vigorous, young boys know how to swim.

In case of the pair of sentences

(5) A young and healthy boy swims

(6) A healthy and young boy swims

the use of the same sequences $\langle 1, 2, 3, 4, 5 \rangle$ and $\langle 1, 4, 3, 2, 5 \rangle$ is not the most
convenient. For, instead of *a* (or instead of *and*), not a great variety of seg-
ments can be used. But *a* and *and* are among most convenient constants for
English. (5) and (6) are globally congrammatical via the pair of sequences:
$\langle a, 1, and, 2, 3, s \rangle$ and $\langle a, 2, and, 1, 3, s \rangle$.

We defined congrammaticality of sentences using a method based on comparing sentences with the same material (except for constants) and discovering
where and how they differ and whether the difference is a systematic feature
of the language or only a local, isolated phenomenon. Note that congrammaticality is reflexive, symmetrical, and transitive. But congrammaticality
with respect to a sequence (the notion more useful than the general congrammaticality) is not transitive.

Obvious changes in the preceding definitions will extend the notion of
congrammaticality to cover a case when a sentence is congrammatical not
with a single sentence, but with two, three, or any finite set of sentences.
Thus

(7) John likes to swim but the weather is unstable

is congrammatical with the set of two sentences

(8) John likes to swim

and

(9) The weather is unstable.

It may happen that two sentences are congrammatical via a given set of
two related sequences and two other sentences are congrammatical via the
same set. This, as a rule, is not sufficient to conclude that there is a strong
grammatical connection between one pair of sentences and the other pair.
Thus

(10) John thinks she is pretty

and

(11) John thinks that she is pretty

can be obtained from the set of related sequences $\langle 1, 2 \rangle, \langle 1, \text{that}, 2 \rangle$. From this set one obtains similarly

(12) John likes painting

and

(13) John likes that painting.

Obviously, the sentences (10) and (11) are grammatically affiliated in many ways in which (12) and (13) are not.

The dissimilarity of these pairs may be explained in two ways.

Firstly, the set of admissible replacers for *she is pretty* in (10) and (11) is considerably different than the set of admissible replacers for *painting* in (12) and (13); many segments which can replace *she is pretty* in the first pair cannot replace *painting* in the second. One can define a co-occurrence[5] difference, on a particular position, between similarly congrammatical pairs of sentences as the set of those segments which can occur at this position in both sentences of the first pair and not in both sentences of the second pair. Slightly more precisely: If X is a sequence in a set A of related sequences, a sentence α is obtained from X by replacing segments for numerals, and every segment obtained by similar replacements (conforming segments for conforming numerals) from every sequence in A is a sentence, then we say that α enters A at X.

If α, α' and β all enter A at X and α' is like α except for containing a segment γ in every place in which α contains a segment that replaces the numeral x_i of X and the segment β' which is like β except for containing γ in every place in which β contains a segment that replaces x_i is not a sentence, then γ is said to belong to the co-occurrence difference on the x_ith place between α and β.

Note that the co-occurrence difference is not symmetrical.

Thus (10) and (12) enter the set $\{\langle 1, 2 \rangle, \langle 1, \text{that } 2 \rangle\}$ at $\langle 1, 2 \rangle$. (11) and (13) enter the same set at $\langle 1, \text{that } 2 \rangle$. The co-occurrence difference on the second place between (12) and (10) is substantial and contains *painting, swimming,* etc. The second place co-occurrence difference between (10) and (12) contains nearly every sentence.

The structural strangeness in relating some sentences (like (10) and (12)) that enter a set of related sequences at the same sequence may be explained by studying their co-occurrence differences. As a rule, greater strangeness goes together with larger sets of co-occurrence differences. Moreover, the co-occurrence differences at various places may differ in size, and in this way "show" the pattern of strangeness between the sentences.

Secondly, besides studying their co-occurrence differences the intuitive unrelatedness of two pairs of sentences (like (10), (11), as against (12), (13)) may be traced to the fact that the sentences of the first pair are each congrammatical with another sentence via some new set of related sequences whereas

---

[5] The notion of co-occurrence was introduced in [4]. Here it is used in a slightly different way. For, firstly, only the co-occurrence difference and not a positive co-occurrence is used here, and secondly co-occurrence was in [4, p. 285], relative to grammatical categories like noun, adjective, etc., whereas here it is relative to a set of related sequences.

there is no sentence which is congrammatical with a sentence of the second pair via this particular set of related sequences. E.g., (10) is congrammatical with

(14)   John thinks hence she is pretty

via sequences $\langle 1, 2 \rangle$ and $\langle 1, \text{hence}, 2 \rangle$ but

(15)   John likes hence painting

is not a sentence.

Hence (10) enters a different set of related sequences than (12).

(10) enters, for example, the set

(A) $\langle 1, 2 \rangle$, $\langle 1, \text{that } 2 \rangle$, $\langle 1, \text{hence}, 2 \rangle$

(12) enters, among others, the set

(B) $\langle 1, 2 \rangle$, $\langle 1, \text{that}, 2 \rangle$, $\langle 1, \text{his}, 2 \rangle$.

It is important that (10) does not enter (B) and that (12) does not enter (A). In the study of a language it is useful to record not only what can occur, but also what quite definitely cannot occur. Therefore it may be helpful to introduce into a set of sequences also negative components. E.g., to characterize (10) more fully we may add *not* $\langle 1, \text{his}, 2 \rangle$ to (A).

Now, a set the elements of which are either sequences or negatives of sequences and which is such that all sequences that take part in it (occurring positively or negatively) together constitute a set of related sequences is called a battery of transformations.[6] In other words a battery of transformations is composed of sequences that form a set of related sequences after all the negatives of sequences are taken as positive occurrences of the same sequences. For a negative of a sequence $\langle x_1, x_2, \cdots, x_m \rangle$ I shall write

$$* \langle x_1, x_2, \cdots, x_m \rangle .$$

(10) enters at $\langle 1, 2 \rangle$ the battery

(A') $\langle 1, 2 \rangle$, $\langle 1, \text{that}, 2 \rangle$, $\langle 1, \text{hence}, 2 \rangle$, $\langle 2, \text{and}, 1 \rangle$, $\langle 1, \text{that}, 1, \text{that}, 2 \rangle$, $* \langle 1, \text{his}, 2 \rangle$, $* \langle 1, \text{the}, 2 \rangle$, $* \langle a, 2, \text{is what}, 1 \rangle$.

On the other hand (12) enters at $\langle 1, 2 \rangle$ the battery

(B') $\langle 1, 2 \rangle$, $\langle 1, \text{that}, 2 \rangle$, $\langle 1, \text{his}, 2 \rangle$, $\langle 1, \text{the}, 2 \rangle$, $\langle 1, \text{that}, 1, 2 \rangle$, $\langle a, 2, \text{is what}, 1 \rangle$, $* \langle 1, \text{hence}, 2 \rangle$, $* \langle 2, \text{and}, 1 \rangle$.

(A') and (B') differ in many components. This fact constitutes the basis for a second explanation of the feeling of strangeness between (10) and (12), the first explanation having been found in the large co-occurrence differences between (10) and (12). That is, although two sentences enter a battery of transformations at the same sequence, one of them may enter another battery which the second sentence does not enter.

There are intrinsic connections between co-occurrence differences of two sentences and the batteries of transformations that they enter. About these connections I would like to propose two hypotheses.

HYPOTHESIS 1.   If two sentences α and α' that enter the same battery A of transformations at the same sequence X have a substantial co-occurrence difference on the kth place, then there are batteries of transformations B and

_____

[6] A battery of transformations is a concept that is a generalization of two (different) notions of transformations, one found in [4], the other in [1] and [2].

B' such that α enters B at X and α' enters B' at X, α does not enter B' nor α' enters B, many sentences resulting from α by putting at the kth place elements of the co-occurrence difference enter B at X, and many sentences obtained from α' by putting at the kth place elements of the co-occurrence difference do not enter B'.

Hypothesis 1 claims, roughly speaking, that if there are substantial differences in what can be substituted at a given place in two sentences, then the two sentences are subject to different batteries of transformations. A battery (B) reflects a large co-occurrence difference.

To state the second hypothesis I need a definition of a refinement.

A sequence X' is a simple refinement of a sequence X if and only if X' is obtained from X by replacing an element by one or by several elements.

A sequence X' is a refinement of the sequence X if and only if there is a finite sequence of sequences which starts by X and ends by X' and is such that each sequence in it is a simple refinement of the preceding one.

A battery B is a refinement of a battery A if and only if for every sequence in A there is a refinement of it in B obtained by a uniform process of replacements.

HYPOTHESIS 2. If α and α' enter a battery A of transformations at the same sequence X and if the co-occurrence difference between α and α' as they enter A is substantial, then there is a battery B such that B is a refinement of A and the co-occurrence difference between α and α' as they enter B is substantially smaller than in the first case.

In other words, refining the segmentations and adjusting the batteries one can considerably reduce a co-occurrence difference.

In this paper batteries of transformations play a similar role to the role played in other approaches by sequences of grammatical categories of successive segments in a sentence. One can therefore take numerals occurring in sequences of a battery as grammatical categories. A grammatical category is, then, relative to a battery. If Hypotheses 1 and 2 are true, then by building suitable batteries of transformations one can obtain more suitable grammatical categories. This does not mean, however, that there exists a uniform method of discovering suitable batteries for a language. There is no substitute for insight. But the methods described here are in many ways close to actually grasping the sentence structures in a language. Moreover, the methods are general enough to abstract from peculiarities of languages on which much of grammatical work is modeled. There is an effort here to present grammatical studies of a language as something open, changing, progressing. There are infinitely many batteries of transformations for a language. We change our grammar, our global view of the language, by shifting our attention from one finite set of batteries to another.

BIBLIOGRAPHY

1. N. Chomsky, *Three models for the description of language*, IRE Transactions on Information Theory vol. IT-2 (1956) pp. 113–124.
2. ———, *Syntactic structures*, 's-Gravenhage, Mouton and Co., 1957.
3. Nelson Goodman, *Graphs for linguistics*, this volume, pp. 51–55.

4. Zellig S. Harris, *Co-occurrence and transformation in linguistic structure*, Language vol. 33 (1957) pp. 283–340.

5. H. Hiż, *Types and environments*, Phil. Sci. vol. 24 (1957) pp. 215–220.

6. S. Leśniewski, *Grundzuge eines neuen Systems der Grundlagen der Mathematik*, Fund. Math. vol. 14 (1929) pp. 1–81.

7. Malcolm W. Pownall, *An investigation of a conjecture of Goodman*, University of Pennsylvania Doctoral Dissertation, 1959.

8. A. Tarski, *Logic, semantics, metamathematics*, Oxford University Press, 1956.

UNIVERSITY OF PENNSYLVANIA,
  PHILADELPHIA, PENNSYLVANIA

GRAPHS FOR LINGUISTICS

BY

NELSON GOODMAN

What I have to say may be no more immediately relevant to mathematical linguistics than would be expected from a philosopher who is neither a mathematician[1] nor a linguist. But I shall be discussing problems in the theory of structure; and not only is linguistics much concerned with structure but it is not so old a science that one can predict what aspects of the theory may eventually prove to be pertinent. Speculations concerning one or two possible applications to linguistics will be offered later in this paper.

The particular investigations of graph-theory I shall consider have to do with the derivation of a graph, given only the information, for each two points or nodes, whether they are or are not within some constant number of steps from each other. The graphs in question are all graphs of symmetric, locally finite, irreflexive, ancestrally connected relations. If the relation—that is, the relation of nextness in the graph—is N, then the relation M of being not more than k steps apart in the graph is the kth power of $N \cup I$ (N plus identity). The problem of constructing the graph from M is thus the problem of determining both N and k—that is, of extracting the roots of the relation M.

The relation M is required to be such that no two nodes in the graph bear the relation to exactly the same nodes; i.e., the M-neighborhoods of each two nodes must be different.[2] This requirement, that M be *separated*, will of course be violated in a finite array if k is too large. The most obvious approach to the problem of reconstructing the graph from M is based on the principle that two nodes are the nearer the more their M-neighborhoods overlap. What makes the problem interesting is that this principle does not by any means always work. It fails for nodes near the ends of linear graphs, for example; and more seriously, it fails to distinguish between next-pairs of nodes and diagonally-opposed pairs in a graph represented by an ordinary tesselation of the plane into squares.[3]

For ordinary linear graphs the problem is not very difficult. But it becomes more complicated if we allow "gaps" or "irregularities",—that is, if we suppose that some nodes are "unoccupied" and that M consists only of pairs of occupied nodes, so that some pairs of nodes are missing from M without violation of the stated conditions. Can we still reconstruct the linear order? Can we insert "gaps" to recover the regularity of the underlying graph? The first question was answered positively in my book [3]; and the second in articles

---

[1] The work reported here could have been carried out only with the cooperation of N. J. Fine and George Schweigert and—more recently—Malcolm Pownall. But there has been no opportunity to show them the present paper before publication, and they are in no way responsible for any blunders it may contain.

[2] A more stringent requirement would be needed to guarantee unique recovery in certain cases; see pp. 274–276 of [3].

[3] I regret that the publication schedule has not left time for the preparation of diagrams.

by Fine and Harrop [1; 2].   The theory is virtually complete for linear arrays.

That any tree without ends may be reconstructed from any relation meeting the stated requirements upon M has also been proved[4], although the problems pertaining to "unoccupied" nodes have been investigated only for linear arrays.

More complex graphs offer much greater difficulties.   Here we can at present deal only with thoroughly homogeneous graphs, disallowing boundaries and any other irregularities.   Not only node-homogeneity but also next-pair homogeneity is required: the relationship of every next-pair to the rest of the graph must be the same as that of every other next-pair to the rest of the graph.   Our problem is then to prove the following conjecture: *Any thoroughly homogeneous, connected, symmetric, irreflexive, and locally finite graph N may be defined from any (not necessarily known) separated power of N∪I.*   Apparently adequate means for such reconstruction in a wide variety of cases have been known for some time[5]; but proof of their adequacy is another matter.   Rather than attempt to prove this at once in full generality, we have had to seek a suitable classification of graphs such that the general proof could be approached through proofs of the conjecture for the several classes.   The classification itself, and some properties of certain types of array, may be of interest for linguistics.

The initial dichotomy, first suggested by George Schweigert, is into *cut-point* graphs, which become disconnected when any node is deleted, and *networks*.   The following auxiliary definitions are needed: The *order-number* o of a node in a graph is the number of nodes next to it in that graph. A *cell* is a minimal N-cycle in the graph; and the *cell-type* t of a graph is the number of nodes in a cell.   A cell is called triangular, square, etc., according as t is 3, 4, etc.   The *cell-number* c of a node is the number of cells to which the node belongs.

The simplest cut-point graphs are trees.   Other cut-point graphs may be derived from trees by replacing each next-pair in a tree by a triangle, square, etc.   Such graphs, consisting of loosely dangling polygons, might be called *chandeliers*.   Certain characteristics of trees and chandeliers are likely to be important with respect to possible applications.   In a tree, there is only one path between any two nodes.   In a chandelier whose cells are odd-numbered polygons, there is more than one path between any two nodes, but only one *minimal* path.   In a chandelier whose cells are even-numbered, there is more than one path between any two nodes, and it is not the case for every two nodes that there is only one minimal path between them.

Malcolm Pownall, in a recent doctoral thesis [4], has made an intensive investigation of the conjecture.   He has temporarily confined himself to graphs that meet the following further restriction: if node x is n steps from node y, then there is a node z next to x that is $n + 1$ steps from y.   This excludes all finite and certain infinite graphs.   Under this "extension" postulate, he has succeeded in proving the conjecture for all cut-point graphs of any order-number, cell-type, and cell-number.   He has also proved the conjecture, under

---

[4] My proof is outlined in [4].

[5] See [3], especially pp. 266–274.

the same restriction, for standard triangular-cell networks (where $o = c = 6$) and standard square-cell networks (where $o = c = 4$). These proofs should be easily extensible to more closely packed networks: triangular-cell networks with $o = c > 6$, and square-cell networks with $o = c > 4$.

But what happens in the case of less closely packed networks? Here I have come upon a rather curious result. Although for $o = c = 4$ there is an infinite square-cell network covering the plane, infinite square-cell networks of various finite diameters covering an infinitely long cylinder, and finite square-cell networks of varying sizes covering a torus, there is for $o = c = 3$ *only one* square-cell network. It consists of eight nodes and is topologically equivalent to the cube.

For triangular-cell networks, the results are similar. Where $o = c = 3$, the unique graph is the topological equivalent of the tetrahedron; where $o = c = 4$, the topological equivalent of the octahedron; and where $o = c = 5$, the topological equivalent of the icosahedron.

In standard pentagonal-cell networks, $o = c = 4$. Pentagonal-cell networks with $o = c > 3$ may be infinite; but with $o = c = 3$, the unique graph is the topological equivalent of the dodecahedron. Networks with larger cells are standard when $o = c = 3$, and may be infinite whenever $o = c > 2$. (Obviously where $o = 2$, whatever t may be, the only graph is a single t-sided polygon.)

That graphs of the five types in question are indeed unique and terminating is easily proved. That these are the *only* unique and terminating homogeneous networks with $o = c$ follows from Euler's theorem; for if there were others, there would be more than the five regular solids. Thus the present theorem complements Euler's. The present theorem derives uniqueness and overall finitude from purely local conditions, while Euler's derives the limitation to five graphs from local conditions plus overall finitude.

In some networks, which may be called *laces*, c does not equal o but rather $o/2$. Informally these graphs may be thought of as having two types of polygon alternating around a node; for example, squares and triangles, or squares and pentagons, or triangles and hexagons, etc. Since only the smaller polygons in each case are minimal cycles, only these count as cells; and there is always an even number of them containing any given node. Strict next-pair-homogeneity is preserved. In the simplest type of lace, each node lies in two triangles and two squares. This terminates: the only such graph consists of the topological equivalent of the cuboctahedron.

Although the terminating graphs obviously do not satisfy Pownall's extension postulate, our general conjecture is easily proved for them. Thus it is proved for all networks where c is equal to o and is less than standard. (It is of course also easily proved for the terminating lace described; but proof for other laces has not yet been attempted.)

The results concerning terminating graphs have a further interest Consider, for example, the following conditions upon a set of elements α and a symmetric, irreflexive, ancestrally connected relation R among elements of α:

  (a) Each element in α bears the relation R to just n others.

  (b) Each element in α belongs to just n different sets of three such that each pair of the three is an R-pair.

Our result concerning terminating graphs tells us that if n is 6 or more, α may be indefinitely large, even infinite; but that if n is 5, α must have exactly 12 elements; that if n is 4, α has exactly 6 elements; and that if n is 3, α has exactly 4 elements. The theorems concerning other terminating graphs may be similarly restated.

As for the relevance of graph-theory to linguistics, Chomsky uses trees for analyzing language structures, and Hiż suspects that more complex graphs are needed for some cases. Furthermore, how networks might enter into consideration is easily illustrated. Suppose we are studying the relationship of modification among words in a phrase. Let Q be the relation obtaining between two words when either modifies the other. Clearly the graph of Q for the phrase "happy and healthy boys and girls" will be:

We can readily build out this graph in square-cell form to represent modification-relationships in a larger set of words, e.g.,

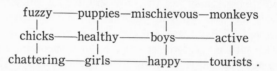

This perfectly reasonable pattern might obtain, but it can hardly be embodied in an English sentence (except by taking repetitions of a word as identical). We could, however, easily construct a language having no such limitation. On the other hand, certain limitations upon patterns that are possible at all in any language, natural or artificial, are set forth in our results concerning terminating graphs. Thus we can compare the scope of the structures permitted by a given language with the scope of those that are linguistically possible at all.

Again, consider the phrase "frosty white ground". We normally insist that the first word must modify either the second or the third exclusively; but we could allow it to modify each. Then we have a triangle:

$$
\begin{array}{c}
\text{frosty} \\
\diagup \qquad \diagdown \\
\text{white} - \text{ground} \; .
\end{array}
$$

On the same principle, every word in Quine's "pretty little girl's camp" might be taken as modifying each succeeding word[6]; and our graph would be a tetrahedron. Triangular-cell arrays of greater extent are quite possible. But if we take Q as R and n as 3, for example, only a set of exactly four words can meet the conditions upon α stated above.

---

[6] Modification-relationships between sequences of more than one word are ignored for the purposes of our example here.

If it seems at the present stage of structural linguistics that nothing more will ever be needed than the familiar rudiments of graph-theory, it probably seemed at a comparable stage in the development of physics that nothing more would ever be needed than elementary arithmetic.[7]

REFERENCES

1. N. J. Fine, *Proof of a conjecture of Goodman*, J. Symb. Logic vol. 19 (1954) pp. 41–44.
2. N. J. Fine and R. Harrop, *Uniformization of linear arrays*, J. Symb. Logic vol. 22 (1957) pp. 130–140.
3. Nelson Goodman, *The structure of appearance*, Harvard University Press, 1951.
4. Malcolm W. Pownall, *An investigation of a conjecture of Goodman*, Doctoral thesis, Department of Mathematics, University of Pennsylvania, January, 1960.

UNIVERSITY OF PENNSYLVANIA,
  PHILADELPHIA, PENNSYLVANIA

[7] This paper was prepared in conjunction with the Transformations and Discourse Analysis Project at the University of Pennsylvania, sponsored by the National Science Foundation.

SOME LOGICAL ASPECTS OF GRAMMATICAL STRUCTURE[1]

HASKELL B. CURRY[2]

1. Introduction. It is a common observation that human progress is most difficult in those fields which do not belong exclusively under one of the accepted major branches of knowledge. With respect to such fields we are frequently in the position of the six blind men and the elephant. According to this story one of the blind men, who got hold of the elephant's leg, asserted that he was like a pillar; a second, who had the animal by the tail, said that he was like a rope; another, who was up against the elephant's side, claimed that he was like a wall; while the remaining three, who touched the elephant's ear, trunk, and tusk, maintained with equal stoutness that he was like a sail, a hose, and a spear respectively.

The field here discussed—general grammar—is preeminently one of that character. It can be approached from the standpoint of linguistics, from that of logic, and from that of psychology; and each of these approaches discloses something not seen from the other. Moreover the logical aspect looks somewhat different from the standpoint of mathematics than from that of philosophy. Even the linguistic aspect is apt to be colored by the particular languages one has specialized in; and there is a suspicion that, in some quarters at least, preoccupation with the Indo-European languages has caused distortion.

In such circumstances progress is probably best made by bold cooperation. By this I mean that we should make as many different approaches as possible without too much fear, at first, of errors due to lack of omniscience; and, that each person should report his observation, in a manner intelligible to the other persons, without worrying about whether the latter have or have not already perceived the same thing.

In this spirit I shall attempt to explain certain impressions of the grammatical elephant as perceived by a blind man who has hold of it in rather an odd place. I do not claim any revolutionary character for these impressions; but, even so, the fact that they arise from the standpoint in question may be of some interest in itself. On that account I have given in §7 some details of the logical motivation.

2. Language and mathematical logic. The standpoint from which

[1] Based in part on a lecture delivered November 23, 1948, to the "comparative literature group", at what was then the Pennsylvania State College, under the title *The logical structure of grammar*. This was mimeographed by a group at the University of Chicago in 1949 and distributed to a number of persons. It was reissued with minor corrections at the Pennsylvania State University, July 27, 1959. The manuscript has been revised, and a new section, §7 has been added; but the elementary character of §§1–6 has been preserved.

[2] Some assistance in connection with preparation of this manuscript has been received from a research grant of the National Science Foundation, U.S.A.

this discussion starts is that of a particular aspect of mathematical logic. It is therefore expedient to begin by a discussion of the logical aspects of language in general.

That there is a close connection between mathematics and logic on the one hand and language on the other has been evident for some time, and is brought to a focus even more strongly by the existence of this symposium. The standpoint of mathematical logic has the following advantages. In the first place mathematics is itself a language in some sense—not, to be sure, in the same sense that English or German or Chinese or Eskimo is, but none the less a language with its own grammar and vocabulary.[3] Moreover it is a language which has been especially evolved for purposes where severe logic is essential; and therefore it is natural to suppose that its grammar would reflect the logical requirements more closely that of the natural languages. In the second place, much recent work in logic has been explicitly concerned with artificial languages of an idealized and simplified sort; and it is reasonable that the solution of the problem in these cases would be a useful prelude to the more complicated problems of the natural languages. Of course, the logical standpoint has its limitations; not the least of these is the circumstance that in all the natural languages logic is only one of the factors to be considered. Nevertheless, within its limitations the logical approach may be suggestive and interesting.

To a logician the term 'language' has acquired a sense different from that to which linguists are accustomed. In the most general sense a *language* is a system of objects called *symbols* which can be assembled into combinations called *expressions*. Here the terms 'symbol' and 'expression' are undefined; but for any given language they are defined by the conventions of that language. However, symbols are understood to be objects not too unlike the phonemes of speech or the letters of print, which can be produced in unlimited quantity. Generally the expressions are the finite linear series (or "strings") of such symbols; in that case I shall say the language is a *linear language*. If the language is or can be used for purposes of communication it will be called a *communicative language*; while a language in the sense of linguistics will be called a *natural language*.

3. A simple language. Before entering on a general discussion it will be expedient to consider a simple artificial language, which we shall call Language A. This shall have three symbols, viz.

$$a, b, c\ ;^4$$

---

[3] In 1937, and thus just a few years after the publication of his book [**Lng**], (for explanation of the letters in brackets see the Bibliography at the end of the paper) Bloomfield submitted to the Linguistic Society of America a manuscript of about 300 pp. entitled *The Language of science*. I was one of the persons who had the privilege of seeing and criticizing this document. It contained many interesting observations on the nature of mathematics. It is unfortunate that he was, apparently, unable to finish it.

[4] We shall regard the letters 'a', 'b', 'c' not as themselves the letters of the language A, but as letters being used in the present context as names for the letters of A. For this reason quotation marks about these letters are omitted.

and the language is to be a linear language, so that the expressions are the finite linear series such as

$$ababcbbca\ .$$

We now define a class of expressions called "sams" as the least class such that: 1) *a* is in the class; and 2) if *b* is added after any member of the class then the new expression is in the class. The sams then comprise all and only those expressions of the infinite list

$$a$$
$$ab$$
$$abb$$
$$abbb$$
$$abbbb$$
$$\ldots\ldots$$

Next we define a class of "tettles" as expressions formed by taking two sams and writing *c* between them. Finally we define the class of "tantets" as the least class of tettles such that: 1) *aca* is in the class; and 2) if *A* and *B* are sams such that *AcB* is in the class, then *AbcBb* is in the class. It is easily seen that the tantets are those tettles whose component sams are alike, i.e., a tantet is a tettle of the form *AcA*, where *A* is a sam.

All these definitions have been made without assigning any meaning to any of the expressions of Language A. Everything which we have done relates only to the way in which the expressions are formed from the symbols. Such considerations are called "syntactical" by most modern logicians.

It is now time to explain the meanings to be conveyed by Language A. This meaning will be introduced in three stages.

To begin with, the tettles of Language A are its sentences. This simple explanation tells us what the grammar of Language A is. The sams are evidently something analogous to nouns; *c* is a two-place verb which forms a sentence when flanked by two nouns, like 'strikes', 'pulls', 'loves', 'is' in English; while *b* is a suffix which forms nouns from nouns.

Next, the tantets of Language A are its true sentences. In that case *c* expresses the relation of equality, which we express in ordinary mathematics by '='.

Finally it will be explained that the sams denote numbers: *a* denotes the number 0, *ab* the number 1, *abb* the number 2, etc. In fact the words 'sam', 'tettle', 'tantet' are anglicized corruptions of the Hungarian words 'szám', 'tétel', 'tantét' which mean respectively 'number', 'sentence', and 'theorem'.

The explanation of meaning is now complete. It will be noted that *b*, employed as a suffix, indicates the operation of forming the successor of a number in arithmetic.

4. Semiotics. There has arisen a whole school of philosophers (and mathematicians) who place great emphasis on quasi-linguistic analysis of the sort just illustrated. Some of them call *semiotics*[5] the study of symbolic

[5] See Morris [**FTS**], and also, to some extent, his [**SLB**]; Carnap [**ISm**].

systems in general, whether artificial or natural, and divide the subject into three parts: 1) *syntactics*, i.e., the study of those considerations which depend only on the structure of the expressions as strings of symbols; 2) *semantics*, i.e., the study of those considerations which require a reference to communicative functions; and 3) *pragmatics*, which includes relations between the language and its users (psychological and physiological factors, etc.) Thus the discussion of Language A, in which we talked about sams, tettles, and tantets, was syntactical without admixture of any semantical or pragmatical element; but when we interpreted these terms we were doing semantics. Pragmatics, although it is, in a sense, the basis from which the other dimensions are formed by abstraction, will not concern us here. The semiotical senses of these words must not be confused with the senses which they have in linguistics; the term 'syntactics' is, perhaps, unfortunate, but it has become established.

As the example of Language A shows, we may conceive of semantics as itself divided into three stages. The first stage is concerned with the formation of sentences; let us call this *grammatics*, where the termination suggests that we are dealing with a theoretical science which is a part of semiotics related to grammar. The second stage is concerned with truth; let us call it *aletheutics*. The third stage may be called *onomatics*.[6]

Several remarks will now be made which are pertinent to this discussion.

In the first place the usage of the term 'semantics' may strike you as a little peculiar. There is some diversity of usage in regard to this term. Some authors seem to use it in the sense of 'onomatics'. This appears to have been the intention of Carnap in **[ISm]**.[7] He distinguished between rules of formation (the present grammatics), rules of truth (the present aletheutics), and rules of designation (the present onomatics). But the strictly onomatical considerations played only a secondary role, and could be dispensed with altogether; practically all the theorems proved in that book can be considered as purely aletheutical. Likewise the work of Tarski appears to identify semantics with onomatics; the notion of truth is defined in terms of a notion of satisfaction which is onomatical. There is also a widespread feeling that the notion of truth is semantical while the notion of sentence is not. But when I once asked a friend, who was stoutly maintaining this thesis, how he told what sentences were, he replied that in the last analysis it depended on the judgment of native speakers; if that is so, then a communicative (and perhaps also pragmatical) element is involved, and the notion is semantical according to the definition adopted here. Any reference to the use of the language for communicative purposes is semantical from the present standpoint.

The Language A teaches us also that, even though a concept is semantical, there may be a syntactical notion which is equivalent to it. Thus the sentences of A are the tettles, and the true sentences are the tantets; but the notions of

---

[6] These terms were first proposed in **[LFS]** and **[MSL]**. See also the discussion in **[CLg]** pp. 35–37.

[7] Cf. footnote 5.

tettle and tantet are purely syntactical. In mathematics, and particularly in mathematical logic, we have less trivial examples of the same situation. In the natural languages many persons think that we have something similar in the case of grammar. Although it has not yet been clearly established whether that is so or not, yet it is certainly admissible as an objective for research to seek for such theories. But we should bear in mind that, since there are known to be logical systems which can formulate their own syntax but not their own truth, it may turn out that a syntactical theory of grammar is impossible, or at least not practically attainable.

We shall be concerned here with grammatics—or grammar if you prefer. This may be defined as the considerations which define what the sentences of the language are. However it is not always clear, and I do not know how to make it clear, just what a sentence is. Thus Chomsky maintains that

Sincerity admires John

is not a sentence of English. As a native speaker of English I disagree. To me it seems a perfectly grammatical sentence, although an absurd one. Absurdity, however, is—at least to my linguistic instincts—not a grammatical concept but an alethetical one. This shows that the line between grammatics and aletheutics is not as sharp as one might suppose. The line is bound to be obscured if one bases his analysis too naively on distribution, since true sentences occur much more frequently in the discourse of sane human beings than false ones. How this difficulty is to be overcome I do not know. Perhaps we shall have to consider still other stages of semantics, intermediate between grammatics and aletheutics,—or other subdivisions of one or the other, corresponding to different levels of grammaticalness. However that may be, I shall suppose for the time being that the category of a sentence is sufficiently well known to form a basis for our present discussion.

After this preliminary discussion let us turn to our main theme, viz. to find concepts and principles for general grammatics.

5. Phrases and their fundamental classification. To begin with, it is evident that (for a linear language) expressions do *not* form a natural class of symbol combinations. Thus in the English sentence

I see both red and blue flowers,

the following expressions occur

see both red,

ed and bl.

On the other hand the words '*both*' and '*and*' together form a semantical unit, and therefore should form a grammatical unit. Let us use the term *phrase* for a symbol combination which forms a grammatical unit, i.e., a unit in the rules for determining what constitutes a sentence. This term we must regard, like 'symbol', 'sentence', and 'expression', as not otherwise defined. A phrase, as we have seen, may consist of detached parts.

Next, what are the main classifications of phrases? In Language A the following classes of phrases occur:

1) Sams. From the grammatical point of view these are essentially *nouns*.

2) Sentences, i.e., tettles.

3) Phrases which combine phrases to form other phrases. Such for instance is the suffix[8] b which, when affixed to a noun, forms another noun; and the infix c which, when placed between two nouns, forms a sentence. Such phrases were called "functors" by the Polish philosopher Kotarbinski, and the term will be adopted here.

A little thought will show that these are the fundamental categories for any conceivable mathematical language. It may be necessary to consider two or more different categories of nouns (such as individual-nouns, class-nouns, relation-nouns, etc.)[9]; but the nominal character of each of these kinds is clear. *Nouns, sentences,* and *functors* are, then, the basic grammatical categories. The first two categories together we call *closed phrases* in contradistinction to functors.

6. Functors. We now consider the functors more closely. Every functor combines one or more phrases, called its *arguments*, to form a new phrase called its *value*. Functors can evidently be classified as to the number and kind of the arguments and the nature of the value. Thus in Language A the suffix b is a functor with one nominal argument, and a nominal value; the infix c is a functor with two arguments, both nominal, and a sentential value. But before going further with this it is necessary to introduce some notation.

A functor is by definition a means of combining phrases to form other phrases. The complete specification of a functor must show how the value is to be made up. In other words we cannot represent a functor without blanks or other devices[10] to indicate where the arguments are to be inserted. In some natural languages certain case endings or word order performs this function. We shall use dashes with subscripts; the first argument is to replace the dash or dashes with subscript 1, the second that (or those) with subscript 2, etc. Thus the two functors mentioned for language A are $-_1 b$ and $-_1 c -_2$ respectively. (These are not the only functors in A; e.g., we have $-_1 bb$.)

At this point let us stop to emphasize that the notion of functor is not confined to words or affixes which are placed before or after their arguments, in the case of two arguments, between them. These, with the proper indication of the position of the arguments, are indeed functors; but they are not the most general ones. We have just seen an example, viz. 'both $-_1$ and

---

[8] The term 'suffix' is used here for a functor which follows the argument or arguments, 'prefix' for one which precedes its arguments, and 'infix' for a functor of two arguments which is placed between them.

[9] The distinction sometimes made between nouns and noun phrases is not taken into account here. From the present point of view these are just different kinds of nouns. Thus the discussion of Hill [ILS] p. 175 may be interpreted as meaning there are seven or more different kinds of nouns in English; Harris [MSL] Chapter 16 requires four or more.

[10] If a functor is described as a prefix, an infix, or a suffix, this may take care of this point, and in such a case further devices may be unnecessary.

$-_2$' of a functor consisting of detached parts. Even more general forms than this are conceivable. What Harris and Chomsky call transformations are also functors. A functor is *any* kind of linguistic device which operates on one or more phrases (the argument(s)) to form another phrase. A functor may, conceivably, so modify its arguments that even the notations involving blanks are inadequate to describe it.

A notation for describing kinds or "categories" of functors will now be introduced. Let X, Y, Z, U be grammatical categories. Then we can represent by

$$\mathsf{F}XY,$$

$$\mathsf{F}_2XYZ,$$

$$\mathsf{F}_3XYZU,$$

. . . .

respectively, the categories of functors with one argument in X and value in Y; those with two arguments, in X and Y, and value in Z; those with three arguments, viz. in X, Y, Z, and value in U; etc. If N represents the category of nouns, and S that of sentences, then the two primitive functors for Language A, together with the categories to which they belong, are:

$$-_1b, \quad \mathsf{F}NN;$$

$$-_1c-_2, \quad \mathsf{F}_2NNS;$$

while the 'both$-_1$ and $-_2$' of the sentence originally quoted above belongs to the category $\mathsf{F}_2(\mathsf{F}NN)(\mathsf{F}NN)(\mathsf{F}NN)$.[11]

In order to attain complete generality we must admit functors with other functors as arguments. As for the value, we note that

$$\mathsf{F}X(\mathsf{F}YZ), \quad \mathsf{F}_2XY(\mathsf{F}_3UVWT)$$

are the same categories respectively as

$$\mathsf{F}_2XYZ, \quad \mathsf{F}_5XYUVWT$$

and so on. In classifying functors we may therefore do either of the following: a) restrict attention to functors of one argument, but allow the value to be a functor, or b) allow functors of any number of arguments but require the value to be closed—in which case we speak of the value as the "closure". The former of these procedures is what is usually followed in linguistics, and is also used in some recent work in logic; the latter is in the spirit of mathematics and the usual symbolic logic. This latter method is more convenient for classification purposes. It should be noted that either method can be unnatural in certain cases. Thus the analysis

$$both-_1 \ and \ -_2 \quad \mathsf{F}_2(\mathsf{F}NN)(\mathsf{F}NN)(\mathsf{F}NN)$$

is more natural than either

$$both-_1 \ and \quad \mathsf{F}(\mathsf{F}NN)(\mathsf{F}(\mathsf{F}NN)(\mathsf{F}NN))$$

or

---

[11] In the original sentence, the phrase "both red and blue" as well as "red" and "blue" are understood to be adjectives (i.e., to belong to the $\mathsf{F}NN$ category).

$$both-_1\ and\ -_2-_3 \qquad \mathbf{F}_3(\mathbf{F}NN)(\mathbf{F}NN)NN .$$

The following table gives some examples of phrases belonging to various categories in the above scheme.[12] The first column gives the category; the second column gives examples from ordinary English; the third column gives examples from the technical language of mathematics. It will be noted that functors are classified into two main classes, primary and secondary: primary functors are those all of whose arguments are closed; secondary functors those of which at least one argument is another functor.

EXAMPLES OF PHRASES

CLOSED PHRASES

N	Proper nouns	$0, 1, 2, \cdots, e$
	Common nouns (tentatively)	
	Pronouns	
S	Sentences in usual sense	$x = y, 1 < 2, 2 = 3$
	Interjections	
	Noun in vocative case	

PRIMARY FUNCTORS

$\mathbf{F}NN$	Attributive adjectives	$\lvert -_1 \rvert$ (absolute value);
	Noun in genitive case	$(-_1)^2$ (square)
$\mathbf{F}_2NNN$	Adjective suffixes	$(-_1) + (-_2)$
	Genitive case ending	
$\mathbf{F}NS$	Intransitive verbs	$-_1 > 0$
$\mathbf{F}_2NNS$	Transitive verbs, copula	$-_1 = -_2, -_1 > -_2$
$\mathbf{F}_3NNNS$	Verbs with two objects	$-_1$ is between $-_2$ and $-_3$
$\mathbf{F}SN$	That $-_1$,	
	Verbal noun transformations	
$\mathbf{F}SS$	Negation	$\rightarrow-_1$
$\mathbf{F}_2SSS$	Coordinating conjunctions	$-_1$ & $-_2$,

SECONDARY FUNCTORS

$\mathbf{F}(\mathbf{F}NN)(\mathbf{F}NN)$	Adverb modifying adjective	Iteration of an operation
	Operation of attribution	Square of a function
$\mathbf{F}(\mathbf{F}NN)(\mathbf{F}(\mathbf{F}NN)(\mathbf{F}NN))$	Suffix '-ly'	Composition of functions
$\mathbf{F}(\mathbf{F}NS)N$	Verbal noun transformations	Least number satisfying a condition
$\mathbf{F}(\mathbf{F}NS)(\mathbf{F}NS)$	Adverbs modifying intransitive verbs	Complement of a condition
$\mathbf{F}N(\mathbf{F}(\mathbf{F}NS)(\mathbf{F}NS))$	Suffixes forming such adverbs from nouns	

[12] For further examples see [CLg] pp. 264–265, 274–275.

7. Concluding remarks. The idea of expressing categories by means of **F** was devised to meet the needs of a certain type of logic. It may help us to understand this notion, and some of its limitations, to describe this application briefly.

In the type of logic called combinatory logic[13] the formal metalanguage—i.e., that part of the language being used which serves to name the formal objects and to express the statements derivable within the system—consists solely of the following: a finite number of basic nouns, a two-argument functor, called *application*, forming a noun from two nouns, and a sentence-forming functor of one nominal argument. Yet in this system very complex types of logical system can be represented. In order to explain the paradoxes which have been known to logicians for about half a century, it was realized at an early date that one would have to formalize distinctions of semantical category within the system. In order to do this one needs: (a) nouns representing basic categories; (b) devices for forming derived categories; (c) axioms assigning categories to primitive notions represented by nouns; and (d) means for proving within the system that notions constructed from the primitives by the operations belong to appropriate categories. Since (XY), i.e., the application of X to Y, is interpreted as the value of X (as function) for the argument Y, an appropriate means of formalizing (b) and (d) is to postulate a notion, **F**, called the functionality primitive, and then to say that when X is an **F**$\alpha\beta$ and Y is an α, (XY) is a β. On this basis it is, I think, possible to treat from a unified point of view all the devices used by various logicians to avoid the paradoxes.[14]

Similar ideas concerning the semantical categories had previously been entertained. Leśniewski apparently placed emphasis on the idea that avoidance of the paradoxes required study of the semantical categories. From H. Hiż I understand that the idea goes back to Husserl. For an account of this earlier work and its recent developments the most accessible references are Ajdukiewicz [**SKn**] and Suszko [**SSS**].[15]

So much for the logical origin of **F**. The application of these ideas to linguistics came somewhat as an afterthought. It is natural to expect that the applications for that purpose would require some modification. But I think it is also true that the consideration of them suggests improvements in current linguistic procedures. I shall close with some comments along these lines.

In the first place, combinatory logic was formulated as a system in which the formal objects were rather differently conceived than was the case in standard formalizations of logic. The standard procedure at that time was

---

[13] For further information concerning this system see [**CLg**], especially Chapters 1 and 8. For briefer treatments see, besides the papers cited in [**CLg**] p. 1, the introductory parts of [**DTC**].

[14] Thus the theory of types, the "definite" notions of Zermelo, Fraenkel and their successors, the "stratification" of Quine are all specializations of this idea, in the sense that they may be treated, at least in principle, by adjoining to the combinatory theory of functionality special assumptions of the sorts considered under (a) and (c).

[15] For the history of these ideas see [**CLg**] p. 273.

to demand that the formal objects be the expressions of some "object language"; this means that they be strings formed from the symbols of that object language by concatenation. In combinatory logic these formal objects, called *obs*, were wholly unspecified; it was merely postulated that there was a binary operation of application among them, that the obs be constructed from the primitive objects, called *atoms*, by these operations, and that the construction of an ob be unique. This means that the obs were thought of, not as strings of atoms, but as structures like a genealogical tree. Now of course there are various ways in which such a tree can be associated with a string. Any method of making such a one-to-one association between the obs and a special class of expressions called *wefs* (i.e., well formed expressions) is called a *representation* of the system. In order that a linear language be a representation in this sense it is necessary that each wef indicate a unique construction (i.e., a unique tree): in such a case the language will be called *monotectonic*.[16]

Now this situation suggests that we may think of a language in an analogous fashion. That is, we may think of it, not as a system of expressions, but as a system of phrases, in the sense of §5, which are formed from the primitive or atomic phrases by the functors. We may even push this a little further, since we regard the functors as themselves phrases, and think of a phrase as a construction by the single operation of application of a functor to its first argument. In this way we may conceive of the *grammatical structure* of the language as something independent of the way it is represented in terms of expressions; and this grammatical structure can be studied by means of **F** (and possibly other similar notions). Of course this will need to be supplemented by a study of the way these phrases are represented by expressions. This gives us two levels of grammar, the study of grammatical structure in itself, and a second level which has much the same relation to the first that morphophonemics does to morphology. In order to have terms for immediate use I shall call these two levels *tectogrammatics* and *phenogrammatics* respectively; no doubt someone will propose better terms later.

One or two examples will illustrate what has just been said. Thus the application operator of combinatory logic may be represented by a functor '$(-_1-_2)$' involving parentheses, or by a prefix '$*-_1-_2$' without parentheses. Both these representations can be shown to be monotectonic. We would thus have two languages for representing combinatory logic; these would have the same grammatical structure, but would differ in their phenogrammatics. Another example is the theory of sams, in which the suffix '$-_1b$' can be replaced by the prefix '$s-_1$'.

Harris and Chomsky have suggested that grammar be divided into three stages, "phrase structure" grammar, transformation grammar, and morphophonemics. But if phrase structure grammar means the building up of phrases by concatenation of adjacent phrases, then it has a phenogrammatical aspect. From the standpoint of tectogrammatics I see no reason to put phrase structure and transformation grammar on separate levels, nor to suppose that

---

[16] In [CFS] I called this property the tectonic property. But I now think the term 'monotectonic' is better, because it leaves the 'polytectonic' for the opposite property.

phrase structure operations necessarily either precede or follow transformation operations.

In the same vein, Lambek[17] has recently proposed a calculus of grammatical structure based on two kinds of functionality notions expressed by slant lines. Thus N/S would mean a functor forming a noun from a sentential argument on its right, while $N\backslash S$ would mean a functor forming a sentence from a nominal argument on the left. This is a classification of expressions in a concatenative grammar rather than a classification of functors in the sense of §6. If we use 'f' as abbreviation for the expression, then Lambek's "'f' is an N/S" would mean the same as "'$f-_1$' is an $\mathsf{F}SN$", whereas his "'f' is an $N\backslash S$" would mean the same as my "'$-_1f$' is an $\mathsf{F}NS$". Thus Lambek's conception has an admixture of phenogrammatics. Moreover it seems to break down completely with reference to functors which are not either prefixes or suffixes.

It is to be expected that grammatical structure will vary less from language to language than does the phenogrammatics. Different languages use entirely different devices for indicating grammatical phrase composition. In some languages word order is important, as it often is in English; but in Latin the three words in

Puer puellam amat

can be arranged in any of the six possible orders without changing the structure. It is not uncommon in such languages to have functors consisting of detached parts, or of parts widely separated from the arguments.

Finally I shall mention two phenomena which occur in the natural languages but are rare in the artificial languages of logic and mathematics. These may be expected to cause some modification in the concepts of grammatics.

The first of these is the phenomenon of ellipsis. It is a common tendency in the natural languages to omit anything which is not necessary for communication in the particular context. Thus almost any single word in the English language is capable of forming a sentence by itself; and one can imagine a question which could be significantly answered by giving a detached suffix. Most languages have pronouns; and, as Harris has recently pointed out,[18] one may have proverbs and promorphenes of other sorts. Any adequate discussion of grammatical structure must take this into account.

The second phenomenon is that the same phrase may be constructed in different ways. By this I am not referring to homonymity, which is the similarity in form of what most of us would regard as distinct phrases, but to the fact that even phrases which we may wish to regard as semantically identical may still be analyzed in different ways. Thus the sentence

The clams were eaten by the children

is described by Chomsky as necessarily obtained from

The children ate the clams

---

[17] See Lambek [**MSS**], also his paper in this symposium.
[18] See Harris [**CTL**].

by the passive voice transformation, which is an F*SS*. But there is an alternative explanation viz. as formed from the F*NS*.

$$-_1 \text{ were eaten by the children}$$

by applying it to 'the clams' as argument. This is the only explanation possible in

The clams were eaten by the seashore.

It is true that the 'by' in the second sentence is merely a homonym for the
'by' in the first (and it would be expressed in German by a different word).
But I cannot follow the argument which says that the second analysis is correct in the second case but not in the first. It is true that the artificial languages of mathematics and logic have generally the property that every
phrase has a unique construction—i.e., these languages are monotectonic. But
it is a fallacy to assume a priori that the natural languages have this property. They may be, and I believe most of them are, polytectonic, and the
equivalence of different constructions of the same sentence is one of the
features which has to be taken account of in an adequate grammar.

These features, as well as the oversimplification in taking N and S as the
only basic categories, can, I think, be taken into account. They do not affect the fundamental point, that we can profitably study grammatical structure as such, apart from its representation in terms of concatenation.

BIBLIOGRAPHY

Works are cited, with or without the author's name, by abbreviated titles consisting
of three letters in brackets, as in the following list. (When the author's name is omitted
entirely the author is usually Curry or Curry and Feys.) Journals are abbreviated according to the practice of Mathematical Reviews.

KAZIMIERZ ADJUKIEWICZ

[SKn] *Die syntaktische Konnexität*, Studia Philos. vol. 1 (1935) pp. 1–27.

LEONARD BLOOMFIELD

[Lng] *Language*, New York, 1933.

RUDOLF CARNAP

[ISm] *Introduction to semantics*, Cambridge, Mass., 1942.

NOAM CHOMSKY

[LSL] *Logical structure in language*, Amer. Documentation vol. 8 (1957) pp. 284–291.

[SSt] *Syntactic structure*, The Hague, 1957.

HASKELL B. CURRY

[DTC] *The deduction theorem in the combinatory theory of restricted generality*, Logique
et Analyse, 3ᵉ Année (1960) pp. 15–39.

[LFS] *Languages and formal systems*, Proceedings of the Tenth International Congress
of Philosophy (1949) pp. 770–772.

[MSL] *Mathematics, syntactics and logic*, Mind vol. 62 (1953) pp. 172–183.

HASKELL B. CURRY and ROBERT FEYS

[CLg] *Combinatory logic*, Amsterdam, 1958.

ZELLIG HARRIS

[CTL] *Co-occurrence and transformation in linguistic structure*, Language vol. 33
(1957) pp. 283–340.

[MSL] *Methods in structural linguistics*, Chicago, Ill., 1951.

ARCHIBALD A. HILL

[ILS] *Introduction to linguistic structure*, New York, 1958.

CHARLES F. HOCKETT

[CML] *A course in modern linguistics*, New York, 1958.

OTTO JESPERSEN

[PGr] *Philosophy of grammar*, London, 1924.

JOACHIM LAMBEK

[MSS] *The mathematics of sentence structure*, Amer. Math. Monthly vol. 65 (1958) pp. 154–170.

CHARLES MORRIS

[FTS] *Foundations of the theory of signs*, Chicago, 1938.

[SLB] *Signs, language and behavior*, New York, 1946.

JOSEF SCHÄCHTER

[PKG] *Prolegomena zu einer kritischen Grammatik*, Vienna, 1935 (cf. its review, Weinberg, Phil. Rev. vol. 46 (1937) pp. 334–335).

ROMAN SUSZKO

[SSS] *Syntactic structure and semantical reference I*, Studia Logica vol. 8 (1958) pp. 213–244.

THE PENNSYLVANIA STATE UNIVERSITY,
    UNIVERSITY PARK, PENNSYLVANIA

GRAPHIC AND PHONETIC ASPECTS OF LINGUISTIC AND MATHEMATICAL SYMBOLS

BY

YUEN REN CHAO

1. Graphs and logographs. In both linguistics and mathematics there is a lot of talk and there is a lot of scribbling. The present paper is a pre-systematic (and pre-computer) stage of discussion, dealing with the ways in which the talk and scribbling is done in the two fields, with some suggestions as to the directions in which possible future developments may take. Since most of the symbolizing in logic has been derived from mathematics, I shall, unless otherwise specified, simply say 'mathematics' to include both mathematics and logic. The plan of the present paper is to look over the usages in linguistics and mathematics in general and summarize them in the form of problems for the future. But before entering upon the subject, I should like to point out that I am not planning to discuss linguistics or mathematics, but only some relatively peripheral aspects of both, namely, those about the symbolism used in the two fields.

It is well known that the language of any given speech community in the world makes use of from about ten to not over 100 distinctive kinds of sounds called 'phonemes'. The ear can detect several times that number of fine shades of acoustic qualities, but of elements out of which meaningful units of speech communication is made, the total number in any one given language is always fairly small.

Now man spoke for centuries and milleniums before he started to record visually what he spoke. At the same time, he drew pictures and made visual marks to record or represent things and ideas independently of speech. In high antiquity the Chinese are said to have run their government by tying knots and the peoples of the Occidental countries of today are still tying knots around their little fingers to represent errands to do—or at least are represented as doing so in the comics. But within historical times writing has largely been a form of recording speech and only to a minor degree an independent system of symbols which bypasses the act of speech. This has been true of the Egyptian hieroglyphics and even more true of the shell and bone inscriptions of ancient China. The so-called pictographs and ideographs are not symbols of things or ideas, but symbols of words, or logographs.[1]

That this has been so almost follows by definition, since there can be no writing of history without a history of writing. History differs from pre-history in that pre-history is what we say now what men did, as inferred from traces they left—pictures, totems, artefacts—while history is what men

---

[1] Peter S. DuPonceau, *A Dissertation on the nature and character of the Chinese system of writing*, Philadelphia, 1838, xi and xii; Y. R. Chao, *A note on an early logographic theory of Chinese writing*, Harvard Journal of Asiatic Studies vol. 5. (1940) pp. 189–191.

have said what they did as recorded in spoken words—whether pictographic, ideographic, or phonetic.

Once the elements of language come to be represented in visual symbols, then their user would begin to name and talk about them, and such talk, in turn, can be and often is represented in either the same or in some other system of visual representation. School teachers, calligraphers, and printers, have whole vocabularies for various graphic aspects of writing.

How does one refer to the visual symbols for spoken words? The simplest way is to say the words they represent. Thus, the spoken sentence [I see a dog][2] is written 'I see a dog' and when I am asked what is the last written word in the written sentence I will say aloud [dog]. Note that what is involved here is not just the possibility of a two-fold representation, namely the phonetic representation of a visual symbol, but a four-fold representation: (1) the phonetic presentation of the spoken word (not necessarily by pronouncing the word), (2) the visual presentation of the spoken word, (3) the spoken representation of the written word, and (4) the written representation of the written word. These distinctions are often neglected, because very often what is true of one aspect is also true of another. For example, to say that the word[3] 'millimeter' occurs frequently in science is applicable both to the written and to the spoken word. On the other hand, the statement that the word 'millimeter' is one millimeter long is false as referring to the word-instance as printed here on this particular page being read by the reader at this point, while it would be nonsense if referring to the word as spoken by me at the meeting at this point.

Most systems of writing consist of recurring parts, corresponding more or less to recurring parts of the language. But below the smallest parts represented by the graphical units, the graphical parts are no longer phonetically relevant. Thus, a Chinese character represents a whole syllable, but parts of the character do not as a rule represent parts of the syllable. In a system of writing using the latin alphabet, each letter corresponds roughly to the phonemes of the language written, but minding one's *p*'s and *q*'s or *b*'s and *d*'s has nothing to do with aspects of the sounds they write, although these shapes have obviously related graphical characteristics. It is only in the Korean *onmon* alphabet that parts of symbols correspond to parts of phonetic elements. It will however take us too far afield to go into that aspect of Korean writing.

2. Letters and characters. Coming now to a level closer to mathematical symbols, let us take up linguistic elements of the size of phonemes. The history of the alphabet may be regarded as the history of approximation to writing of language with symbols for its phonemes. In fact, until the late 19th Century, people talked indiscriminantly about letters and sounds. Now

---

[2] I shall dispense with phonetic or phonemic notation when it is not relevant to the discussion and let square brackets indicate that it is the sentence as spoken aloud that is being referred to.

[3] We operate with the word as a unit of convenient size, but most of the remarks in this connection will apply to larger or smaller segments of language.

how does one mention and talk about the sounds of language? To one who is used to an alphabetic system of writing, it seems to be the simplest thing to talk about the sound 'o', the sound 'e', the sound 'l' [ɛɫ], the sound 'b' [bi:], or even the sound 'w' [ˈdʌblju:]. But to one used to a logographic system of writing like the Chinese, or a syllabic system of writing like the Japanese, the nature of sound segments in the form of consonants and vowels is not at all obvious and even seems highly abstract. As an intermediate type we may cite Sanskrit or Tibetan writing in which each symbol has what is called an inherent vowel in addition to a consonant, so that it will represent a syllable with a vowel of generally [a]-quality, unless marked otherwise.

With the emphasis on the distinction between sound and symbol in modern pedagogy and the necessity for mentioning sounds audibly to a group of persons, there has arisen a usage of mentioning vowels as they are, but consonants by adding the neutral vowel [ə]. In the Chinese National Phonetic Letters, some of the consonants are named by the nearest homorganic vocalization. For example, the consonant 's' is named by adding a z-like vocalization after it, the palatal consonant [ɕ] by adding a palatal vowel [i], while the majority of the consonants are named by adding the natural vowel [ə], as [lə] for 'l', [nə] for 'n'.

Among language teachers, especially among linguists, I have noticed a difference in usuage between Americans and Europeans. In Europe, there is more use of the sound itself, adding the neutral vowel [ə] in the case of consonants, while in America there is a tendency to use the names of the letters representing the sounds, e. g., the sound 'el' rather than [l] and [ɫ], or circumlocutions like 'the sound represented by the lower-case "e" in the IPA'. Where no ordinary single letters are available, a foreign name, as 'shwa' for [ə], or a made up name, as 'eng' for [ŋ], or 'esh' for [ʃ], or 'barred eye' for [ɨ], is used.

So far I have made a brief review of the phonetic aspects of linguistic symbols, namely the manners in which linguists have spoken, aloud, of the symbols used either traditionally or systematically to represent the sounds of languages. As for the graphic aspects of linguistic symbols, those systems of writing which are in logographic units naturally have more complicated forms than those using smaller units, such as the phoneme. It is often stated that ideographic (read 'logographic' in our view) writing is two-dimensional, while alphabetic writing is one-dimensional. This is true in one sense and false in another sense. In so far as words occur in one single succession, the logographs writing them are in one single succession, just as the succession of letters is in alphabetic writing. On the other hand the internal formation of the letters of an alphabet, as opposed to dots and dashes in the Morse code, are two-dimensional, just as Chinese characters are. The significant difference here is that a character being one out of several thousand, its information value is of the order of 12, while that of a letter of the alphabet is of the order of 5.

In one sense, trivial at the present stage of discussion, all visual symbols are one-dimensional, since any two-dimensional or multi-dimensional manifold can be mapped on one single line, a fact known intuitively centuries, and more rigorously at least 100 years, before the advent of the scanning method of sending television signals, or, for that matter, before the invention of half-tone engraving, with its rows of dots.

The salient fact about the graphic aspect of linguistic symbols is that of arbitrary convention. This is largely true of the so-called ideographic system of writing and, of course, true of alphabetic systems of writing, including the somewhat systematized scheme of phonetic transcription, such as the IPA. The only serious attempt at iconic representation of sound by shape is that of Bell's Visible Speech,[4] which, however, has never been adopted widely. Frege's two-dimensional notation for logic has never been popular, either, though certain logical formulae gain symmetry and elegance by being displayed in two-dimeñsions. For example:

$$\begin{array}{l}(\forall x)(\exists y) \\ \qquad\qquad A(x, y, u, v) \\ (\forall u)(\exists v)\end{array}$$

arranged linearly will take the more lengthy and less elegant form:

$$(\exists f)(\exists g)(\forall x)(\forall u)A(x, f(x), u, g(u)),[5]$$

where '$(\forall \cdots)$' is to be read as 'for all $\cdots$' and '$(\exists \cdots)$' as 'there is a $\cdots$ such that'. Algebraic matrices or determinants are typically two-dimensional arrays, and recent trials in stringing them along serially to save printing expenses have met with opposition by users because of loss of some visual aspects, which are thus rendered inaccessible to inspèction, with consequent loss of chance of intuitive discovery of relationships.[6]

3. Segmentation and individuation. In both the phonetic and the graphic aspects of linguistic symbols there are the two problems of segmentation and individuation. The first problem is, how much of a chunk is to be counted as one symbol? The other one is, what perceptually distinguishable instances—tokens—are to be classed together and called the same symbol —a type? The cutting up of the stream of speech into discrete segments or the cutting up of writing in long hand into discrete letters (or "radicals" and "phonetics" from a column of Chinese cursive script) is a problem of the first type; while the grouping of different sounds into phonemes or different styles of lettering under the same alphabetic letter is a problem of the second kind. I shall not go into the details of the phonetic aspects of these problems, since they have been well covered, if not entirely solved, by linguists—it means practically the whole of phonological theory. The graphic aspects for linguistic symbols, however, have suffered comparative neglect from linguists.[7]

---

[4] Melville Bell, *Visible speech: The science of universal alphabetics*, London, 1867.

[5] I am indebted to Professor Leon Henkin for this example, as well as for several other points of mathematics here.

[6] See Notices Amer. Math. Soc. vol. 6 (1959) p. 496, in which H. A. Pogorzelski proposes the contraction sign, consisting of a bold-face downward pointing righthand half arrow, to be read as 'the next line reads'.

[7] The most direct attack on this problem so far, so far as the latin alphabet is concerned, is of course that by Murray Eden, *On the formalization of handwriting*, this volume, pp. 83–88.

The problem of segmentation is fairly simple, but the usage as to what tokens are grouped under the same type has had a history as casual and
fortuitious as that of any human institution.

To begin with, we have the 26 letters of the Latin alphabet. But this was
already not the original list to begin with: 'i' and 'j' were graphic variants
of 'the same' letter. So were 'u' and 'v'; and 'w' betrays its lateness by its
very name. Then there has always been the hesitation as to the identity or
difference between caps and small letters, between print and script, between
roman and italics, etc. Linguists, especially those doing comparative work
on different languages or different periods will naturally need more than 26
different symbols and so an informal convention has arisen by regarding as
distinctive types what were previously regarded as non-distinctive tokens:
printed small 'a' for front [a], script small 'a' for back [ɑ], small capital 'a'
for medium [ᴀ] (after Otto Jespersen), italics for linguistic forms mentioned,
single quotes for glosses, and finally made-up or modified letters 'ŋ', 'ɦ', 'ʂ',
etc., and letters borrowed from other systems of writing 'β', 'φ', 'ø' and diacritical marks (less often used in IPA than in American usage) to answer
the needs for necessary graphic distinctions in phonetic symbolism. The point
I want to make here is that there is no complete uniformity of usage and
even within the scope of one type of writing, say that represented by IPA,
the usage has grown gradually rather than been designed systematically.

4. Talking about the graphs. It is one thing to name the sounds
of language as we observed above, e.g., 'the sound [ə]', 'the sound represented by the English letter E', it is another to quote the graphic shape of the
symbols used to represent those sounds. Here, the usage has been just as
fortuitous as with the graphic aspects. Printers do have a fairly full if not
too systematic set of unambiguous names for various types. During the 1930's,
when Academia Sinica was in Nanking and its publications were printed in
Shanghai, I once drew up a very elaborate table of names for linguistic symbols, so that there would be no mistake about setting them up at the hands
of the printers, who read little or no English. In our phonetics laboratory
we more or less talked about the symbols the same way and gave the print-
er printing and proof-reading instructions in those terms. For example, to
call the symbol 'ɛ' we would say [faan san] (which is Mandarin for [reversed
figure three]), just as American linguists talk about the [barred eye] for 'ɨ'.
In general linguists do not usually make a significant distinction between roman and italics or between ordinary type and bold face. But the difference
in shape between caps and lower case (e.g., r, ʀ) and between printed and
script (e.g., z, ʒ) is often made distinctive. Diacritical marks are usually employed to represent a modification or differentiation of a sound, thus becoming
a meaningful symbol in a complex of symbolic compound rather than an arbitrary graphical modification to change a letter into another symbolically
unanalyzed unit.

Numerical figures and prime marks are rarely used as linguistic symbols.
Sinologists have used superscripts '1', '2', '3', '4' to indicate the four tones
of Mandarin Chinese and semanticists have used subscripts to a word to label

its different meanings, but on the whole not much use is made of numerals in linguistic symbols. However, accents and other diacritical marks, though avoided as a matter of policy by users of the IPA, play an important part in the hands of other linguists. They often serve as unit symbols, with operational meanings of their own on top of those of the letters (physically, of course, sometimes at the bottom).[8]

5. Primarily non-linguistic graphs. Outside the main current in the development of systems of writing, however, there are various lines of symbolic development which either take autonomous courses of their own, or, as often happens, branch off from writing and form independent systems of written language, giving rise to true written language, as distinguished from language written. For example, when you see on a European street the letter 'P' marked over with a big red slant slash, it is supposed to say 'no parking', but to a Frenchman it says 'défense de stationner', or whatever is said nowadays. Here the letter 'P' is obviously derived from the first phoneme in the English spoken word [parking], while the negative command is represented by the visual symbol, the slash, without specific reference to any spoken word in any language. On the other hand, in a picture of an anchor with a slash across it, no part of it is related directly to any word in any language.[9]

An interesting intermediate case between direct visual language and spoken language written is that of the variant Japaneses readings of Chinese characters. Most Chinese characters used in Japanese writing have two or three, sometimes even more, alternate readings, depending upon context. There are to each character usually two *on* readings, i.e., readings by (Chinese) sound, based on ancient Chinese sound, for example the character ㅅ for 'man, human being' is pronounced 'nin' or 'jin' (< ancient Chinese ńźi̯ĕn). In addition there is a *kun* or 'glossing' meaning, the character being used for writing a native Japanese word, in this case *hito*. It is as if one writes 'etc' and pronounces it (1) [et kētera], (2) [et set (e) ra], (3) [and so forth], or (4) [and so on], where (1) and (2) would be *on* readings and (3) and (4) *kun* readings. The only difference is that while this is rare in English, it is the normal situation for most characters in Japanese. The status of Chinese characters in Japanese is therefore somewhere between that of an independent system of writing directly representing meaning and that of writing as a system of logographs. It is, however, much closer to the latter, since there is, usually, not more than one *kun* reading for each character.

Symbols used in mathematics, whether iconic (e. g. '>', '<', '=', 'Δ', '∠') or, more frequently, non-iconic (e. g. '+', '−', '×', '÷'), do not usually represent the spoken words for the entities symbolized, but are intended to represent

---

[8] In a tape recording of a Seminar in Ethnolinguistics at Indiana University I received just before this Symposium, Max Zorn led a discussion of, among other things, the question as to the status of letters and diacritics in representing terms and relations. For instance, is the accent grave a letter?

[9] It is another matter that the anchor is iconic, while the slash is conventional, though a common convention in many cultures. But the point does not concern us here.

them directly.   Thus, the cardinal number 3, defined as the class of all classes whose members are in 1 to 1 correspondence with the class consisting of the members Tom, Dick, and Harry,[10] is a mathematical entity which is usually symbolized by '3', but pronounced in as many ways as there are languages and dialects in the world.[11] Because of the relatively loose connection between mathematical entities and the spoken words connected with them, what is generally called by mathematicians 'L', the language of the mathematics being studied, 'L'' the metalanguage used to talk about 'L', etc., is usually applied to the system of written symbols and only incidentally, or or even casually, to the ways those symbols are pronounced or mentioned in various contexts and in various languages.   Thus, a tradition of casual ways of oral naming of the symbols of mathematical entities has arisen within the framework of each natural language, quite in line with the natural growth and change in the language as a whole, but quite out of line with the systematic relations of the mathematical entities that are talked about.

6.   Symbols and symbol complexes. Here a distinction should be drawn between (1) the arbitrariness of symbol to its denotatum and (2) the presence or absence of systematic relation between symbols and their denotata.   The very nature of symbolism consists in the arbitrariness of associations and it is of no particular advantage that Chinese characters are written one, two, and three strokes for the numbers one, two, and three, especially as that is given up from four on.   On the other hand it is of definite advantage symbol-wise that the numbers 11, 12, $\cdots$ 20, 21, $\cdots$ 30, $\cdots$ are called ten-one, ten-two, $\cdots$ two-ten, two-ten-one, $\cdots$ three-ten, etc., as against the German order, which does not correspond to the graphic symbols.   It is true that before adopting such a way of saying the numbers, it ought to be shown that it is unique and consistent.   But the ancient Chinese apparently found that out when they used the scheme and met with no difficulty in practical applications for several thousand years.

When we consider larger symbol complexes in mathematics we shall see all the more that they are constructed quite apart from linguistic considerations, even though they began as a generalization of linguistic forms, forming an extended language.   In the first place, mathematical symbols are not always serially ordered as linguistic symbols are, as we have noted in connections with matrices.   Two-dimensional forms do not lend themselves readily to being read aloud in a string of spoken words.   That was how Einstein ran into difficulty once when he tried to cable a formula across the Atlantic.   The

---

[10] This is an equivalent paraphrase of the formal (apparently circular) definition of the number 3 as the class of all triads.

[11] It is true, to be sure, that even in linguistics, one discourses on classes rather than individuals.   A phoneme is a class of allophones, and even an allophone, say the unaspirated [k] in 'school' is a perceptually recognizable type, represented by different tokens in different utterances.   It is only when one inquires into a specific instance of the use of a word in an actual setting, such as in a philological inquiry, that the word is taken as an actual token.   Thus, one might simplify the distinction between linguistics and philology by regarding linguistics as the study of types and philology as the study of tokens.

problem of hierarchy of immediate constituents, even when all elements are arranged serially, is more complex in mathematical than in linguistic symbols. Ordinary language itself does get into ambiguities of construction, due to the unavoidable nature of linear modification. You all know the story of the customer who wanted to buy a comb and on being asked by the salesgirl if he wanted to buy a narrow gentleman's comb replied haughtily, "No, I want a comb for a stout gentleman, with rubber teeth." In mathematical symbolism parentheses and brackets, or the dots in logical symbolism, take care of the immediate constituents, but this graphic part of the symbolism cannot, or does not usually, have a clear way of oral presentation. The use of 'left parenthesis' for '(' and 'right parenthesis' for ')' like 'quote' and 'unquote', can often be helpful, but not adequate to take care of all eventualities. Pauses and intonation can also serve as markers of construction in language, but will have only very limited application beyond simple cases like:

a, plus b-squared

as against:

a plus b, squared.

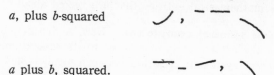

From the preceding we see that the oral usage in mentioning mathematical symbols has so far received only scant attention and has never been considered on its own account as worthy of scientific or practical concern, for no doubt the usually good reason that so far mathematicians have gotten along pretty well the way they have.

7. Trivial aspects becoming non-trivial.

What makes it worthwhile to look more closely now at the graphic and phonetic aspects of linguistic and mathematical symbols, and to look at them together, is that these apparently trivial aspects of both linguistics and mathematics are becoming less and less trivial as these aspects of symbolism become more and more relevant in problems of communication, recording, machine translation and even control systems. So let us consider from the point of view of efficiency of use those aspects of symbolism which we have so far been looking at from the point of view of the status quo only.

The development of telecommunication and computer technology has had the effect of cutting the size and shape of natural language to fit the straight jacket of the machine. Because the make and break of the telegraph key make a minimum demand on the channel capacity, letters of the alphabet have to be coded into dots and dashes. Because computers operate best with the make and break of the electric circuit or with magnetized and demagnetized states, everything has to be transferred into permutations of the two elements, 1 and 0, and no other. It is true that duality is an important feature of nature, and even of human nature, when we remember that the ultimate element of action in the brain is that of make and break at the synapse between neurons, with no intermediate state. And linguistic analysis by a binary dichotomy has turned out to be very fruitful and effective, as demonstrated by Jakobson in his system of distinctive features.[12] However, at higher stages of organization, both in man and in machine, things look as if they were on an analogical rather than digital basis. This has been possible and practical just as the physical world of discrete particles has been amenable to treatment by differential equations for the molar or even some of the larger molecular aspects of things. Thus a realistic and practical approach to the communicational aspects of symbols will, in addition to the binary approach, deal with the whole multi-space of shapes and sounds and qualities, and even though the brain and the computer operate by elements of make and break, the input-output stages will still take the form of spoken words and/or typed letters.

8. Looking to the future. By way of resume, I shall wind up by raising certain problems concerning possibilities of conscious planning.

(1) SHAPE AND QUALITY OF UNIT SYMBOLS. The first problem to look into is what shapes and qualities are generally available for unit symbols? If we were ink-emitting squids swimming freely in three-dimensional water, we would probably have invented a way of fixing our spoken words in 3 dimensions, to the great advantage of literal and graphic representation of linguistic or mathematical entities. That would still be far from visualizing multi-space, but it would be a great step—witness the lame efforts we have made in constructing solid models and drawing families of curves on one sheet of paper. Colors have so far been of limited use and things like traffic lights, green indexes to the yellow pages of the telephone book, ad hoc uses of colored chalks by professors of mathematics (rarely going into print), etc. have never developed into any large-scale system.

Thus it leaves most of the symbolism used in linguistics and mathematics to ringing changes on the letters of the latin alphabet. Here and there one resorts to additional shapes by borrowing from other alphabets, but there seems to have been no overall survey or experimental test of all easily distinguishable shapes of letters.[13] But a systematic exploration of simple forms: Greek and Hebrew letters, turned and reversed letters, and especially importantly, all the common simple forms of Chinese characters, most of which are not duplicates of any letters of occidental alphabets, has not been undertaken. Various systems of stenography usually start with consideration of all possible forms of strokes, but there the primary consideration is speed, while clear differentiation is only of secondary importance. It is true that for technological transmission and recording of symbols one may find it most desirable to recode them into shapes '1' and '0' or their electrical or magnetic equivalents, but there is still much room for systematic development on the perceptual level to explore all possibilities in the design of new shapes

---

[12] Roman Jakobson and Morris Halle, *Fundamentals of language*, The Hague, 1956.

[13] This is not to say that large collections of shapes and letters have not been listed without analytic classification. See, for example, Anwezige, 6, 8, *en* 10 *Punts Matrijzen voor Wetenschappelijke Werken*, Zaltbommel, van de Garde & Co.'s Drukkerij, 1953, 19 pp.; Style Manual of American Institute of Physics, 2nd edition, New York, 1959, iii + 42 pp.

and in the classification, indexing,[14] and mechanical recognition of old shapes.

(2) ORAL NAMING. Secondly, what manner of calling the symbols are possible for clear and unambiguous oral discourse or acoustic communication? Tradition has made the names of 'b', 'd', 'p', 't' end in the vowel [iː] and those of 's', 'm', 'n' begin with the vowel [ɛ]. Telephone companies and military organizations have designed formulae for clear identification, one version of which is:

Alfa	Foxtrot	Kilo	Papa	Uniform	Zulu
Bravo	Golf	Lima	Quebec	Victor	
Charlie	Hotel	Mike	Romeo	Whisky	
Delta	India	Nectar	Sierra	X-ray	
Echo	Juliett	Oscar	Tango	Yankee	

But in ordinary English, only the shapes 'h', 'l', and 'm' have written names 'aitch', 'ell', and 'em', though on my way to this meeting the man at the gate of the airport called out my seat number 'C-3' in the form of [Charlie three]. The above list, though internationally oriented on the whole, was based on tests made with English-speaking users, so that 'Mike for M' may not be as good as 'Metro for M'. Thus, apart from perceptual suitability, the consideration of linguistic background of the user also looms large as a pragmatic factor.

(3) PROBLEM OF NAMES OF SYMBOLS IN DIFFERENT LANGUAGES. Thirdly, if some system of oral reference to symbols is to be arrived at, is it a separate system for each language or one system for all languages? The latter alternative would hardly be feasible now, because it would amount to proposing an international language. For certain regions of science, uniformity is relatively easy for graphic symbols (e. g. the chemical elements), but it would be impracticable to try to satisfy all the different phonemic makeups of the major languages of the world. What about setting up a systematic way of oral naming of symbols and symbol complexes for each language and then define the oral form of each symbol as the class of all the oral forms (or, more strictly, a function of those forms defined in specified ways)? In any case a survey of how mathematical operations and formulae are read aloud in different languages will certainly be of value to one who knows only one way of reading them. For example, to a Chinese school boy who knows only to read '3/4' as 'four-parts less three', it must be illuminating to know that it is also three quarters.

(4) SIZE OF SYMBOLS. Fourthly, the size of symbols is an important consideration. The letters of the alphabet are already identified by Alfa, Bravo,

---

[14] The problem of indexing of cursive shapes, i.e., arranging all shapes of a given set in a determinate serial order, has never been throughly explored. For some promising schemes, see Sukeyuki Endō, *Sōsho Daijiten*, Tokyo, 1935; Fang-yü Wang, *Introduction to Chinese cursive script*, New Haven, 1958, especially pp. 216–240; and M. Halle and K. N. Stevens, *Analysis by synthesis*, Proceedings of the Seminar on Speech Transmission and Processing (W. Wathen-Dunn and L. E. Woods, Editors), December, 1959. AFCRC-TR-59-198. vol. II, Paper D-7. Cf. also Note 7.

Charlie, etc. at great expense of informational redundancy.[15] But besides oc-
cupying more channel, that is, using more equipment and time, a large symbol occupies a large field of the user's span of attention. This is an advantage
when concentration on one item is desired; for example 'Monument' or [monu-
ment] may be easier to carry in one's head than the too fleeting 'MO' or
[mow]. But more often than not, one has to hold a complex of symbols in
one span and then small size will enable more units to come within one span.
For example, if I have to keep a seven-symbol telephone number while walk-
ing from the chained phone book to the telepeone booth, say, MO-3-7851, I
would rather say it to myself as [mo san, chi ba wuu i] than [mow three,
seven eight five one], not because I am more used to Chinese numerals—I
doubt that I am—but because Chinese numerals are shorter and more of them
can be held in one span for one who is equally familiar with both. It is to
be sure of small importance whether one can hold a telephone number or
one's social security number in one's head, but it is important to be able to
hold a large complex in one span in order to see or discover new relations.

When a symbol complex is sufficiently important or occurs with high frequency, it is of course common practice in mathematics to use a new unitary
symbol for it and then enter into further complexes at a higher level of organization. This is in fact how much mathematics is built up. At the same
time there is still the same heuristic advantage at high levels in being able
to hold a large complex in one span.[16] Compare this with the use of abbreviations for frequently occuring phrases such as: AAAS, FBI, UNESCO, Voco-
der, FIDO (Fog, Intense Dispersal Of), Hazel (Homogeneous assembly zero
level), Nester (Neutron source thermal reactor), REGAL (Range Elevation
Guidance Approach Landing), TIROS (Television Infrared Observation Satel-
lite), etc. A distinction should be made here between calling them by the
names of the letters and pronouncing these as words when pronounceable. If
called by letters, e. g., [ei ei ei es], [ef bi: ai], there is a waste of phonemes or
a redundancy of about 200%, while pronounced with the *values* of the letters
the brevity in sound is of the same order as that in letters and thus allows
a correspondingly greater span, just as the equating of simple letters to whole
formulas. Note that it takes just as many phonemes to say 'x' [eks], 'y' [wai],
'o' [ou] or [zi: rou], as to say 'lim', 'cos', 'log' or 'val'. In this connection I
might mention that in Chinese abbreviations, it is the first syllables (written
with single characters) taken from each polysyllabic word that are strung together to make abbreviations. A string of four syllables takes the same

---

[15] In this connection it is interesting to note how 'eigenvalue', a half-foreign word,
has held its ground against possible native competitors 'characteristic value', 'proper
value', or even 'latent value', with its three or even four-consonant cluster [-t(ə)ntv-],
which is a bit too chewy, as compared with 'eigenvalue'. See Arthur Sard's letter to
the editor in Notices Amer. Math. Soc. vol. 6 (1959) p. 361.

[16] See George A. Miller, *The magical number seven, plus or minus two: Some limits
on our capacity for processing information*, Psychological Review vol. 63. (1956) pp. 81–97.
Miller proposed (p. 92) the suggestive and useful distinction between *bits* of information
and *chunks* of information. A span of immediate memory is limited to about 7 chunks,
but much information (more bits) can, by recoding, be put into one chunk.

length of time and is equally spannable with a string of four initial letters pronounced, as they usually are, by their names, but since each syllable is a morpheme out of more than several thousand, the form will give 40 or 50 bits of information in one span, as against less than 20 bits (4×5) from forms like [Wye Em See Ay]; or again, to say [Cal Tech] takes less time than [Em Eye Tea], but gives more information.[17]

(5) SUBSTITUTION STEPS. Fifthly, how does symbolism in linguistics and mathematics compare with regard to the problem of balance between the advantages of (1) substitution and abstraction and (2) keeping close in view as much as possible the original objects under investigation? In the old days, in the so-called geometrical proofs, such as Galileo used in his *Two new sciences*, there was less substitution steps in letters and one could get a better *anschaulich* view of what's going on, like driving on country roads. But when one uses straight analysis, the proofs may be good and rigorous, but one is flying by instrument, or, to unmix my metaphor, one is driving by following the verbal directions on the sign boards, such as doing three right turns to make one left. The technique is powerful, but it may be something of an impediment to originality and inventiveness. The linguistic counterpart to intuitive investigation in mathematics, then, is the performance of the Thomas Cook type of a polyglot; he is usually looked down upon by the true linguistician, who nevertheless always stands to gain even in his theoretical work if he cultivates an active knowledge of a few languages.

(6) INTERDISCIPLINARY UNIFORMITY. Sixth, to what extent is it possible or desirable to arrive at uniformity of usage in symbolism between linguistics and mathematics? The different senses in which the signs '$>$' and '$<$' are used in linguistics and mathematics are of no great concern when the context will normally tell which sense is to be taken. So is the difference in the use of single quotes for giving glosses in linguistics and for citing a mentioned form in mathematics.[18] But it is often of substantive import and wide application to regularize the use of subscripts and superscripts. In mathematics a superscript normally has some very specific use, such as a power index, while a subscript usually has an adjectival function, usually indicating serial order. There is no corresponding usage among linguists. Thus, one cannot tell whether $[a^n]$ is a nasalized [a] or the vowel [a] *followed* by an imperfectly articulated nasal consonant. Some linguists have even used superscripts in exactly the same sense in which mathematicians have used *sub*scripts, as 'a^2' in the sense of 'a_2' or 'a''' in mathematics, that is, second 'a' in a series of 'a''s. I have proposed the using of superscripts and subscripts as far as possible without conflict with mathematical usage and I think most Chinese linguists have now accepted my proposal. Thus $[a_r]$ mean an r-colored [a] but $[a^r]$ means [a] followed by an r-colored ending.

(7) STATUS OF NON-CONSTITUENTS. Seventh, the analysis of complexes into

---

[17] On this problem see also Science vol. 131 (May, 1960), editorial page.

[18] Leonard Bloomfield found it advisable to follow non-linguistic usage by citing words in single quotes instead of italics in his *Linguistic aspects of science*, International Encyclopedia of Unified Science vol. 1, Chicago, 1939, p. 5. An advantage of quotes over italics is that for a second step one can quote quotes, but can't italicize italics.

hierarchies of immediate constituents has sometimes been called into question in linguistics and mere frequency of occurence has influenced the cutting of immediate constituents, for example, 'by/strength of will' vs. 'by means of/will'. Compare this with the notation 'dy/dx' for $\lim_{x=0}\Delta y/\Delta x$ being now written 'Dy', where the apparently nonsensical 'd/dx' acquires status as a constituent, notationally at least, and then symbolized as 'D'. Such developments of analysis in both mathematics and linguistics seem worth looking into, though I am now entering into more substantive problems than matters of symbolism.

(8) OTHER INTERDISCIPLINARY SYMBOLISMS. I have so far considered problems of sound and shape only in linguistics and mathematics. Many of these problems will also be present in other fields wherever symbols and terminology are involved, and it will be desirable to avoid duplication and incompatibility between departments of science. In the biological sciences, especially in taxonomy, there has been much concern among workers all over the world for uniformity. But has any botanist or zoologist stopped to think of the phonetic aspects of taxonomy with regard to communicational efficiency (as to ease of uttering, hearing, memorizing, and seeing relationships) as well as with respect to international uniformity? Chemistry is another field in which there is nearly complete uniformity in visual symbols, less in nomemclature, and few chemists have interested themselves in inquiring into the efficiency of the phonetic aspects of names of elements and compounds. In the Chinese names for the elements, there is some advantage in having every element called by one syllable. As there are about 1300 existing syllables and several times that many possible syllables to choose from, it should be easy to take care of the one hundred odd elements. And yet, both sulfur and lutecium are pronounced 'liou', both nitrogen and tantalum are called 'dann', then with differences in tone, silicon, selenium, and tin (stanum) are all pronounced 'shi', and yttrium, ytterbium, and iridium are all pronounced 'i'.[19] As for the status of the names of compounds, especially those for polymers, they are systematic enough and do have a useful isomorphism with the elements and structures they represent. But I doubt that a thorough examination of the phonetic possibilities in chemical nomenclature, say, by reducing polysyllabic Greek morphemes to the size of monosyllables and syllables to the size of phonemes, will not yield something which may serve scientific purposes better. The trade makes up, unsystematically, handier usable names for commercial purposes. Why can't the science make up, systematically, phonetic forms which will carry on efficiently in the seminar, in the laboratory, and above all in the chemist's thinking, much of which must consist of talking to himself?

I shall not go on citing separate problems, but will conclude with a hope for some cooperative survey by mathematicians, logicians, linguists, perhaps

---

[19] In characters, they are respectively,

硫², 鎦²; 氮⁴, 鉭⁴; 矽⁴, 硒¹, 錫²; 釔³, 鐿⁴, 銥¹,

where the superscripts indicate the tones.

also biologists and chemists and other scientists,[20] in the mechanics—by which I mean the graphics and phonetics—of their symbolism with a view to its more effective use in these days of fantastic performances of tools of communication.

UNIVERSITY OF CALIFORNIA,
    BERKELEY, CALIFORNIA

---

[20] In reply to a question from the floor, this phrase will of course include in an important way workers in psycholinguistics.

ON THE FORMALIZATION OF HANDWRITING

BY

MURRAY EDEN[1] [2]

It is the object of this study to describe cursive English writing. It will be seen that a good many of the results are applicable to other scripts as well—certainly to varieties of a Latin Script, used in writing French, Italian, German and the like, but it also seems likely that with rather natural modifications the analytic procedure may be used for Gothic, Cyrillic and perhaps Arabic and Sanskrit.

A handwritten specimen may be regarded as a bounded function in the plane, defined on some interval of the real line and continuous almost everywhere. It seems natural to disregard the fact that the written line has finite thickness, microscopic irregularities, microscopic discontinuities and the like.[3]

Within a particular natural language, it is obvious that one handwritten specimen will be judged by a person literate in that language, to be equivalent to a number of other specimens as well as to other physical signals. The name our observer will give to the equivalence class will be a *word* in the language. (The name of the class of equivalence classes is "word".) He will also say that each word is characterized by a finite linear sequence or string of letters.

However, the letters used in a word have no unique representation when they are thought of as functions. In fact it is obvious that the number of representations for a letter are uncountable. This follows immediately from the fact that the partition of two letters is not uniquely defined nor is it clear how such a partition could be defined. In addition, if we consider an arbitrary finite sequence of letters rather than dictionary words known to the observer, once such a word has been represented by a particular handwritten specimen it can be partitioned into several different letter sequences, rather than uniquely into the sequence that gave it rise. For example, the letter *c* is embedded in the letter *d* or *l* in *b*.

We regard as our task that of generating the class of representations of an

[1] This report is based on work conducted in collaboration with Professor Morris Halle, R. L. E. and Modern Language Department, M. I. T.

[2] The research reported in this document was made possible in part by support extended the Massachusetts Institute of Technology, Research Laboratory of Electronics jointly by the U. S. Army (Signal Corps), the U. S. Navy (Office of Naval Research), and the U. S. Air Force (Office of Scientific Research, Air Research and Development Command), under Signal Corps Contract DA36–039–sc-78108, Department of the Army Task 3–99–20–001 and Project 3–99–00–000.

[3] We are obviously not concerned with the aspects of the physical signal that arise from the fact that a pencil line is actually a collection of a finite number of carbon particles or that the paper is uneven. The problem of identifying an abstract function with a physical line has been considered by J. Perkal; *On the ε-length* Bull. de l'Acad. Polon. des Sciences, CL. III, vol. 4 (1956) pp. 399–403; *Sur les ensembles ε-convexes*, Colloquium Mathematicum vol. 4 (1956) pp. 1–10.

arbitrary word given a finite set of symbols and rules for operating on these symbols. We define a set of objects called *strokes* exhibiting the following properties. Each stroke is a real number and a pair of points, the points being ordered in at least one of two (not necessarily orthogonal) coordinates.[4] The motivation for the real number is essentially this:

Associate a unit vector with one of the points. (The initial direction of the vector and the specification as to which is the "first" point will be uniquely specified by rules to be found in the text.) Imagine the vector tangent to some path terminating at the second point. The magnitude of the real number mentioned above is identified with the angular rotation of the vector and the sign refers to the sense of rotation, i.e., positive if rotation is counterclockwise.

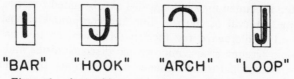

"BAR"   "HOOK"   "ARCH"   "LOOP"

Figure 1.   A graphic portrayal of the four segments.

The strokes are generated from a subset of four strokes, called *segments*. A representation of these segments is given in Figure 1. A representation of the set of 18 strokes that are sufficient to describe all English upper and lower case letters[5] are given in Figure 2. Every handwritten letter in English can be described as a unique sequence of these strokes. A table of English letters is given in Figure 3.[6]

We first define a set Σ of elements called *segments* of the form

$$\sigma_j = (\alpha_{j1}, \beta_{j1})(\alpha_{j2}, \beta_{j2}), \theta_j.$$

We specify four elements of Σ which we shall call *bar, hook, arch* and *loop* respectively

$$\sigma_1 = [(1, 0), (0, 0), 0]\quad bar,$$
$$\sigma_2 = [(1, 1), (0, 0), \pi]\quad hook,$$
$$\sigma_3 = [(1, 0), (1, 1), \pi]\quad arch,$$
$$\sigma_4 = [(1, \varepsilon), (0, 0), \pi]\quad loop, \quad 0 < \varepsilon < 1.$$

The set Σ is generated by a group $\mathcal{G}$ of transformations, ρ_i acting on the σ_j.

---

[4] Two types of "horizontal" ordering are required; they differ by a condition on the relative ordering to the next stroke in the string of a word.

[5] Certain diacritic marks e. g. the dot of the "i" and the cross of the "t" are not considered. They are in any case redundant in the handwriting under discussion.

[6] We wish to call attention to certain analogies between the structure presented here and that proposed for spoken language. Thus the segments are analogous to the distinctive features (Jakobson, Fant and Halle, *Preliminaries to speech analysis*, Cambridge, Massachusetts Institute of Technology Press, 1952); the strokes are analogous to phonemes, the letters to morphemes and the words to words. There is no counterpart in linguistics to our primitive notions of point pair ordering and angular rotation.

$$\rho_1(\sigma_j) = [(\alpha_{j2}, \beta_{j1})(\alpha_{j1}, \beta_{j2})\theta],$$
$$\rho_2(\sigma_j) = [(\alpha_{j1}, \beta_{j2})(\alpha_{j2}, \beta_{j1})\theta],$$
$$\rho_3(\sigma_j) = [(\alpha_{j1}, \beta_{j1})(\alpha_{j2}, \beta_{j2}) - \theta].$$

The set S of *strokes* (of English script) are obtained by applying an additional set F of transformations:

$$f_+(\sigma_j) = [(\alpha_{j1} + 1, \beta_{j1})(\alpha_{j2} + 1, \beta_{j2})\theta_j],$$
$$f_-(\sigma_j) = [(\alpha_{j1} - 1, \beta_{j1})(\alpha_{j2} - 1, \beta_{j2})\theta_j],$$

and the restriction

$$f(\sigma) = s \in S \text{ if and only if}$$
$$\alpha_1(\sigma) > \alpha_2(\sigma) \quad \text{or} \quad \alpha_1(\sigma) = \alpha_2(\sigma) \text{ and } \beta_2(\sigma) > \beta_1(\sigma).$$

Thus S is restricted to those elements of $f(\Sigma)$ for which the *initial* node is *above* the *terminal* node or if these nodes are not ordered then the initial node is to the *left* of the terminal node.

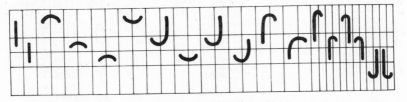

Figure 2. A graphic portrayal of the strokes of cursive
English script.

Associated with each stroke there is a property we shall call *direction*. If for any s_j, $[(\beta_{j2} - \beta_{j1}) \times \theta_j] > 0$, then the *initial* direction, $D_{j1} = \pi/2$ and is read "the initial direction is up." Otherwise $D_{j1} = -(\pi/2)$, i.e., "down." The *final* direction $D_{j2} = (D_{j1} + \theta_j) \pmod{2\pi}$.

A *letter* is defined as a unique n-tuple of $s_j \in S$. That is every letter in English script will be identified with a particular $\lambda_\alpha = (s_{\alpha 1}, s_{\alpha 2}, s_{\alpha 3}, \cdots, s_{\alpha n})$.

Given a sequence W of λ_j, i.e., $(s_{11}, s_{12}, \cdots, s_{1n})(s_{21}, s_{22}, \cdots, s_{2m}) \cdots (s_{k1}, s_{k2}, \cdots, s_{kl})$, compute recursively a new sequence W^*. W^* is called the *collation* of W.[7] Two collation rules are required; the first holds for the concatenation of $s_{h,i-1}, s_{h,i}$; the second[8] holds for $s_{h-1,n}, s_{h,1}$:

$$\beta_1^*(s_{11}) = \beta_1(s_{11}),$$
$$\beta_s^*(s_{11}) = \beta_2(s_{11}),$$
$$\beta_1^*(s_{h,i}) = [\beta_2^*(s_{h,i-1})]h, \qquad i \neq 1$$
$$\beta_2^*(s_{h,i}) = \beta_1^*(s_{h,i}) + (\beta_2 - \beta_1)(s_{h,i}),$$
$$\text{Min}\{\beta_1^*(s_{h,1}), \beta_2^*(s_{h,1})\} = \text{Max}\{\beta_1^*(s_{h-1, n-1}), \beta_2^*(s_{h-1, n-1})\} + 1.$$

Note that W^* does not exhibit letter parentheses.

A word, W', is defined as a class of continuous (finitely many-valued) bounded functions (not necessarily continuous in their first derivatives) on a

---

[7] An illustration of the application of the collation rules is given in Figure 4.

[8] The symbol $[x]$ taken to mean: the largest integer less than x.

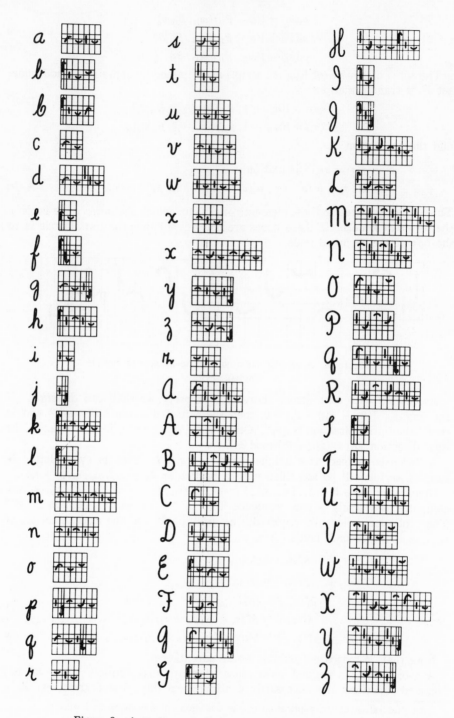

Figure 3. A stroke representation of the English alphabet.

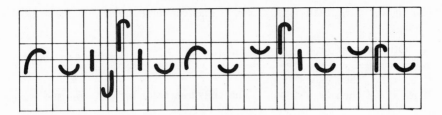

Figure 4. The stroke representation of the world "globe" and its
representation following the application of the collating rules.

closed interval of the real line with the following properties:
1. W' is obtained from W^* by substituting

$$\theta'_j = (\theta^*_j + \delta_j) \qquad \text{for} \quad \theta^*_j ,$$

$$\theta'_{j+1} = (\theta^*_{j+1} - \delta_j) \qquad \text{for} \quad \theta^*_{j+1} .$$

Thus, in general $\theta'_j = \theta^*_j + \delta_j - \delta_{j-1}(-\pi/2 < \delta_i < \pi/2)$.
2. $\psi \in W'$ is a concatenation of continuous functions, continuous in their
first derivatives, i.e.,

$$\psi(s'_1, s'_2, \cdots, s'_k) = \psi_1(s'_1) \circ \psi_2(s'_2) \circ \cdots \circ \psi_k(s'_k) .$$

Let $(\xi, \psi)_i$ be the Cartesian coordinate variables of $\psi_i(s'_i)$. Define:

$$d\tau = \sqrt{(d\xi)^2 + (d\psi)^2} .$$

τ_i will thus be a single-valued continuous function of $\psi_i(s'_i)$. Define:

$$\phi = \arctan \frac{d\psi}{d\xi} .$$

Then for each $\psi_i(s_i)$: $-\operatorname{sgn}(d\phi/d\xi) = \operatorname{sgn}\theta'_i$,

$$\phi(\tau_i = 0) = D_1(s_i) .$$

Define: $\tau_i = n$ by

$$\int_{\tau_i=0}^{\tau_i=n} d\phi = \theta_i .$$

If we denote the values of $\psi(s_i)$ at $\tau_i = n_i$ by $(\xi_n, \psi_n)_i$, then $(\xi_n, \psi_n)_i = (\xi_0, \psi_0)_{i+1}$.

I. If $(\alpha_{i2}, \beta_{i2}) = (\alpha_{1+i}, {}_1\beta_{1+i,1})$ and
(a) if $\beta_{i2} < \beta_{i1}$ then $(\xi_n)_i < (\xi_0)_i$,

(b) if $\alpha_{i2} < \alpha_{i1}$ then $(\psi_n)_i < (\psi_0)_i$. The converse holds for $\beta_{i2} > \beta_{i1}$ and $\alpha_{i2} > \alpha_{i1}$.

II. Otherwise *if* $(\alpha_{i2}, \beta_{i2}) \neq (\alpha_{1+i,1}\beta_{1+i,1})$

$\exists \tau_i; \tau_i = y, 0 < y \leq n_i$,

if $\beta_{i2} < \beta_{i1}$, then $(\xi_y)_i < (\xi_0)_i$,

if $\alpha_{i2} < \alpha_{i1}$, then $(\psi_y)_i < (\psi_0)_i$. The converse holds for $\beta_{i2} > \beta_{i1}$ and $\alpha_{i2} > \alpha_{i1}$.
Also,

$\exists \tau_{i+1}; \tau_{i+1} = z, 0 \leq z < n_{i+1}$

if $\beta_{1+i,2} < \beta_{1+i,1}$, then $(\xi_n)_{i+1} < (\xi_z)_{i+1}$,

if $\alpha_{1+i,2} < \alpha_{1+i,1}$ then $(\psi_n)_{i+1} < (\psi_z)_{i+1}$,

and the converse holds as well.

It will be noted that the class of functions equivalent to a given word will include some that are rather bizarre. Whether they would be legible or not— and this is the ultimate test of equivalence for a natural language—is open to empirical investigation. There are also a large number of specimens that are legible and that will be associated with a particular equivalence class even though the specimens cannot be generated from the appropriate W' for that class. It is obvious that the literate observer needs a good deal less than the complete W' description in order to identify a specimen so long as he has reason to believe it is a word in the language. As we have already stated, if it is not a word in the language, the specimen may well be generated by several W'_j. In reading, the literate person will reject the alternative readings because they are not words in the language so far as he knows; or if two or more are words in his vocabulary he will have to make his decision by criteria involving the context of the word, i.e., the string of words in which it is embedded.

MASSACHUSETTS INSTITUTE OF TECHNOLOGY,
  CAMBRIDGE, MASSACHUSETTS

ON THE ROLE OF SIMPLICITY IN LINGUISTIC DESCRIPTIONS[1]

MORRIS HALLE

Almost from the very beginning of abstract concern with language there have been proposals for schemes to classify the sounds of speech. This is hardly suprising since it is almost self-evident that speech sounds form various intersecting classes. Thus, for instance, the final sounds in the words *ram*, *ran*, *rang* share the property of *nasality*; i.e., the property of being produced with a lowered velum, which allows air to flow through the nose. In a similar fashion, the sound [m] shares with the sounds [p] and [b] the property of being produced with a closure at the lips, or, as phoneticians would say, of having a bilabial *point of articulation*. The individual speech sounds can then be characterized as complexes of nasality, particular points of articulation and other properties, which together make up the various classificatory frameworks.

The proposed frameworks differ, of course, from one another, and up to the present phoneticians have not agreed on any single framework that is to be used in all linguistic description. In the following I shall utilize the *distinctive feature* framework, which is due primarily to Roman Jakobson. This framework differs from others in that it consists exclusively of binary properties. If we adopt the distinctive features as our classificatory scheme, we commit ourselves to speaking about speech sounds exclusively in terms of two-valued attributes; i.e., of properties which a given sound may or may not possess.

The manner in which individual speech sounds are characterized in terms of distinctive features is illustrated in Figure 1. In this framework [s] is characterized as nonvocalic, consonantal, nongrave, noncompact, strident, non-nasal, continuant, voiceless; or [m] is characterized as nonvocalic, consonantal, grave, noncompact, nonstrident, nasal, noncontinuant, voiced. Consequently, the alphabetic symbols *s* and *m* by which we conventionally designate these sounds are nothing but abbreviations standing for the feature complexes just mentioned. It is as feature complexes, rather than as indivisible entities that speech sounds will be regarded hereinafter. It will be shown that this decision opens the way for further advances in the theory.

We note, moreover, that we can use the features to refer conveniently to classes of speech sounds. Thus, for instance, all sounds represented in Figure 1 belong to the class of consonants and as such they share the features nonvocalic and consonantal. We note furthermore that the consonants [s z č ž š ž] are the only ones that share the features nongrave and strident; or [p b f v m]

[1] This work was supported in part by the U. S. Army (Signal Corps), the U. S. Navy (Office of Naval Research), and the U. S. Air Force (Office of Scientific Research, Air Research and Development Command), and in part by the National Science Foundation.

	p	b	m	f	v	k	g	t	d	θ	ð	n	s	z	č	ǯ	š	ž
vocalic	−	−	−	−	−	−	−	−	−	−	−	−	−	−	−	−	−	−
consonantal	+	+	+	+	+	+	+	+	+	+	+	+	+	+	+	+	+	+
grave	+	+	+	+	+	+	+	−	−	−	−	−	−	−	−	−	−	−
compact	−	−	−	−	−	+	+	−	−	−	−	−	−	−	+	+	+	+
strident	−	−	−	+	+	−	−	−	−	−	−	−	+	+	+	+	+	+
nasal	−	−	+	−	−	−	−	−	−	−	−	+	−	−	−	−	−	−
continuant	−	−	−	+	+	−	−	−	−	+	+	−	+	+	−	−	+	+
voiced	−	+	+	−	+	−	+	−	+	−	+	+	−	+	−	+	−	+

Figure 1. Distinctive feature representation of the consonants of English

alone share the features grave and noncompact. On the other hand, [m] and [s] share no features which would distinguish them from all other consonants. If we wanted to designate the class containing the sound [m] and [s] in distinctive feature terminology, we should have to give a long, cumbersome list of features. We shall say that a set of speech sounds forms a *natural class* if fewer features are required to designate the class than to designate any individual sound in the class. Hence the first three sets of sounds form natural classes, whereas the set containing [m] and [s] is not a natural class.

Jakobson has shown that in describing the most varied linguistic facts, we commonly encounter sets of sounds which form natural classes in the distinctive feature framework, and that only rarely does one meet classes of sounds that require long, cumbersome lists of distinctive features for their characterization. As a case in point, consider the formation of English noun plurals. As every English speaker knows in practice, if and only if a noun ends in [s z š ž č ǯ], the plural is formed by adding the extra syllable [ɪz]. But as we have already seen it is precisely this class of consonants that is exhaustively characterized by the features nongrave and strident. This coincidence is important, for the distinctive features were not postulated with the express purpose of affording a convenient description of the rules for forming the English plural.

The preceding remarks imply a special notion of descriptive economy. I should like to suggest that in the part of a linguistic description that deals with the phonic aspect of language, economy should be measured by the number of distinctive features utilized. The fewer features mentioned in a description, the greater its economy. It is not difficult to show that in simple cases the criterion does indeed perform as one would expect. Given two statements of which one applies to all consonants, whereas the other applies only to strident consonants, we should say without a doubt that the former is more general, more economical. This fact would also be reflected in the number of distinctive features that would have to be mentioned in the two statements, for in order to speak of the class of all consonants we need to mention only the features nonvocalic and consonantal, whereas to designate the class of strident consonants we must mention the feature strident in addition to those which designate the class of all consonants. In an analogous fashion we should consider a rule that applies without restriction, more general and hence simpler than a rule that applies in specific contexts only. The second rule would also require mention of more features, for we would need to mention at least one distinctive feature in order to characterize the context in which the second rule applies.

The proposed criterion, however, has other interesting consequences. To see these we turn again to the formation of plurals of English nouns. The facts can be stated as follows:

To form the plural:

(a) [ɨz] is added if the stem ends in a sound which is nonvocalic, consonantal, nongrave, and strident.

(b) [s] is added if the stem ends in a sound which is nonvocalic, consonantal, voiceless, and nonstrident; or nonvocalic, consonantal, voiceless, strident, and grave.

(c) [z] is added if the stem ends in a sound which is vocalic; or nonvocalic, consonantal, voiced, and nonstrident; or nonvocalic, consonantal, voiced, strident, and grave.

It is to be noted that the above three statements are not ordered with respect to each other, and it is this which makes them so cumbersome. If we impose an order on the application of the statements, we can simplify them markedly as follows:

To form the plural:

(A) [ɨz] is added if the stem ends in a sound which is nonvocalic, consonantal, nongrave, and strident.

(B) [s] is added if the stem ends in a sound which is nonvocalic, consonantal, and voiceless.

(C) [z] is added.

The relative lengths of the two sets of statements graphically reflect their relative simplicity. Ordering, therefore, is mandatory in the present instance, if we want to satisfy our criterion of simplicity.

The proposal that an order be imposed on the application of the rules is not novel. Every description that makes use of phrases like "in all other cases" so as to eliminate the need for spelling out in detail what these "other cases" might be, makes use of an order among the descriptive statements. The only novelty here is that the reason for establishing an order is made explicit: it is a direct consequence of the proposed criterion of simplicity. Note, however, that the ordering established by the criterion may not be total, since in some instances it will not result in a simplification of the description.

Consider now a hypothetical dialect of English[2] which differs from the

<hr>

[2] A dialect with almost exactly these features has been described by my colleague Dr. J. R. Applegate of M. I. T. In order to illustrate my point more clearly, I have modified the facts sightly. This modification, however, in no way affects the plausibility of the constructed example.

standard language in the following two respects:

Where the standard language has a continuant consonant in noninitial position, the dialect has the cognate noncontinuant (stop) consonant.

Where the standard language has several identical noncontinuant consonants
in a word, the dialect replaces all but the first of these by a glottal stop.

EXAMPLES:

I		II		III	
cuff (cup)	[k′ʌp]	puff	[p′ʌp]	pup	[p′ʌʔ]
gave (Gabe)	[g′eb]	brave	[br′eb]	babe	[b′eʔ]
sauce (sought)	[s′ɔt]	toss	[t′ɔt]	taught	[t′ɔʔ]
lies (lied)	[l′ajd]	dies	[d′ajd]	died	[d′ajʔ]

It is to be noted that the dialect admits words with several identical noncontinuant consonants, as can be seen in the examples in Column II, but in
every one of these examples the second noncontinuant corresponds to a fricative in the standard language.

The phonetic peculiarities of this dialect are handled by the following two
ordered rules, which do not function in the standard language:

1. If in a word there are several identical nonvocalic, consonantal noncontinuants, all but the first become nonvocalic, nonconsonantal noncontinuants
(i.e., glottal stops in distinctive feature terminology). Examples in Column III.

2. In noninitial position, nonvocalic, consonantal continuants become noncontinuant.

I believe that this solution, proposed by Applegate, is preferable to the
alternative of postulating a different phonological system for the dialect than
for the standard language. It seems to me intuitively more satisfactory to
say, as we have done here, that the dialect differs from the standard language
only in the relatively minor fact of having two additional low-level rules,
rather than to assert—as we should have to do, if we rejected the proposed
solution—that the dialect deviates from the standard language in the much
more crucial sense of having either a different phonemic repertoire than the
standard language, or of having a strikingly different distribution of phonemes.
It must be stressed that in the proposed solution the ordering of the rules
is absolutely crucial, for if Rule (1) is allowed to operate after Rule (2) the
noncontinuants produced by Rule (2) would be turned into glottal stops by
Rule (1); i.e., the examples in Column II could not be accounted for. Without
ordering of the rules we are forced to accept the unintuitive alternatives mentioned above.

If we regard the process of synthesizing an utterance as a sort of calculation whose final results are transmitted as instruction to the speech organs,
which in turn produce the acoustical signal that strikes our ears, then the
descriptive rules discussed above are simply steps in the calculation. We
have found that by ordering these steps in a particular way the entire calculation becomes less laborious. We might now ask whether the order of the
rules does not also reflect the chronology of their appearance in the language.
Did, for example, the English dialect just discussed pass first through a stage
where it was identical with the standard language, and then through another

stage where it differed from the standard language only in having glottal stops as required by Rule (1), but lacking the noncontinuants produced by Rule (2)?

If the order of the rules can be regarded in this light, then the proposed criterion of descriptive simplicity becomes an important tool for inferring the history of languages, for it allows us to reconstruct various stages of a language even in the absence of external evidence such as is provided by written records or by borrowing in or from other languages.

This way of looking at the phonological rules of a language is anything but novel. As a matter of fact, I should like to argue that the reconstruction of the history of the Indo-European languages, which is perhaps the most impressive achievement of nineteenth century linguistics, was possible only by making use of the proposed criterion of economy to establish an order among the descriptive statements; the order was then assumed to reflect their relative chronology. This can perhaps be illustrated most graphically by a discussion of the so-called Laws of Grimm and of Verner, which, with good reason, are considered among the most solid achievements of Indo-European studies. The Laws describe stages in the evolution of the Germanic languages from the Indo-European proto-language, stages which, it should be noted, are not attested by any external evidence.

The Indo-European proto-language is supposed to have had a single continuant consonant [s], which was voiceless; and a fairly complex system of noncontinuants, of which for present purposes we need consider only two, one voiced and the other voiceless. Grimm's and Verner's Laws describe what happened to these consonants in the course of the evolution of the Germanic languages.

The part of Grimm's Law that is of interest here consists of two rules which can be formulated as follows:

G-1. In certain contexts where condition C_1 (the precise nature of which need not concern us here) is satisfied, nonconvocalic, consonantal, voiceless noncontinuants become continuant. (It is by virtue of this Law that English *five* is said to be cognate with Greek *pente*, Russian *pjat'*, and Sanskrit *pañca*.)

G-2. Nonvocalic, consonantal, voiced noncontinuants become voiceless. (G-2 establishes the correspondence between English *ten* and Greek *deka*, Russian *desjat'*, and Sanskrit *daça*.)

The handbooks tell us that these two rules came into the language in the order indicated, because—and this is particularly important here, for there is no other evidence—if G-2 had operated before G-1 the voiceless continuants produced by G-2 would have become noncontinuants as a consequence of rule G-1. This argumentation, however, is identical with the reasoning which we gave above in justifying the ordering of the rules in the example from the English dialect. The only new factor here is that the order of the rules, which in the English example had no chronological significance, is given such significance here.

At some later time Germanic underwent the effects of Verner's Law which can be formulated as follows:

V. In contexts where C_2 holds, nonvocalic, consonantal, voiceless continuants become voiced.

If we believe with the majority that Verner's Law was later than G-1, then we must assume that at this stage the language possessed voiceless continuants from two sources: the [s] which descended unchanged from the Indo-European proto-language, and the voiceless continuants produced by the operation of Grimm's Law (Rule G-1). The fact that Verner's Law applies without distinction to voiceless continuants from both sources is always cited as the crucial evidence in favor of regarding Verner's Law later than Grimm's Law. This evidence, however, carries weight only if we accept a criterion of descriptive economy much like the one that was stated above, for—as in the case of the plural of English nouns—the facts can also be accounted for fully by the following three unordered rules:

In contexts where both condition C_1 and C_2 are satisfied, nonvocalic, consonantal, voiceless noncontinuants become voiced and continuant.

In contexts where C_1 but not C_2 is satisfied, nonvocalic, consonantal, voiceless continuants become continuant.

In context C_2, [s] (i.e., its total feature specification, which requires mentioning a fair number of features) becomes voiced.

By the proposed criterion of simplicity we must reject the unordered rules, for they require more features than the ordered alternatives G-1 and V. Since there is no external evidence that the language changed in the manner indicated by Grimm's and Verner's Laws, the acceptance of these Laws as historical fact is based wholly on considerations of simplicity. But these are very weighty considerations indeed, for as Professor Quine has remarked, we construct the picture of our world on the basis of "what *is* plus *the simplicity of the laws* whereby we describe and extrapolate what is."

MASSACHUSETTS INSTITUTE OF TECHNOLOGY,
    CAMBRIDGE, MASSACHUSETTS

THE PROBLEM OF LINGUISTIC EQUIVALENCE

BY

ROBERT ABERNATHY

An essential trait of a language—as distinguished from certain mathematical systems, for instance that of the natural numbers—is that it admits of more than one occurrence of the same element. Therefore linguistics has an interest in what Peirce conveniently christened as the distinction between "types" and "tokens." Questions of this nature can arise in various connections: say, in a study of how children learn their native language, in investigation of speech perception or efforts to reproduce such perception mechanically, and, of course, in theories of linguistic description. Formally, the problem is most often thought of as one of establishing a many-one correspondence between tokens on the one hand and types on the other, in other words of inducing an equivalence relation on the set of tokens.

Practical solutions of this problem in one concrete form—namely, that of supplementing an existing speech-communication system by one using written marks instead—go back in history for some thousands of years. The best of these solutions were so good for the purpose in hand that, ever since, people in literate communities have been prone to confuse speech with writing in their thinking about both subjects. The Greeks, when they were being careful, recognized a difference between γράμματα and στοιχεῖα τῶν γραμμάτων, and Latin writers similarly between *litterae* and *elementa litterarum*, but it is only in modern times that the questions implied by such distinctions have been seriously reopened. It now seems plain that the matter of establishing a graphic alphabet for a spoken language is only a special case of a more general problem, which is that of type-token relationships. The shape this will take in specific linguistic theories naturally depends on what initial assumptions are made about the conditions of access to information about language, and then on what it is proposed to do with the data. There has been a great deal of discussion relating in one way or another to these points, much of it unfortunately hampered by terminological ambiguities. It seems possible to distinguish two main viewpoints with regard to the status of minimal elements of linguistic representation, starting from the supposition that what is given is a supply of tokens and the problem of assigning them to types; these two kinds of theory might be labeled "evidential" and "inferential". (This is just a summary classification, which does not seek to do justice to nuances; for surveys of the subject cf. R. Jakobson and M. Halle, *Fundamentals of language*, 's-Gravenhage, 1956, pp. 7–19, and W. Haas, *Relevance in phonetic analysis*, Word 15.1 (1959) pp. 1–18.) The evidential is the older and seemingly the more natural point of view; it simply assumes that the elements of a linguistic description are determined by some decision procedure which, given any token, assigns it to one and only one type. The inferential kind of theory, which is characteristically associated with structuralism in linguistics, expressly refrains from granting this premise for all linguistic elements, or, in other words, it supposes that we want to describe some features of a language for which—because they are too minute, impossible to obtain or produce in isolation, or the like—there does not exist any such straightforward decision procedure, hence that the identification of such features must proceed by inference from knowledge about the complex wholes of which they are parts. A predominance of one or the other theory can perhaps be detected in the diverse principles (always more or less compromised in practice) which seem to inspire different historical solutions of the problem of devising a practical script, e. g. the Chinese character writing as contrasted with European orthographies.

The present paper is an attempt to formulate more exactly certain proposals of the inferential kind. In line with the prevailing tendency in the literature alluded to above, the interpretation primarily intended is that in terms of linguistic description. The formulation is, however, meant to be broad enough to admit the possibility of various interpretations (say in connection with a model of child language learning, or with a "learning" process which might be realized by a machine).

Given: (1) An at most denumerable set S, and a relation $>$ such that, for $x, y, z \in S$, the following conditions are satisfied:

$$(x)(y) \sim [x > y \cdot y > x] ,$$

$$(x)(y)(z) [(x > y \cdot y > z) \rightarrow x > z] ,$$

$$(x)(y)(z) [(x > y \cdot x > z) \rightarrow (y > z \, V z > y)] ,$$

$$(x)(y)(z) [(x > y \cdot z > y) \rightarrow (x > z \, V z > x)] .$$

Let $S(x)$ be the longest sequence $\langle \alpha_1, \cdots, \alpha_n \rangle$ such that, for some $i, x = \alpha_i$, and, for all $i < n, \alpha_{i+1} > \alpha_i$.

(2) A second set T which is likewise at most denumerable.

(3) R_z such that, for all $x \in S$, if $S(\alpha_i) = \langle \alpha_1, \cdots, \alpha_i, \cdots \rangle$, then $R_\beta S(\alpha_i) = \langle \alpha_1, \cdots, \alpha_{i-1}, \beta, \alpha_{i+1}, \cdots \rangle$.

(4) F such that, for all $x, y \in S, FR_x S(y) \in T$.

S is partially ordered by $>$, in such a way that it is a sum of completely ordered disjoint subsets. The set T might be merely, say, the first k natural numbers, or all the natural numbers. We have further an operator R_z which replaces the designated element y of a sequence $S(y)$ by $x \in S$. In particular, evidently $R_x S(x) = S(x)$. Finally, there is a function F which maps each of the $R_x S(y)$ into some element of T.

On this basis, we can obtain some new relations on S, in addition to the ordering relation $>$. First, for all $x, y \in S$, let C be defined as follows:

$$(x)(y) [C(x, y) \equiv (FR_x S(y) = FR_y S(y))] .$$

I. e., x bears the relation C to y if and only if replacement of y by x in the sequence containing the former $(S(y) = R_y S(y))$ does not alter the image of this sequence in T. $C(x, y)$ might be read "x is substitutable for y".

Next, define D by:

$$(x)(y) [D(x, y) \equiv (C(x, y) \cdot C(y, x))] .$$

$D(x, y)$ might be worded as "x and y are mutually substitutable" or "interchangeable". Obviously D is reflexive and symmetrical, whereas C has only the former property.

Finally, let E be defined, for $x, y, z \in S$, by:

$$(x)(y)[E(x, y) \equiv (z)[C(x, z) \equiv C(y, z)]]$$

and, conversely, E^*:

$$(x)(y)[E^*(x, y) \equiv (z)[C(z, x) \equiv C(z, y)]] \, .$$

It can easily be seen that E and E^* are reflexive, symmetrical, and transitive. The above relations form a series of increasing restrictiveness: we have $D \subset C$, and both $E \subset D$ and $E^* \subset D$, but not in general $E = E^*$; though these are both equivalence relations, they are not identical. This can be illustrated by a simple example: Suppose that, for $\alpha, \beta, \gamma \in S$, we have substitutabilities $C(\alpha, \beta)$, $C(\beta, \alpha)$, and $C(\gamma, \alpha)$, but C does not hold otherwise except when $x = y$. Then there is an equivalence $E(\alpha, \beta)$, but $E^*(\alpha, \beta)$ fails to hold, and in fact no two distinct elements are equivalent by E^* (which in this instance is a refinement of E, but of course no such relationship will apply generally). Moreover, once we have two equivalence relations on the same set, we can immediately get more: $E \cap E^*$ and $E \cup E^*$ are again equivalence relations, which may conveniently be abbreviated E_0 and E_1 respectively.

Interpretation of this symbolic scheme with reference to the linguist's aims will go more or less as follows: The data from which we hope to construct a language description are supposed to be available in the form of "words" (in a loose sense, merely as a less awkward label than "minimum identifiable configuration" or the like). These may be composed of elements which are not themselves words. We are able to expand this initial stock of word-tokens by making from each one copies which differ from the original by virtue of the substitution, for just one of its elements, of another element found anywhere in the stock. The replacement operator R_z answers to a variety of devices which have been suggested or tried—ranging from cutting and splicing of mechanical recordings, through methods relying on the human capacity for mimicry, to purely conceptual experiments.

It is further supposed that we have some way of identifying each form in the expanded stock as a token of some word-type (or of none), or, at least, of deciding for each pair of forms whether they are "the same" or "different". Such a procedure is usually envisaged as a crucial experiment of a psychological nature; for instance, the linguist somehow manages to confront a native informant with a problematic pair of forms, and registers a decision about their identity on the basis of the response evoked. (It might be added that the linguist and his informant are not necessarily distinct individuals; the linguist may, as Quine puts it, have begun by "ingesting" the informant.) The function F in (4) above might be variously realized; for the present purpose, it is essential only that there exist a decision procedure of some sort.

Relations defined on S thus become as many different prescriptions for classifying parts of a body of data, with the aim of representing it in terms of a (preferably finite) "alphabet" of types. It is immediately evident that some proposals for dealing with this problem are not adequate to the place they are meant to occupy in linguistic theory, since they amount to assigning tokens to the same type if they satisfy relations C or D, while taking for granted that the alphabet should be a set of mutually exclusive alternatives. A hidden assumption is involved here, namely that the systems to which the prescribed mode of description is to apply are of a more restricted kind than that defined by (1)–(4), so that one need take into account only limiting cases such as that in which $C = D = E$. But there is some reason to believe that natural language data will not always conform to such cases. Cf. Eli Fischer-Jørgensen's reported findings (*The commutation test and its application to phonemic analysis*, For Roman Jakobson, 's-Gravenhage, 1956, pp. 140–151); in this experiment R_x was realized by interchanging portions of tape-recorded Danish utterances (and tests were performed to ascertain that the invariance $FR_xS(x) = FS(x)$ in fact held true under the experimental conditions), and the decision procedure was statistical, since a number of listeners' responses were collated. The results show $C \neq D$, e. g. substitutions of $[t]$ for $[k]$ (explosions of postaspirated Danish stops) uniformly produced a "different" response, but substitutions of $[k]$ for $[t]$ elicited a judgment of "no difference". Thus for Danish segmented in this way substitutability of one element for another does not imply that they are equivalent. On the other hand, results obtained for a coarser segmentation—$[th]$, $[kh]$, etc.—were apparently compatible with such an assumption.

It has been pointed out above, however, that equivalence relations can be induced on the underlying set in a more general class of systems than those for which $C = E$ or $D = E$; in fact, this can be done in more than one way, so that such a system can have diverse but equally valid "alphabets". The relations E, E^*, E_0, E_1, with their relation of inclusion, form a Boolean lattice; the alphabet corresponding to E_1 might be called the "least alphabet" of a given system, in the sense that it will contain the smallest number of characters, and conversely E_0 will give the maximum number. Just what consequences this may have for linguistics is not immediately clear. It is, in effect, very commonly held that a least alphabet is a prime desideratum of linguistic description; but it is not recognized that a choice of alternative descriptions may be involved other than at the level of distributional analysis (which however presupposes the selection of one or another kind of equivalence). Perhaps the existence of unrecognized choices is responsible for some of the obscurities and misunderstandings which have arisen in discussion of these questions.

MASSACHUSETTS INSTITUTE OF TECHNOLOGY,
    CAMBRIDGE, MASSACHUSETTS

THE JOINTS OF ENGLISH[1]

BY

HANS G. HERZBERGER

Sentences can be taken apart in a number of ways, leading to different structural characterizations. A method that has proved fruitful in preliminary mechanical operations on English[2] involves the decomposition of a sentence into a *center* and its *adjuncts*. We shall record some observations about adjunction-analysis, and exhibit some of its connections with other known types of structure.

Each method of analysis can be construed in terms of a structural relation whose domain is a set of sentences.[3] With each sentence in its domain, the relation associates a set of elements that can be taken as an analysis of that sentence. A finite statement of the relation specifies its domain together with analyses: it is a grammar of the domain.

Structural relations may be defined over the whole set of sentences, or over strategic subsets which they characterize naturally.[4] It is often instructive to consider relations restricted to particular sets of sentences, and in this spirit to examine the groupings which structural relations impose on the set of sentences. Structures of English which are characteristic but not ubiquitous would only be obscured by a uniform structural relation for the whole language. For example, zeroings under conjunction cut across other linguistic structures. The sentence: *If he won't go, then I will go* has the zeroed or elliptical form: *If he won't go, then I will*. The set Z of sentences without such zeroings forms an umbrella over the language (every sentence is either in Z or is a part of some sentence in Z) which has a much tighter structure than the whole language has: and we restrict our attention to such a set. Within its perhaps restricted field, each relation induces a set of elementary sentences as generators, and a set of derived sentences.[5] Sentences elemen-

[1] This paper was written in connection with the National Science Foundation Transformations and Discourse Analysis Project at the University of Pennsylvania, and is intended as a report on some aspects of the work of that project. The paper owes much to discussions with Professors Z. S. Harris, H. Hiż, and the other members of the project, as well as with Professors R. McNaughton, W. Craig, and N. Chomsky.

[2] Cf. p. 103 of this paper, and TDAP (1959).

[3] An element x is in the domain of a binary relation R if and only if there is an element y such that $R(x, y)$.

[4] By a natural characterization we mean, in part, one where the relation $R(x, y)$, or some allied relation, has a uniform interpretation in semantic or behavioral terms: e.g. x *modifies* y, or x is *categorized* (perceived, remembered) as a y, etc.

[5] In the extreme case one or both of these sets may be null: each may be a set of abstract strings representing a set of sentences. The generators will represent a subset (not necessarily a proper subset) of the set of sentences represented by the whole domain of the relation.

tary with respect to one type of structure may be derived with respect to another.

One type of analysis which has received considerable attention in linguistics parses a sentence into its constituents. The sentence: *He was a scavenger* can be decomposed into its subject noun-phrase *he*, with the residue as verb-phrase, which in turn can be broken into the copula *was* and the noun-phrase *a scavenger*. The relation underlying such analysis arranges distinguished segments of the sentence into a hierarchical pattern, or segmental analysis. A segmental analysis of a string *s* is a decomposition of the string into a set of continuous stretches, including *s* itself and its atomic parts, such that no two of these segments cross in *s*: the only overlap in the set is inclusion. Formally, a segmental analysis of a string *s* is a set *A* of strings satisfying the conditions[6]:

(i) $x \subset s$ (for all $x \in A$),

(ii) $s \in A$,

(iii) $(x)(y)[(x \subset s)$ & $(y \subset x \rightarrow y = x) \rightarrow x \in A]$,

(iv) $x \circ y \rightarrow [x \subset y \lor \subset x]$ (for all $x, y \in A$).

A segmental analysis can be displayed in a number of ways. If we form all inclusion-chains in the set *A*, we obtain a rooted tree,[7] with the string *s* (called the *product* of the analysis) as root. As an example, we can decompose the string *abcde* into itself, its letters and the segments *bc, bcd*. This decomposition can be represented by a bracketing of the string: $a[(bc)d]e$, with superfluous brackets omitted around the string and its individual letters. The tree can be diagrammed:

$$a \quad b \quad c \quad d \quad e$$

with each node representing the longest segment its straight branches span. A set of such analyses having the strings of a set L as products will be called a segmental system for L.[8]

Adjunction is a special relation within segmental structure that allows us to describe a range of complex sentences on the basis of a set of elementary

---

[6] These remarks and formal conditions presume that no letter recurs in a string. In the general case occurrences of a letter could be kept distinct by alphabetic replacement.

We use the horseshoe for weak inclusion, the arrow for implication, and the small circle for overlap. We understand inclusion in such a way that segments are continuous: $(x)(y)[x \subset y \rightarrow (\exists u)(\exists w)(y = uxw)]$. An element x overlaps an element y if and only if x and y have a common part.

[7] A tree is a set of elements ordered and connected in such a way that there is a unique path between any two elements. If one element of a tree is designated in some way, the tree is said to be rooted in that element.

[8] Such a system is ordinarily constructed over an extension of the terminal vocabulary, with auxiliary letters (constituent-types) used to label the nodes of the trees: Cf. Chomsky (1959). Cf. Tamari (1954) for abstract representations of relevant features which may be of considerable interest in the theory of these systems.

clauses supposed available. We will use the term *phrase* to mean any string of words or morphemes, and the term *clause* to mean a sentence or an adjunct-string. The main sources of adjuncts are relative clauses[9] and predicates (objects of the copula *be*, including adjectives, participles, prepositional phrases, and so on). The great bulk of these adjuncts can be shown by co-occurrence analysis[10] to be positional variants of sentences, deformed and bound to particular syntactic positions within sentences. We also extend the notion of clause to a few strings not derivative from sentences, including certain adverbs, quantifiers, and the like.

The constituents of a sentence can be built up by repeated adjoining of strings to a center. We can develop the noun-phrase *our interpretation* into *our interpretation of the silence* into *our interpretation of the silence around us*, and so on. English has adjunction to nouns, verbs, noun and verb phrases, whole sentences, to adjuncts, and so on. Adjuncts appear to the right of, to the left of, and sometimes embedded within, their centers. A number of these cases are illustrated in the example: *He was, [after all], a scavenger [of the mind], [or so it seemed]*. Adjunction can be viewed as a set of operations on phrases. The result of adjoining a phrase to a constituent of a sentence is a constituent (of the same type); adjoining to an adjunct yields an adjunct (of the same type). Adjoining to any segment in a sentence produces a new sentence with essentially the same structure.

We can develop this pattern on various levels of detail. Consider a binary asymmetric relation of *attachment*, that holds between two strings when the first is adjoined to the second or to some segment in the second; and a set of elementary strings called *centers*. The centers are the elementary sentences and adjuncts. A schema for the rules of formation is: an elementary sentence is well-formed; and an adjunct can be attached to a particular position in a string already introduced. Since an occurrence of an adjunct cannot be attached to two different positions, much less to two distinct segments, the structure of any sentence is a rooted tree with respect to attachment, with an elementary sentence as root. It is attached to no clause, and all other clauses are ancestrally attached to it. In the direction of decomposition, every sentence is a clause, a clause consists of a center together with its attachments, and an attachment is a set of clauses. When we examine adjunction more closely, we can see that every clause has a center together with adjuncts at various positions, and that each adjunct is a sequence of clauses. When more than one clause is adjoined to the same point, they turn up consecutively in the sentence, as in *the indifference [of the natural world][to the constructions of art]*.

A segmental system accomplishes a tree-ordering of distinguished segments of a sentence. Given a segmental system for a set of centers (elementary sentences and adjuncts) and some adjunction-operations, we can extend the

---

[9] Under relative clauses we include sentences deformed by the zeroing of an element and affixing an element of a certain "relative" class, viz.: *that he came, in which they lived, where they left him, whoever he was,* and the like.

[10] Cf. Harris (1957).

system to a larger set of more complex sentences. Adjoining may have two sorts of effect on the final shape of a sentence, depending on the point of adjunction. The parts of a sentence can appear as connected segments or as nested inside one another. Both occur in: THE *small* FIGURES, *balanced like careful riders*, HAILED US *in Arabic* (the center of the sentence is ITALIC). A string is *split* when a clause adjoins it at an interior point, and adjoining to an endpoint *extends* the string. Extending can result from adjunction to the whole string, or to one of its rightmost or leftmost segments. In splitting, the course of a string is interrupted, and this can, under suitable conditions,[11] indefinitely separate the parts of an elementary clause, producing what appears as a discontinuous clause. These discontinuities are either nested or disjoint: splitting is asymmetrical, and can never result in the crossing of elementary clauses. Splitting is hereditary under attachment. Any attachments to a splitting clause stretch discontinuities. The study of such discontinuities (dependencies), their lengths and kinds, is of some interest as a tool for the investigation of the gross structure of a language.

Attachment structure, which records adjunction but not the point of adjunction, can be diagrammed with solid lines for splits and broken lines for extensions. The previous example, with notational conventions, would look like:

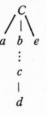

[Let $C =$ *The figures hailed us*, $a =$ *small*, $b =$ *balanced*, $c =$ *like riders*, $d =$ *careful*, $e =$ *in Arabic*.]

Sentences elementary with respect to adjunction fall into two main classes in English. Some of them are simple, like *Puzzles confused him*, and others are derivative forms of the same structure except that a clause occupies the position of a noun: *Whatever he tried confused him*. The set has common principles of organization, with one class taking its elements from the terminal vocabulary and the other from the elementary clause-generator as well. Along with the elementary sentences we have a parallel set of elementary adjuncts: *whom I saw*, *from the window*, *coming across the lawn*, and so on. The first elementary class is a finite set of strings: an upper bound to the length of these strings is determined by the size of the vocabulary. The second class of sentences elementary with respect to adjunction can be analyzed in terms of a replacement operation which converts a simple elementary sentence into a composite one. The two operations, adjunction and replacement, exhaust the

---

[11] Provided only that clauses attach to some interior points, and that adjuncts themselves include some points of adjunction.

recursive aspects of segmental structure.[12]

The set E of elementary sentences induced by adjunction overlaps the so-called kernel set k induced by transformational analysis.[13] E but not K will presumably contain comparative sentences like *The more you earn, the more she spends*, and interrogatives like *Why did he come?*: while K but not E will presumably contain sentences with adverbials, like *He fell down the stairs*.

The structure we have described serves as the basis for the computable syntactic analysis developed at the University of Pennsylvania,[14] which breaks each sentence at its joints and undoes all adjunction, isolating the center of the sentence (subject, verb, object) and marking its modifiers. The grammar underlying this program specifies a close superset of the sentences of English. The program associates a segmental structure from this grammer with each sentence of an input text, with alternative readings for homonymous strings.

BIBLIOGRAPHY

1. N. Chomsky, *Syntactic Structures*, 's-Gravenhage, 1957.
2. ———, *On certain formal properties of grammars*, Information and Control vol. 2, (1959) pp. 137–167.
3. Z. S. Harris, *Co-occurrence and transformation in linguistic structure*, Language vol. 33 (1957) pp. 283–340.
4. D. Tamari, *Monoides préordonnés et chaines de Malcev*, Bull. Soc. Math. France vol. 82 (1954) pp. 54–98.
5. Transformations and Discourse Analysis Projects (TDAP) reports, mimeographed, Philadelphia, 1959, pp. 15–21.

UNIVERSITY OF PENNSYLVANIA,
  PHILADELPHIA, PENNSYLVANIA

---

[12] The form of grammatical statement for adjunction is a combinatorial production which develops a chosen letter into a string containing it; that for replacement develops a letter into a string which does not contain it. Cf. Chomsky (1959) for detailed studies of grammars as combinatorial systems.

[13] Cf. Chomsky (1957) and Harris (1957).

[14] Cf. TDAP (1959).

AUTOMATIC SYNTACTIC ANALYSIS AND THE PUSHDOWN STORE[1]

BY

ANTHONY G. OETTINGER

1. Introduction. The problems of syntactic analysis have received considerable attention in recent years from three types of investigators, namely: mathematical logicians interested in the structure of formal "artificial" languages, applied mathematicians concerned with the design and translation of languages suitable for programming automatic information-processing machines, and mathematical linguists seeking algorithms for automatic translation among "natural" languages or for automatic information retrieval. Although these three types of investigators have different central objectives, a perusal of the works listed in the bibliography should convince the reader that there is a strong underlying kinship not only in the problems under investigation, but also in the methods of study and in the kinds of solutions sought or obtained.

One important common problem is that of obtaining an algorithm for distinguishing sentences from nonsentences or, in more formal terms, well-formed strings from not well-formed strings. Although the pure form of this problem has received more attention from logicians than from the others, it is of equal importance in automatic programming, where a fail-safe translator or compiler capable of detecting and rejecting not well-formed input data could eliminate much tedious debugging effort, and in automatic translation, where the problem of guaranteeing that each sentence is well-formed and has been correctly analyzed still looms large.

A second common problem is that of obtaining the simplest, in some sense, of a set of otherwise equivalent algorithms. Since this is a problem of practicality and economy rather than of existence, it has been of more vital concern to applied mathematicians and to mathematical linguists seeking algorithms that can be executed in a reasonable time at a reasonable cost than to logicians for whom this matter may have only aesthetic significance, since an exhaustive treatment of all cases is theoretically sufficient whenever "all" is finite.

In many cases of interest both of these problems seem amenable to solution by the application of techniques based on the use of what some computer people have come to call a "pushdown" store, namely a linear array of storage locations in which information is entered or removed from one end only, in accordance with a "last-in-first-out" principle. Although the full range of applicability of pushdown store techniques still remains to be determined, the cases studied so far all have structures that can be described in terms of trees or graphs akin to trees.

The work detailed in this paper and sketched at an earlier conference (Oettinger [19; 20]) grew out of reflections on a syntactic analysis technique devised

---

[1] This work has been supported in part by the National Science Foundation and by the Rome Air Development Center of the United States Air Force.

by Rhodes [22; 23; 24] at the National Bureau of Standards and adopted with modifications by Sherry [29] and others at Harvard, on the formalization of the syntax of Łukasiewicz's parenthesis-free notation given by Burks, Warren, and Wright [3] and applied by Miehle [16] and Oettinger [18], on the analytic and explanatory linguistic models of Chomsky [5] and Yngve [32; 33], and the related psychological model of Miller [17], on the syntactic analysis theories of Wundheiler and Wundheiler [31], Bar Hillel [1; 2], Lambek [14], and Riguet [25], and on such theoretical studies of automatic programming as those by Rutishauser [27], Janov [12], and Ljapunov [15]. Several authors, particularly Kanner [13], Ingerman [9], and Gorn [8], have thought along similar directions. The importance and the simplicity of the pushdown store have been clearly and independently recognized by Samelson and Bauer [28], whose paper appeared just as this one was being completed.

The Rhodes method of "predictive" syntactic analysis is based on the observation that in scanning through a Russian sentence from left to right it is possible, on the one hand, to make predictions about the syntactic structures to be met further to the right and, on the other hand, to determine the syntactic role of the word currently being scanned by testing what previously made predictions it fulfills. The predictions are stored in a linear array called the "prediction pool" which behaves approximately as a pushdown store. Before a new sentence is scanned, a set of initial predictions is entered in the pool. The first word of the sentence is then admitted, and a test is made to see if the topmost prediction in the pool will accept it. If so, the successful prediction is erased from the prediction pool, and new predictions based both on lexical data about the word obtained from a dictionary and on syntactic rules embodied in the predictive analysis system are entered into the prediction pool on top of whatever earlier predictions may have remained there. The system is then ready to process the next word in the sentence. To a fair degree of approximation, this technique may be regarded as the inverse of the system for sentence generation outlined by Yngve [33], in which a pushdown store is clearly used.

The foregoing is necessarily a grossly simplified account of the predictive analysis method. Somewhat more detailed descriptions have been given by Rhodes [22; 23; 24], Sherry [29], and Oettinger [19]. Empirical results obtained for Russian at the National Bureau of Standards and at Harvard are extremely encouraging, but it must be strongly emphasized that no claim is made of any final solution of the problems of automatic translation. Recent work at Harvard by Bossert, Giuliano, and Grant on the application of predictive analysis to English is equally encouraging. Detailed reports on both Russian and English are in preparation.

Predictive analysis yields a description of the syntactic structure of a sentence in terms consonant, although not identical, with old-fashioned parsing, immediate constituent theory (e.g., Wells [30]), or phrase-structure theory (Chomsky [5]). It remains to analyze the exact relation of the predictive method to these theories, as well as to those of Bar Hillel, Lambek, and Riguet, and to those of the logicians who, like Ajdukiewicz, inspired the latter investigators. A model by Sherry, described in a report in preparation, that extends some of the results given later in this paper to account for significant properties of predictive analysis, may help to shed more light on this question.

For present purposes, the most important properties of predictive analysis are (1) that in the ideal case and, indeed, in many simple practical cases, a correct syntactic analysis of a sentence is obtained after a single scan of the sentence from left to right, each word being used once and only once, and (2) that the method incorporates very natural checks for well-formation, and therefore has desirable fail-safe properties. As applied to natural languages in the general case, the technique of predictive analysis has an empirical, approximative and, in some instances, iterative character. It seemed natural to ask whether an exact and interesting theoretical counterpart exists for some suitable simple artificial languages. The remainder of this paper answers this question in the affirmative. Familiarity with the work of Burks, Warren, and Wright [3] is assumed in what follows; references to their article will henceforth be made with the abbreviation "BWW". It should be noted that the *register* in the Evaluator of BWW (p. 56) is essentially a pushdown store.

2. The languages P_1, P_2, P_3, **and** L. In the following definitions "δ_{jk}" designates the kth member of a set of elements of degree j. Elements δ_{0i} are usually called variables, and elements for which $j \geq 1$ are called functors or operators of degree j. Discussion will be confined to $0 \leq j \leq 2$, since the "parenthetic" languages to be defined do not admit of functors of degree >2. The symbol "$\varDelta_j$" denotes an arbitrary formula in L, while "$\varDelta_j^i$" denotes an arbitrary formula in P_i. Left and right parentheses designate themselves. In all cases, "$\varLambda$" designates the null formula, and for any $\varDelta$, if $\varDelta \neq \varLambda$, $\varDelta$ is of finite length.

Well-formed formulas in the languages P_1, P_2, P_3, and L are defined as follows:

DEFINITION 1 (P_1). (a) δ_{0i}; and (b) if $\varDelta_1^1$ and $\varDelta_2^1$, then $(\delta_{1j}'\varDelta_1^1$, and also $(\varDelta_1^1\delta_{2k}'\varDelta_2^1$.

DEFINITION 2 (P_2). (a) δ_{0i}; and (b) if $\varDelta_1^2$ and $\varDelta_2^2$, then $\delta_{1j}'\varDelta_1^2)$, and also $\varDelta_1^2\delta_{2k}'\varDelta_2^2)$.

DEFINITION 3 (P_3). (a) δ_{0i}; and (b) if $\varDelta_1^3$ and $\varDelta_2^3$, then $(\delta_{1j}'\varDelta_1^3)$, and also $(\varDelta_1^3\delta_{2k}'\varDelta_2^3)$.

DEFINITION 4 (L). (a) δ_{0i}; and (b) if $\varDelta_1$ and $\varDelta_2$, then $\delta_{1j}\varDelta_1$, and also $\delta_{2k}\varDelta_2\varDelta_1$.

P_1, P_2, and P_3 will be referred to respectively as left-parenthetic, right-parenthetic, and simple full-parenthetic languages. Except for the restriction to functors of degree ≤ 2, L is the Łukasiewicz parenthesis-free language, as described in BWW and in Rosenbloom [26], Chapter IV.

Mappings among P_1, P_2, P_3, and L are defined as follows:

DEFINITION 5. (a) $\varLambda \longleftrightarrow \varLambda$, $\delta_{0i} \longleftrightarrow \delta_{0i}$, that is, the null formula and the variables are, for the sake of simplicity, assumed to be the same in all four languages.

(b) if $\varDelta_j^1 \longleftrightarrow \varDelta_j^2 \longleftrightarrow \varDelta_j^3 \longleftrightarrow \varDelta_j$

and $\delta_{jk}' \longleftrightarrow \delta_{jk}, j > 0$, then

$$(\delta_{1j}'\varDelta_1^1 \longleftrightarrow \delta_{1j}'\varDelta_1^2) \longleftrightarrow (\delta_{1j}'\varDelta_1^3) \longleftrightarrow \delta_{1j}\varDelta_1 ,$$

and also

$$(\varDelta_1^1 \delta'_{2k} \varDelta_2^1 \longleftrightarrow \varDelta_1^2 \delta'_{2k} \varDelta_2^2) \longleftrightarrow (\varDelta_1^3 \delta'_{2k} \varDelta_2^3) \longleftrightarrow \delta_{2k} \varDelta_2 \varDelta_1 \;.$$

EXAMPLE 1. Let $\delta_{0i} = x_i$, $\delta'_{11} = \sim$, $\delta'_{21} = +$, $\delta'_{22} = \cdot$, $\delta_{11} = N$, $\delta_{21} = A$, $\delta_{22} = M$; then

$$(\sim((x_1 + x_2 \cdot x_3 \longleftrightarrow \sim x_1 + x_2) \cdot x_3)) \longleftrightarrow (\sim((x_1 + x_2) \cdot x_3)) \longleftrightarrow NMx_3 Ax_2 x_1 \;.$$

Algorithms for effecting the mappings of Definition 5 can easily be devised with the aid of a pushdown store. Let p be a pushdown store. Let the input formula be scanned character-by-character from left to right, and let the output formula be produced by adjoining each new character to the left of those previously generated. With these conventions, the following simple translation algorithms may be defined:

DEFINITION 6. Translation from P_2 to L.

If the current input character is

(1) a variable, adjoin it to the output formula;

(2) a right parenthesis, adjoin the character currently at the top of p to the output formula, then remove it from p;

(3) a functor, put its image (Definition 5) at the top of p.

DEFINITION 7. Translation from P_1 to L.

If the current input character is

(1) a left parenthesis, put a "v" at the top of p;

(2) a functor, replace the character currently at the top of p by the image (Definition 5) of the functor;

(3) a variable

(a) adjoin it to the output formula; then

(b) check p; if it is empty or has a "v" on top, proceed to the next input character; otherwise adjoin the character currently at the top of p to the output formula, then remove it from p, and repeat step (b).

EXAMPLE 2. (For ease in printing, the pushdown store is laid on its side, opening toward the left; viewed this way, it is obviously analogous to a tape on a Turing machine or on a real computer.) The formulas are those of Example 1. On each line, the current character, the pushdown store p, and the output formula are shown after application of the rules of Definition 6 or Definition 7.

$P_2 \to L$			$P_1 \to L$		
$\sim$	N	$\varLambda$	(	v	$\varLambda$
x_1	N	x_1	$\sim$	N	$\varLambda$
$+$	AN	x_1	(	$v\,N$	$\varLambda$
x_2	AN	$x_2 x_1$	(	$v\,v\,N$	$\varLambda$
)	N	$Ax_2 x_1$	x_1	$v\,v\,N$	x_1
$\cdot$	MN	$Ax_2 x_1$	$+$	$Av\,N$	x_1
x_3	MN	$x_3 Ax_2 x_1$	x_2	$v\,N$	$Ax_2 x_1$
)	N	$Mx_3 Ax_2 x_1$	$\cdot$	MN	$Ax_2 x_1$
)	$\varLambda$	$NMx_3 Ax_2 x_1$	x_3	$\varLambda$	$NMx_3 Ax_2 x_1$

Note that in both Definition 6 and Definition 7 the characters adjoined to the output obviously depend on p as well as on the current character, but that in Definition 6 the sequence of operations depends solely on the current input character. In Definition 7, "v" clearly "marks the place" of a left parenthesis occurrence, and "v" is used instead of (simply to avoid compounding homography and autonymy. Example 2 also clearly shows that P_1, P_2, and P_3 are equivalent in the sense that grouping remains unambiguous even when either all left parentheses or all right parentheses are removed from an expression in P_3.

3. A notation for algorithms. Definitions 6 and 7 are simple enough to be readily understood as given. More complex algorithms require more formal and precise definitions, especially if it is of importance to establish certain of their characteristics by formal proofs. The notation of BWW is adequate for formal proofs, but it does not lend itself readily to a rapid grasp of the essence of a given algorithm nor to experimentation with the definition of new ones. Conventional flow chart notations used in computer programming lack in rigor and universality, since they often rely on *ad hoc* devices, or on devices tailored too closely to the characteristics of specific real machines. The notation adopted for this paper is a simplified version of a new notation recently devised by Iverson [10] which shows great promise of lucidity, precision, and universality. A detailed definition of the notation and of its varied applications is given by Iverson and Brooks [11].

BWW use juxtaposition in the syntax language to denote juxtaposition in the object language. It proves more convenient for our purposes to use a "vector" notation, for example "$[(, \delta'_{1j}, \Delta^1_1]$" instead of "$(\delta'_{1j}\Delta^1_1$" or "$[(, \sim, (, (,$ $x_1, +, x_2,), \cdot, x_3,),)]$" for "$(\sim((x_1 + x_2) \cdot x_3))$". The dimension of a vector is equivalent to length in the sense of BWW. Thus, if $y = [(, \delta_{01}, \delta'_{11}, \delta_{02},)]$, $L(y) = 5$, and if $y = [(, \Delta^3_1, \delta'_{11}, \Delta^3_2,)]$, $L(y) = 3 + L(\Delta^3_1) + L(\Delta^3_2)$. No distinction is made between a vector of dimension 1 and a scalar.

Vectors whose components are taken from the set $\{0, 1\}$ are called *logical* vectors. If, in the logical vector $[a_1, a_2, \cdots, a_n]$, the first k components $= 1$ and the remaining components $= 0$, the vector is designated by "h^k"; if the last k components $= 1$ and the remaining components $= 0$, the vector is designated by "t^k"; if only the kth component $= 1$, the vector is designated by "e^k"; finally, if all components $= 1$, this "unit" vector is designated by "e" without any superscript.

The following operations, among those defined by Iverson, will be used in this paper:

DEFINITION 8. (a) *Scalar multiplication.*

If c is a scalar, and w is a logical vector, then $(cw)_i = cw_i$. For example, if $c = \delta_{01}$ and $w = [0, 1, 1, 0, 1, 1]$, then $cw = [0, \delta_{01}, \delta_{01}, 0, \delta_{01}, \delta_{01}]$.

(b) *Compression.*

If w is an arbitrary vector, and u a logical vector of the same dimension as w, then the result u/w of a compression of w by u is a vector whose sole components are the components w_i of w for which $u_i = 1$. For example, if $w = [(, \delta_{01}, \delta'_{21}, \delta_{02},)]$ and $u = [1, 0, 0, 0, 1]$, $u/w = [(,)]$.

(c) *Complementation.*

If u is a logical vector, then $v = \bar{u}$ is the complement of u if $v_i = 0$ when $u_i = 1$, and vice versa. In the example of (b), we have $\bar{u} = [0, 1, 1, 1, 0]$, hence $\bar{u}/w = [\delta_{01}, \delta'_{21}, \delta_{02}]$. Note that if $h^1 = [1, 0, 0, 0, 0]$ then $h^1/w = [()$, and $\bar{h}^1/w = t^4/w = t^{L(w)-1}/w = [\delta_{01}, \delta'_{21}, \delta_{02})]$.

(d) *Reduction.*

If x and y are arbitrary vectors of equal dimension, and $\mathscr{R}$ is a binary relation defined on their components, the reduction $x\mathscr{R}y$ is a logical vector u of the same dimension such that $u_i = 1$ if $x_i \mathscr{R} y_i$ holds and $u_i = 0$ otherwise. For example, let $x = [1, 2, 3, 4, 5]$, $y = [5, 4, 3, 2, 1]$, and $\mathscr{R} = >$. Then $x > y = [0, 0, 0, 1, 1]$.

EXAMPLE 3. Let $a = [(, (,), \delta_{0i}, \delta'_{1j}, \delta'_{1j}, \delta'_{2k}, \delta'_{2k}]$ and $b = [s, v, u, u, t, \delta_{1j}, t, \delta_{2k}]$. Then if $c = \delta'_{1j}$ and e is the unit vector we have by reduction, $(a = ce) = [0, 0, 0, 0, 1, 1, 0, 0]$, and by a subsequent compression we obtain $(a = ce)/b = [t, \delta_{1j}]$. Similarly, if $c =)$, $(a = ce)/b = u$.

In Iverson's notation, as in conventional computer programming, an algorithm is specified by a sequence of statements, as illustrated in Figure 1, where a formal expression of Definition 6 is shown. The expression "$x \varDelta^2$", for example,

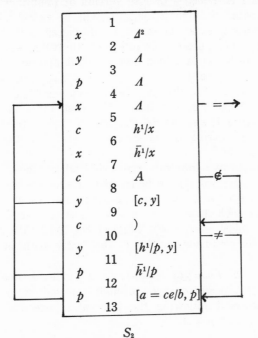

$$S_2$$

$$A = \{\delta_{0i}\}$$
$$a = [\delta'_{11}, \cdots, \delta'_{1j}, \delta'_{21}, \cdots, \delta'_{2k}]$$
$$b = [\delta_{11}, \cdots, \delta_{1j}, \delta_{21}, \cdots, \delta_{2k}]$$

Translation from P_2 to L

Figure 1

may be read as "x is specified to be Δ^{2}", and "y $[c, y]$" is equivalent to "y is specified to be $[c, y]$" or to "the new y is the result of juxtaposing c to the left of the old y". Equivalent expressions in many common flow chart notations would be "$\Delta^2 \to y$" and "$[c, y] \to y$", but arrows are superfluous within elementary statements.

The diagram of Figure 1 is normally read from top to bottom, and the order of execution of the statements is normally the order of listing. A line directed outward from a statement indicates a branch point, namely a break in the normal sequence. If the line is unlabeled, the statement next to it is read according to the definition of the preceding paragraph, but the next statement to be executed is never the one listed next, but always that to which the directed line leads. The unlabeled line thus marks an unconditional branch. For example, "x Δ" and not "c $)$" follows "y $[c, y]$". If the directed line is labeled, the statement next to it is interpreted as a *comparison*, not as a specification, and the branch is a conditional one. Thus, "c A" is equivalent to "$c \in A$?" or to "does c belong to the set A?", and the mark "$\notin$" on the line indicates that "c A" is followed by "c $)$" if "$c \notin A$ and by "y $[c, y]$" if $c \in A$. The reader may now easily verify, with the aid of Definition 8, that the diagram of Figure 1 is indeed a precise version of Definition 6.

A notation for paths through a diagram will be useful. For purposes of reference to statements, each statement is associated with the number immediately above it. For purposes of reference to paths, each number is associated with the *interval* in which the numeral appears. The expression "(m, n)" designates any path starting at interval m and terminating at interval n, without restriction as to allowable intermediate subpaths. For example "$(1, 4)$" designates a path encompassing the first three statements of the algorithm S_2 in Figure 1, and "$(4, 4)$" designates any nontrivial path starting at interval 4 and terminating at the same interval after one or more cycles with arbitrary subpaths.

At a branch point, two intervals are coalesced into one. The expression "r/s" indicates that interval r is to be treated as equivalent to the interval s. The expression "$(4, 9/4)$" designates a path starting at 4 and returning via the unconditional branch which identifies interval 9 with interval 4. The path $(4, 8/9, 12/4)$ is one taken when $c =$), while $(4, 8/9, 10/12, 13/4)$ is followed when c is a functor. No confusion results if the latter path is simply labeled "$(4, 13/4)$".

The expressions "$n : y = a$" or "$(m, n) : y = a$" indicate that at interval n (possibly following a prior passage through interval m) y has the value a before the statement following the interval is executed. Thus, in S_2, $(1, 4) : x = \Delta^2$, $y = \Delta$, and $p = \Delta$.

4. Δ_M-theorems; fail-safe translation. An algorithm T_3, for translation from L to P_3, and an algorithm S_3, for translation from P_3 to L, are given in §§5 and 6, respectively. These algorithms have the following interesting properties:

(1) Internal storage consists essentially of a single pushdown store.

(2) The input formula is scanned in one direction only.

Each character in the input formula is used once and only once and in sequence, eliminating the need either for storing the input formula in internal memory or else for repeated backward and forward reading of tapes, as is required in Rutishauser's method and its derivatives.

(3) The amount of internal storage is independent of the length of the input formula, and depends only on the depth of the deepest nest in the formula.

(4) The characters of the output formula are generated practically simultaneously with the scanning of the input characters, so that translation is completed almost as soon as the last input symbol is read. In translation from P_3 to L, the characters of the output formula are generated in proper sequence either for immediate evaluation by a pushdown evaluator in the manner of BWW or for further translation into a computer program by a device quite analogous to the BWW pushdown evaluator, which is essentially what Samelson and Bauer propose.

(5) It will be shown that each algorithm operates successfully if and only if the input formula is well-formed. The algorithms are therefore ideally fail-safe.

(6) For each algorithm, a theorem of the following type (Δ_M-theorem) can be proved:

Let $\Delta = [\Delta_H, \Delta_M, \Delta_T]$ be any formula of the domain of translation, split into a head Δ_H, a middle Δ_M, and a tail Δ_T. The formula Δ_M is assumed to be well-formed in the domain, while Δ_H and Δ_T are arbitrary residues, possibly null, determined by the choice of Δ_M. At a certain point in the execution of the algorithm, the remaining input formula will be $[\Delta_M, \Delta_T]$, an image Δ'_H of Δ_H will have been generated, and p (as defined in Definition 6 or Definition 7) will be $p(\Delta_H)$, namely a function of Δ_H only. While the characters of Δ_M are being scanned, p naturally becomes a function of Δ_M as well as of Δ_H, but all contributions to p due to Δ_M will be "above" those due to Δ_H in the pushdown store. The Δ_M-theorem effectively guarantees that, once the remaining input formula has become Δ_T,

(a) p will again be $p(\Delta_H)$, that is, no contributions due to Δ_M remain at the top of the pushdown store; and

(b) the image Δ'_M of Δ_M, which is well-formed in the range of translation, will have been adjoined to Δ'_H.

5. Translation from L to P_3.

An algorithm T_3 for translating from L to P_3 is given in Figure 2. The properties of this algorithm are presented in a series of theorems. In the following, all paths are paths in T_3.

DEFINITION 9. Any path $(4, 13/4)$ such that at no time $4 : x = \Lambda$ and $p \neq \Lambda$, is called a *formula cycle* of T_3.

DEFINITION 10. T_3 is *strictly effective* for a formula Δ of L if and only if:

(a) $\Delta = \Lambda$; or

(b) for $\Delta \neq \Lambda$, a formula cycle of T_3 is traversed once and only once to obtain $(4, 13/4) : x = \Lambda$.

DEFINITION 11. T_3 is *effective* for a formula Δ of L if and only if, for $\Delta \neq \Lambda$, a formula cycle of T_3 is traversed a finite number of time to obtain

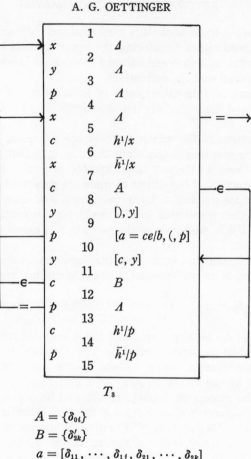

$$A = \{\delta_{oi}\}$$
$$B = \{\delta'_{2k}\}$$
$$a = [\delta_{11}, \cdots, \delta_{1j}, \delta_{21}, \cdots, \delta_{2k}]$$
$$b = [\delta'_{11}, \cdots, \delta'_{1j}, \delta'_{21}, \cdots, \delta'_{2k}]$$

Translation from L to P_3

Figure 2

$(4, 13/4) : x = \Lambda$.

DEFINITION 12. When $4 : x = \Lambda, 4 : y = T_3\Delta = \Delta^3$ is the T_3-*image* of Δ in P_3.

LEMMA 1. (a) $(1, 4) : x = \Delta, y = \Lambda, p = \Lambda$,
          (b) $(4, 13/4) : p = \Lambda$.

The proof is obvious.

LEMMA 2. $T_3\Delta = \Lambda$ *and* T_3 *is strictly effective or effective for* Δ *if and only if* $\Delta = \Lambda$.

PROOF. Obviously if $\Delta = \Lambda$, $T_3\Delta = \Lambda$, and T_3 is strictly effective. If $T_3\Delta = \Lambda$ and T_3 is strictly effective or effective for Δ, but $\Delta \neq \Lambda$, either Δ contains an element of A, hence when $4 : x = \Lambda, y \neq \Lambda$, or it contains no element of A, hence when $4 : x = \Lambda, p \neq \Lambda$, hence T_3 can be neither effective nor strictly effective. Therefore $\Delta = \Lambda$.

The definition of well-formation given by BWW (Definition 3F) is shown to be equivalent to Definition 4 by the following lemma:

LEMMA 3. $\varDelta \neq \varLambda$ *is a well-formed formula if and only if it is of the form* $\varDelta = [\delta, \varDelta_{D(\delta)}, \cdots, \varDelta_1]$, *where each* $\varDelta_j$ *is well-formed.*

PROOF. (a)   If $\varDelta = [\delta, \varDelta_{D(\delta)}, \cdots, \varDelta_1]$, then either

   (i) $D(\delta) = 0$, hence $W(\delta) = 1$, and $\varDelta = \delta$ is positive and well-formed; or

   (ii) $D(\delta) > 0$; then $\varPhi = [\varDelta_{D(\delta)}, \cdots, \varDelta_1]$ is a positive formula (BWW, Theorem IA) and $W(\varPhi) = D(\delta) > 0$. Since $W(\delta) = 1 - D(\delta)$, we have $W(\varDelta) = W(\delta) + W(\varPhi) = 1 - D(\delta) + D(\delta) = 1$. Hence $\varDelta$ is positive and of weight 1, that is, well-formed.

   (b)   If $\varDelta$ is well-formed, then $\varDelta = [\delta, \varPhi]$, where either $\varPhi = \varLambda$ or $\varPhi$, being the tail of a positive formula, is positive. If $\varPhi = \varLambda$, the result follows at once that $\varDelta = \delta$, and $D(\delta) = 1 - W(\delta) = 0$. If $\varPhi \neq \varLambda$, then since $1 = W(\varDelta) = W(\delta) + W(\varPhi) = 1 - D(\delta) + W(\varPhi)$, we have $W(\varPhi) = D(\delta)$, and by Theorem IA (BWW) $\varPhi = [\varPhi_{D(\delta)}, \cdots, \varPhi_1]$ whence the conclusion follows at once that $\varDelta$ is of the form $[\delta, \varDelta_{D(\delta)}, \cdots, \varDelta_1]$.

LEMMA 4.   *Every well-formed formula can be written in the form* $\varDelta = [\varDelta_H, \varDelta_M, \varDelta_T]$, *where* $\varDelta_M$ *is some well-formed formula embedded in* $\varDelta$, *and where* $\varDelta_H$ *and* $\varDelta_T$ *are respectively the residual (possibly null) head and tail of* $\varDelta$.

PROOF. Note that any $\varDelta_j$ of Lemma 3 can serve as $\varDelta_M$ and that, since $\varDelta_j$ itself has a decomposition $\varDelta_j = [\delta, \varDelta_{jD(\delta)}, \cdots, \varDelta_{j1}]$ any $\varDelta_{jk}$ likewise, and so on.

LEMMA 5.   *For arbitrary* $\varDelta = [\varDelta_H, \varDelta_M, \varDelta_T]$, *there exists a path* $(1, 4)$ *such that*

$$(1, 4) : x = [\varDelta_M, \varDelta_T] ,$$
$$y = y_I(\varDelta_H) = y_I ,$$
$$p = p_I(\varDelta_H) = p_I .$$

PROOF. Clearly $(1, 4) : x = [\varDelta_M, \varDelta_T]$ sometime. Consider a path leading to 4 at this time. Since $(4, 6) : c = h^1/x = h^1/\varDelta_M$ marks the first appearance of a character of $\varDelta$ not belonging to $\varDelta_H$, $(1, 4) : y = y(\varDelta_H), p = p(\varDelta_H)$.

THEOREM 1 ($\varDelta_M$-THEOREM).   *For arbitrary* $\varDelta = [\varDelta_H, \varDelta_M, \varDelta_T] \neq \varLambda$, *where* $\varDelta_M$ *is well-formed, there exists a path* $(4, 13)$ *starting at*

$$4 : x_8 = [\varDelta_M, \varDelta_T] ,$$
$$y_8 = y_I ,$$
$$p_8 = p_I ,$$

such that

   (A) $13 : x_f = \varDelta_T ,$
$$y_f = [y_f(\varDelta_M), y_I] ,$$
$$p_f = p_I ;$$

   (B) $y_f(\varDelta_M) = T_8 \varDelta_M = \varDelta_M^8$ *and is unique, and* T_8 *is strictly effective for* $\varDelta_M$.

The proof is by induction on the length $L(\varDelta_M) > 0$ of $\varDelta_M$.

(a) $L(\varDelta_M) = 1$. Since $\varDelta_M$ is well-formed by hypothesis, $\varDelta_M = \delta_{0i}$. The path (4, 8/10, 13) is followed, and

(A) $13 : x_f = \bar{h}^1/x_s = \varDelta_T$,

$$y_f = [c, y_I] = [h^1/x_s, y_I] = [\delta_{0i}, y_I],$$

$$p_f = p_I;$$

(B)   Let $\varDelta_H = \varDelta_T = \varLambda$: then $y_I = p_I = \varLambda$ (Lemma 1), and

$$13 : x_f = \varLambda,$$

$$y_f = \delta_{0i} = y(\varDelta_M),$$

$$p_f = \varLambda;$$

hence the path continues to 4. Since $4 : x = \varLambda, y_f(\varDelta_M) = \delta_{0i} = \varDelta_M^3$, and is unique by (A). Since 4: $p = \varLambda$, (4, 8/10, 13/4) is a formula cycle traversed once and only once, and T_3 is strictly effective for $\varDelta_M$.

(b) $L(\varDelta_M) > 1$.

CASE I. $\varDelta_M = [\delta_{1j}, \varDelta_1]$.

(A)   The path (4, 10/4) is followed and

$$(4, 10/4) : x_a = [\varDelta_1, \varDelta_T],$$

$$y_a = [), y_I],$$

$$p_a = [\delta'_{1j}, (, p_I].$$

Applying the induction hypothesis to $\varDelta_1$, we obtain a path (4, 10/4, 13) such that

$$(4, 13) : x_b = \varDelta_T,$$

$$y_b = [\varDelta_1^3,), y_I],$$

$$p_b = p_a.$$

Since $p_b = [\delta'_{1j}, (, p_I] \neq \varLambda$, the path (13, 15/10, 13) is traversed twice yielding

$$(4, 13) : x_f = \varDelta_T,$$

$$y_f = [(, \delta'_{1j}, \varDelta_1^3,), y_I],$$

$$p_f = p_I.$$

(B)   Let $\varDelta_H = \varDelta_T = \varLambda$; then $y_I = p_I = \varLambda$ (Lemma 1), and

$$13 : x_f = \varLambda,$$

$$y_f = [(, \delta'_{1j}, \varDelta_1^3,)] = y_f(\varDelta_M),$$

$$p_f = \varLambda;$$

hence the path continues to 4.

Since $4 : x = \varLambda, y_f(\varDelta_M) = [(, \delta'_{1j}, \varDelta_1^3,)] = \varDelta_M^3$, and is unique by (A). Since $4 : p = \varLambda$, (4, 13/4) is a formula cycle traversed once and only once, and T_3 is strictly effective for $\varDelta_M$.

CASE II. $\varDelta_M = [\delta_{2k}, \varDelta_2, \varDelta_1]$.

(A)   The path (4, 10/4) is followed and

$$(4, 10/4): x_a = [\Delta_2, \Delta_1, \Delta_T],$$
$$y_a = [), y_I],$$
$$p_a = [\delta'_{2k}, (, p_I].$$

Applying the induction hypothesis to Δ_2, we obtain a path $(4, 13)$ such that

$$(4, 13): x_b = [\Delta_1, \Delta_T],$$
$$y_b = [\Delta_2^3,), y_I],$$
$$p_b = [\delta'_{2k}, (, p_I].$$

The path $(13, 15/10, 12/4)$ is followed next, yielding

$$(4, 4): x_c = [\Delta_1, \Delta_T],$$
$$y_c = [\delta'_{2k}, \Delta_2^3,), y_I],$$
$$p_c = [(, p_I].$$

Applying the induction hypothesis to Δ_1, we obtain a path $(4, 13)$ such that

$$(4, 13): x_d = \Delta_T,$$
$$y_d = [\Delta_1^3, \delta'_{2k}, \Delta_2^3,), y_I],$$
$$p_d = [(, p_I].$$

Finally, the path $(13, 15/10, 13)$ is followed, yielding

$$(4, 13): x_f = \Delta_T,$$
$$y_f = [(, \Delta_1^3, \delta'_{2k}, \Delta_2^3,), y_I],$$
$$p_f = p_I.$$

(B)   Proof parallel to that for Case I.

THEOREM 2.   *For every* POSITIVE $\Delta_M = [\Delta_{W(\Delta_M)}, \cdots, \Delta_1] \neq \Delta$ *(BWW, Theorem* 1) *there exists a path* $(4, 13/4)$ *starting at*

$$4: x_s = [\Delta_M, \Delta_T],$$
$$y_s = y_I,$$
$$p_s = p_I,$$

such that if $p_I = \Delta$, *then*

(A) $(4, 13/4): x_f = \Delta_T,$
$$y_f = [y_f(\Delta_M), y_I],$$
$$p_f = p_I = \Delta,$$

(B) $y_f(\Delta_M) = T_s\Delta_M = [\Delta_1^3, \cdots, \Delta_{W(\Delta_M)}^3] = \Delta_M^3$ *and is unique,* T_s *is effective for* Δ_M, *and the formula cycle is traversed* $W(\Delta_M)$ *times.*

The proof is by induction on $W(\Delta_M)$.
Applying Theorem 1 to $\Delta_{W(\Delta_M)}$ we obtain

$$(4, 13): x_a = [\Delta_{T'}, \Delta_T], \Delta_{T'} = [\Delta_{W(\Delta_M)-1}, \cdots, \Delta_1],$$
$$y_a = [\Delta_{W(\Delta_M)}^3, y_I],$$
$$p_a = p_I = \Delta.$$

Since $p_a = \Lambda$, the path may be continued to (4, 13/4) with the same values of x, y, and $\check{p}$, and constitutes a formula cycle, the first traversed. Since T_3 is strictly effective for $\Delta_{W(\Delta_M)}$ (Theorem 1) it is also effective (Definitions 10 and 11) and $\Delta^3_{W(\Delta_M)}$ is unique (Theorem 1).

If $W(\Delta_M) = 1$, $\Delta_{W(\Delta_M)} = \Delta_M$, $\Delta_{T'} = \Lambda$, hence these results provide the basis for the induction. If $W(\Delta_M) > 1$, the same results give the first part of the induction step.

Applying the induction hypothesis to $\Delta_{T'}$, $W(\Delta_{T'}) = W(\Delta_M) - 1$, we obtain at once

(A) $4 : x_f = \Delta_T$,

$$y_f = [\Delta^3_{T'}, \Delta^3_{W(\Delta_M)}, y_I] = [\Delta^3_1, \cdots, \Delta^3_{W(\Delta_M)-1}, \Delta^3_{W(\Delta_M)}, y_I],$$
$$p_f = p_I = \Lambda;$$

(B) $y_f(\Delta_M)$ clearly has the requisite form and is unique, T_3 is effective for Δ_M, and the formula cycle has been traversed $1 + W(\Delta_{T'}) = W(\Delta_M)$ times.

THEOREM 3. *If* $\Delta = [\Delta_{W(\Delta)}, \cdots, \Delta_1] \neq \Lambda$ *is positive* (*BWW Theorem* 1), *then* T_3 *is effective,* $T_3\Delta = [T_3\Delta_1, \cdots, T_3\Delta_{W(\Delta)}] = [\Delta^3_1, \cdots, \Delta^3_{W(\Delta)}] = \Delta^3$ *is the unique* T_3-*image of* Δ, *and the formula cycle is traversed precisely* $W(\Delta)$ *times.*

PROOF. Let $\Delta = [\Lambda, \Delta, \Lambda]$, and the proof follows directly from Lemma 1 and Theorem 2.

THEOREM 4. *If* $\Delta \neq \Lambda$ *is well-formed, then* T_3 *is strictly effective and* $T_3\Delta = \Delta^3$ *is the unique* T_3-*image of* Δ.

PROOF. This result follows directly from Definitions 10 and 11 and the specialization of Theorem 3 to the case $W(\Delta) = 1$.

THEOREM 5. T_3 *is effective only if* $\Delta \neq \Lambda$ *is positive.*

PROOF. If Δ is not positive, then for some integer $i \leq L(\Delta)$ there exists a $\emptyset = t^i/\Delta$ such that $W(\emptyset) < 1$. Let $j + 1$ be the smallest such integer. Then $\psi = t^j/\Delta$ is either null or positive, and $e^{j+1}/\Delta = \delta$ is such that $-1 \leq W(\delta) < 1$, i.e., $\delta = \delta_{1j}$ or $\delta = \delta_{2k}$. Let $\Delta = [\Delta_H, \delta, \psi] = [\Delta_H, \Delta_M, \Delta_T]$, where $\Delta_H = h^{L(\Delta)-j-1}/\Delta$.
With the aid of Lemma 5 we obtain, at some time

$$4 : x_a = [\delta, \psi],$$
$$y_a = y_a(\Delta_H),$$
$$p_a = p_a(\Delta_H).$$

Since $\delta \notin A$, there is a path (4, 10/4) such that

$$(4, 10/4) : x_s = \psi,$$
$$y_s = [), y_a],$$
$$p_s = [\delta', (, p_a].$$

If $\psi = \Lambda$, then, since $p \neq \Lambda$, no formula cycle is possible and T_3 cannot be effective. If $\psi \neq \Lambda$, $W(\psi) = 1$ since for $W(\psi) > 1$ and $W(\emptyset) = W(\delta) + W(\psi) < 1$ we would require $W(\delta) < -1$ which is impossible in L as defined. Therefore

ψ is well-formed. In this case, $\delta = \delta_{2k}$, since if $\delta = \delta_{1k}$ we would have $W(\emptyset) = W(\delta_{1k}) + W(\psi) = 0 + 1 = 1$ contrary to hypothesis. Applying Theorem 1 to $\psi = [\psi, \Lambda]$

$$13 : x_f = \Lambda \, ,$$
$$y_f = [\psi^3,), y_a] \, ,$$
$$p_f = [\delta'_{2k}, (, p_a] \, .$$

The path (13, 15/10, 12/4) is followed next, yielding

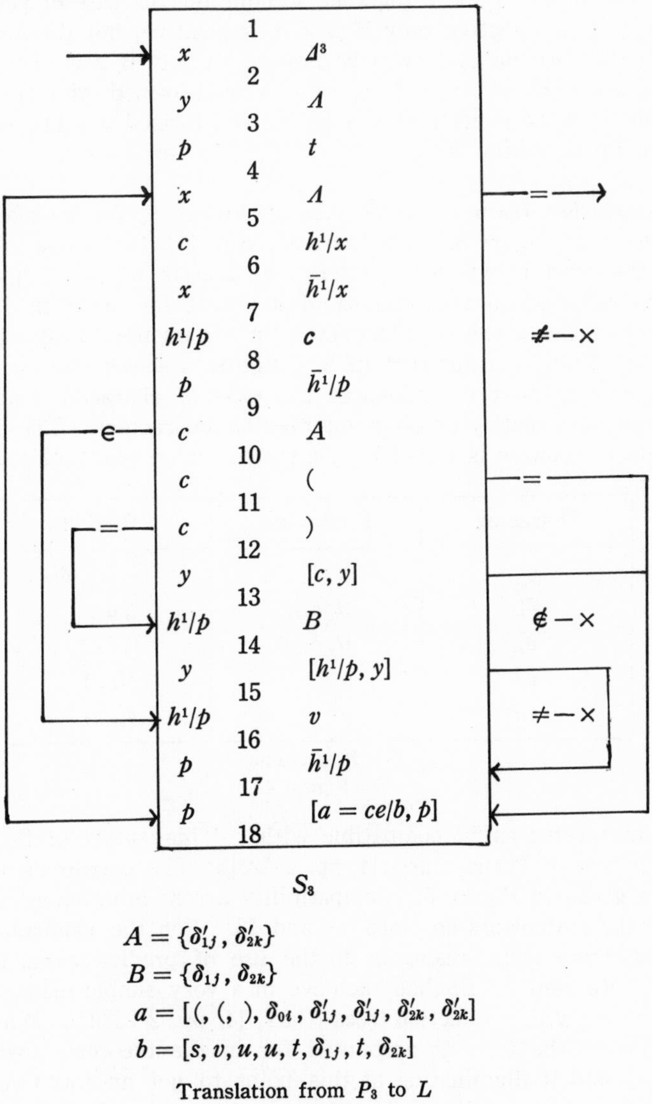

S_3

$$A = \{\delta'_{1j}, \delta'_{2k}\}$$
$$B = \{\delta_{1j}, \delta_{2k}\}$$
$$a = [(, (,), \delta_{0t}, \delta'_{1j}, \delta'_{1j}, \delta'_{2k}, \delta'_{2k}]$$
$$b = [s, v, u, u, t, \delta_{1j}, t, \delta_{2k}]$$

Translation from P_3 to L
Figure 3

$$4 : x = \varLambda \, ,$$
$$y = [\delta'_{2k}, \, \psi^3, \,), \, y_a] \, ,$$
$$p = [(, \, p_a] \neq \varLambda \, .$$

No formula cycle is possible, hence T_3 cannot be effective, and the proof is complete.

THEOREM 6. *T_3 is effective if and only if $\varDelta \neq \varLambda$ is positive, and strictly effective if and only if $\varDelta$ is well-formed or $\varDelta = \varLambda$.*

PROOF. Theorems 3 and 5 together account for the case of positive $\varDelta$. By Theorem 5, T_3 is effective only if $\varDelta \neq \varLambda$ is positive, but the number of traversals of the formula cycle will be precisely 1 only if $\varDelta$ is also well-formed. Hence T_3 is strictly effective only if $\varDelta$ is well-formed; this result, together with Theorem 4, accounts for the case of well-formed $\varDelta$. The case of $\varDelta = \varLambda$ is covered by Definition 10.

6. Translation from P_3 to L. An algorithm S_3 for translating from P_3 to L is given in Figure 3. It is characteristic of L that there are no restrictions on the order in which characters may appear in well-formed formulas, a property reflected in the absence of any test for order in T_3 and in the dependence of the proof of Theorem 5 on arguments based on tail weight only. The situation is different in S_3. Figure 4 shows that occurrence of a character of a given type influences the type of character that may occur next, either immediately or after intervening characters. The compatibility of adjacent characters is tested by the statement on line 7 of S_3, where "$\approx$"

Character	Predictors	Predicts
(	$[s, v]$	$(, \delta_{0i}, \delta'_{1j}$
δ'_{1j}	$[t, \delta_{1j}]$	$(, \delta_{0i}$
δ'_{2k}	$[t, \delta_{2k}]$	$(, \delta_{0i}$
δ_{0i}	u	$\delta'_{2k},)$
)	u	$\delta'_{2k},)$

Predictions

Figure 4

is to be interpreted as "is compatible with". This feature of S_3 is analogous to the pair test of Perlis (Carr, [4, pp. 2–223]). The conditions under which $h^i p \approx c$ are given in Figure 5. Compatibility across intervening characters is tested by the statements on lines 13 and 15. For the elementary language P_3 at least, these tests, analogous to the use of predictions in the syntactic analysis of Russian or English, achieve in a very simple manner what Carr attempts to do with production trees (Carr, [4, pp. 2–233ff]). While the mode of operation of the tests is accounted for in the theorems that follow, the reader may find it illuminating at this point to get an intuitive feeling for their operation by applying S_3 to a few short formulas, both well-formed and not.

Character	Accepted by
(	s, t
δ'_{1j}	s
δ'_{2k}	u
δ_{0i}	s, t
)	u

Compatibility Conditions
Figure 5

DEFINITION 13. S_3 is *strictly effective* for a formula $\varDelta^3$ of P_3 if and only if
(a) $\varDelta^3 = \varLambda$; or (b) for $\varDelta^3 \neq \varLambda$
  (i) at no time $4 : x = \varLambda$ and $p \neq u$; and
  (ii) at no time $7 : c \nleftrightarrow h^1/p$,
  (iii) at no time $13 : h^1/p \notin B$,
  (iv) at no time $15 : h^1/p \neq v$.
A path in which all the conditions of (b) are met is an *effective* path; otherwise it is *ineffective*.

DEFINITION 14. When $4 : x = \varLambda, 4 : y = S_3 \varDelta^3 = \varDelta$ is the S_3-image of $\varDelta^3$ in L.

LEMMA 6. $(1, 4) : x = \varDelta, y = \varLambda, p = t$.

The proof is obvious.

LEMMA 7. $S_3 \varDelta^3 = \varLambda$ and S_3 *is strictly effective for* $\varDelta^3$ *if and only if* $\varDelta^3 = \varLambda$.

PROOF. Obviously, if $\varDelta^3 = \varLambda, S_3 \varDelta^3 = \varLambda$ and S_3 is strictly effective. If $S_3 \varDelta^3 = \varLambda$ and S_3 is strictly effective but $\varDelta^3 \neq \varLambda$, then either $\varDelta^3$ contains a variable, hence when $4 : x = \varLambda, y \neq \varLambda$, or it contains no variable and ends:
  (i) with a right parenthesis; then either $13 : h^1/p = \varLambda \notin B$ and S_3 is not strictly effective, or $13 : h^1/p \neq \varLambda$, hence when $4 : x = \varLambda, y \neq \varLambda$; or
  (ii) with a left parenthesis or a functor; then, when $4 : x = \varLambda, p \neq u$ and S_3 is not strictly effective.
  Therefore $\varDelta^3 = \varLambda$.

LEMMA 8. *Every well-formed formula can be written in the form* $\varDelta^3 = [\varDelta^3_H, \varDelta^3_M, \varDelta^3_T]$, *where* $\varDelta_M$ *is some well-formed formula nested in* $\varDelta^3$, *and where* $\varDelta^3_H$ *and* $\varDelta^3_T$ *are respectively the residual (possibly null) head and tail of* $\varDelta^3$.

The proof is a direct consequence of the definition of well-formation in P_3 (Definition 3).

LEMMA 9. *For every* $\varDelta^3 = [\varDelta^3_H, \varDelta^3_M, \varDelta^3_T] \neq \varLambda$, *there exists a path* $(1, 4, 18/4)$ *such that*

$$4 : x = [\varDelta^3_M, \varDelta^3_T] ,$$
$$y = y_I(\varDelta^3_H) = y_I ,$$
$$p = \begin{bmatrix} s \\ t, p_I \\ u \end{bmatrix}, p_I = \bar{h}^1/p ,$$

where $p_I = p_I(\Delta_H)$ either $= \Lambda$ or contains only instances of "v" or of members of B.

PROOF. Showing that x and y have the stated properties and that $p_I = p_I(\Delta_H^3)$ is trivial (see Lemma 5). The remainder may be proved by induction on $L(\Delta_H)$.

If $L(\Delta_H^3) = 1$ we have

$$(1, 4): p = t, (4, 9): p = \Lambda .$$

A path $(16, 17)$ cannot add characters to p. Eventually, therefore, the path $(1, 4, 9, 18/4)$ is followed resulting in $4 : h^1/p = s, u$, or t, and $4 : \bar{h}^1/p = v, \delta_{1j}, \delta_{2k}$, or Λ, as a consequence of the definition of the vectors a and b (Figure 3).

For $L(\Delta_H^3) > 1$, applying the induction hypothesis to $\bar{t}^1/\Delta_H^3$ yields

$$4 : p = \begin{bmatrix} s \\ t, p_I \\ u \end{bmatrix} ,$$

where p_I has the desired properties. Applying an argument similar to that for $L(\Delta_H^3) = 1$ to the remainder t^1/Δ_H^3 of Δ_H^3 is then sufficient to complete the proof.

DEFINITION 15. If, in Lemma 9, $p = \begin{bmatrix} s \\ t \end{bmatrix}, p_I$, Δ_M is *properly nested*.

THEOREM 7 (Δ_M^3-THEOREM). *For every $\Delta^3 = [\Delta_H^3, \Delta_M^3, \Delta_T^3]$, where Δ_M^3 is well-formed and properly nested, there exists a path $(4, 18/4)$ starting at*

$$4 : x_s = [\Delta_M^3, \Delta_T^3] ,$$

$$y_s = y_I ,$$

$$p_s = \begin{bmatrix} s \\ t \end{bmatrix}, p_I ,$$

such that

(A) $\qquad\qquad (4, 18/4): x_f = \Delta_T^3 ,$

$$y_f = [y_f(\Delta_M^3), y_I] ,$$

$$p_f = [u, p_I] ,$$

(B) $\qquad\qquad y_f(\Delta_M^3) = S_3\Delta_M^3 = \Delta_M$

and is unique, and S_3 is strictly effective for Δ_M^3.

COROLLARY. *If, in Theorem 7, Δ_M^3 is not properly nested, S_3 is not strictly effective for Δ_M^3.*

The proof of the corollary follows directly from Definitions 13 and 15, and the compatibility conditions (Figure 5). If $p = [u, p_I]$, then since every well-formed formula begins either with (or with δ_{0i}, it follows at once that $7 : c \neq h^1/p$, hence S_3 cannot be strictly effective.

The proof of Theorem 7 is by induction on the length $L(\Delta_M^3)$ of Δ_M^3.

(a) $L(\Delta_M^3) = 1$. Since Δ_M^3 is well-formed by hypothesis, $\Delta_M^3 = \delta_{0i}$. The path $(4, 13/17, 18/4)$ is followed; hence we have

(A) $\qquad\qquad\qquad 4 : x_f = \Delta_T^3 ,$

$$y_f = [\delta_{0i}, y_I] ,$$

$$p_f = [u, p_I] .$$

(B) Let $\Delta_H = \Delta_T = \Lambda$. Then $y_I = \Lambda$ and $p_s = t$ (Lemma 6), hence $p_s = [t, \Lambda]$, that is, $p_I = \Lambda$. We have, therefore

$$4 : x_f = \Lambda ,$$
$$y_f = \delta_{0i} ,$$
$$p_f = u .$$

Clearly $y_f(\Delta_M) = \delta_{0i}$ is the S_3-image of Δ_H^3 and is unique. Since $4 : x = \Lambda$ and $p = u$, and since, in (A), $7 : c \eqcirc h^1/p$ and there are no subpaths (13, 14) or (15, 16), S_3 is strictly effetive for Δ_M^3.

(b) $L(\Delta_M^3) > 1$.

CASE I. $\Delta_M^3 = [(, \delta'_{1j}, \Delta_1^3,)]$.

(A) The path $(4, 7, 11/17, 18/4)$ yields

$$4 : x_a = [\delta'_{1j}, \Delta_1^3,), \Delta_T^3] ,$$
$$y_a = y_I ,$$
$$p_a = [s, v, p_I] .$$

We note that $7 : c \eqcirc h^1/p = s$ or t. Continuing with the path $(4, 7, 10/15, 18/4)$, we obtain

$$4 : x_b = [\Delta_1^3,), \Delta_T^3] ,$$
$$y_b = y_I ,$$
$$p_b = [t, \delta_{1j}, p_I] ,$$

noting that $7 : c \eqcirc h^1/p = s$, and $15 : h^1/p = v$. Now, applying the induction hypothesis to Δ_1^3, we obtain

$$4 : x_c = [), \Delta_T^3] ,$$
$$y_c = [\Delta_1, y_I] ,$$
$$p_c = [u, \delta_{1j}, p_I] .$$

Finally, the path $(4, 7, 12/13, 15/16, 18/4)$ is followed, yielding

$$4 : x_f = \Delta_T^3 ,$$
$$y_f = [\delta_{1j}, \Delta_1, y_I] ,$$
$$p_f = [u, p_I] .$$

(B) Let $\Delta_H = \Delta_T = \Lambda$. Then $y_I = p_I = \Lambda$. It follows that $y_f(\Delta_M^3) = [\delta_{1j}, \Delta_1] = \Delta_M$. The process of (A) shows that Δ_M is unique and that S_3 is strictly effective.

CASE II. $\Delta_M^3 = [(, \Delta_1^3, \delta'_{2k}, \Delta_2^3,)]$.

(A) As in Case I, the path $(4, 7, 11/17, 18/4)$ yields

$$4 : x_a = [\Delta_1^3, \delta'_{2k}, \Delta_2^3,), \Delta_T^3] ,$$
$$y_a = y_I ,$$
$$p_a = [s, v, p_I] ,$$

and $7 : c \eqcirc h^1/p = s$ or t. Applying the induction hypothesis to Δ_1^3, we obtain

$$4 : x_b = [\delta'_{2k}, \Delta_2^3,), \Delta_T^3] ,$$
$$y_b = [\Delta_1, y_I] ,$$
$$p_b = [u, v, p_I] .$$

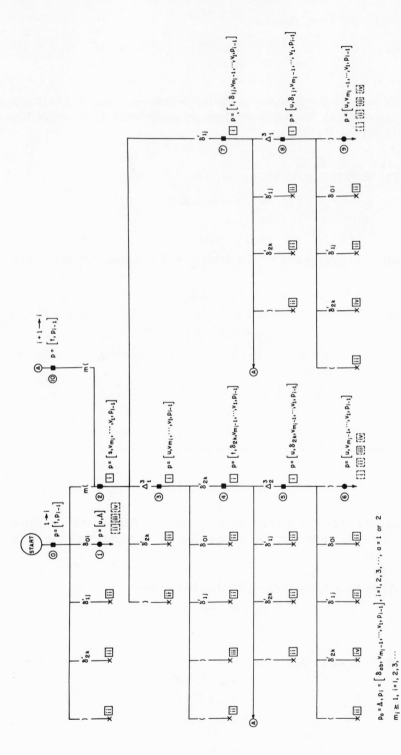

Effective and Ineffective Paths
Figure 6

The path $(4, 7, 10/15, 18/4)$ then yields

$$4 : x_c = [\varDelta_2^3,), \varDelta_T^3] ,$$
$$y_c = [\varDelta_1 , y_I] ,$$
$$p_c = [t, \delta_{2k}, p_I] ,$$

and $7 : c \leftrightharpoons h^1/p = u$, and $15 : h^1/p = v$. Now, applying the induction hypothesis to $\varDelta_2^3$, we obtain

$$4 : x_d = [), \varDelta_T^3] ,$$
$$y_d = [\varDelta_2 , \varDelta_1 , y_I] ,$$
$$p_d = [u, \delta_{2k}, p_I] .$$

Finally, the path $(4, 7, 12/13, 15/16, 18/4)$ is followed, yielding

$$4 : x_f = \varDelta_T^3 ,$$
$$y_f = [\delta_{2k}, \varDelta_2 , \varDelta_1 , y_I] ,$$
$$p_f = [u, p_I] .$$

(B)   As in Case I.

THEOREM 8.   *If $\varDelta^3 \neq \varLambda$ is well-formed, then S_3 is strictly effective, and $S_3\varDelta^3 = \varDelta$ is the unique S_3-image of $\varDelta^3$.*

PROOF.   Let $\varDelta^3 = [\varLambda, \varDelta^3, \varLambda]$, and the proof follows directly from Lemma 6 and Theorem 7.

THEOREM 9.   *S_3 is strictly effective only if $\varDelta^3 \neq \varLambda$ is well-formed.*

PROOF.   The proof is by induction, following a pattern illustrated by Figure 6. The crosses mark the ends of ineffective paths, the Roman numeral in the square box indicating which of the conditions of Definition 13(b) is violated. The heavy squares and dots each mark a return to line 4 of S_3; the circled numerals next to these are for reference. The value $4 : p$ is given in each case, and the Roman numeral in the square box denotes a violation of the conditions of Definition 13(b) in case $4 : x = \varLambda$. Dots are associated with possible terminals of effective paths, while squares denote that a path terminating at the point is ineffective. Connectors are used in the conventional flow chart fashion. The notation "$m($" indicates the presence of m left parentheses in $\varDelta^3$, $m \geq 1$.

(A) $L(\varDelta^3) = 1$.   Reference to S_3 and to Definition 13 shows that for $L(\varDelta^3) = 1$, only $\varDelta^3 = \delta_{0i}$ leads to an effective path.

(B) $L(\varDelta^3) > 1$.

POINT 0 (Figure 6).   Clearly formulas beginning with $)$, δ_{2k}', or δ_{1j} lead at once to ineffective paths in S_3.

If $h^1/\varDelta^3 = \delta_{0i}$, point 1 is reached. If $\varDelta^3 = \delta_{0i}$, it is well-formed and $L(\varDelta^3) = 1$, a case already covered. If $\varDelta^3 = [\delta_{0i}, \varDelta_T^3]$, $\varDelta_T^3 \neq \varLambda$, then, since $p = [u, \varLambda]$ at point 1, all characters $\delta = h^1/\varDelta_T^3$, except $)$ and δ_{2k}', lead to ineffective paths in S_3 by virtue of condition (ii) of Definition 13(b). The characters $)$ and δ_{2k}' in turn lead to ineffective paths by virtue of conditions (iii) and (iv) of Definition 13(b), respectively. Hence $\varDelta^3$ can begin with δ_{0t} and S_3 be strictly effective only if $\varDelta^3 = \delta_{0t}$ and therefore is well-formed.

The remaining case is $h^1/\varDelta^3 = ($. Here the situation is complicated (a) by the possibility that $m > 1$ initially, namely that several left parentheses occur in succession, and (b) by the possibility that $m > 1$ also after the points leading to the connectors, in which case $i > 1$, $m_i \geqq 1$.

When $i = 1$, $m_1 = 1$, it is easy to verify that, if $\varDelta^3$ is well-formed, the paths from point 0 to points 9 and 6 correspond respectively to Case I and Case II in the proof of Theorem 7.

(B1) Consider now $i = 1$, $m_1 = 1$, $\varDelta^3 \neq \varLambda$ arbitrary except $L(\varDelta^3) > 1$. Since $h^1/\varDelta^3 = ($ by hypothesis, a path leads to point 2, where $p = [s, v]$. Since $L(\varDelta^3) > 1$ by hypothesis, we have $\varDelta^3 = [(, \varDelta_T^3], \varDelta_T^3 \neq \varLambda$.

POINT 2. If $h^1/\varDelta_T^3 =)$ or δ_{2k}', there exists no further effective path in S_3. Consideration of the case $h^1/\varDelta_T^3 = \delta_{1j}'$ will be deferred. If $h^1/\varDelta_T^3 = ($, and (is not the head of a well-formed formula, then $m_1 > 1$, contrary to hypothesis. The only remaining cases are $h^1/\varDelta_T^3 = \delta_{0t}$ or $h^1/\varDelta_T^3 = ($, where (is the head of a well-formed head of $\varDelta_T^3$. In either case, $\varDelta_T^3$ has a well-formed head $\varDelta_1^3$. Since $\varDelta_1^3$ is well-formed, Theorem 7 guarantees that there is a path to point 3, where $p = [u, v]$. If $\varDelta^3 = [(, \varDelta_1^3]$, the corresponding path in S_3 is ineffective, since $p \neq u$. Consider therefore $\varDelta^3 = [(, \varDelta_1^3, \varDelta_T^3], \varDelta_T^3 \neq \varLambda$.

POINT 3. There is a further effective path in S_3 only if $h^1/\varDelta_T^3 = \delta_{2k}'$. Such a path corresponds to one leading to point 4, where $p = [t, \delta_{2k}]$. If $\varDelta^3 = [(, \varDelta_1^3, \delta_{2k}']$, the corresponding path in S_3 is ineffective, since $p \neq u$. Consider therefore $\varDelta^3 = [(, \varDelta_1^3, \delta_{2k}', \varDelta_T^3], \varDelta_T^3 \neq \varLambda$.

POINT 4. If $h^1/\varDelta_T^3 =)$, δ_{2k}', or δ_{1j}', there exists no further effective path in S_3. If $h^1/\varDelta_T^3 = ($, and (is not the head of a well-formed formula, then $i > 1$, contrary to hypothesis. The only remaining cases are $h^1/\varDelta_T^3 = \delta_{0t}$ or $h^1/\varDelta_T^3 = ($, where (is the head of a well-formed head of $\varDelta_T^3$. In either case, $\varDelta_T^3$ has a well-formed head $\varDelta_2^3$. Since $\varDelta_2^3$ is well-formed, Theorem 7 guarantees that there is a path to point 5, where $p = [u, \delta_{2k}]$. If $\varDelta^3 = [(, \varDelta_1^3, \delta_{2k}', \varDelta_2^3]$, the corresponding path in S_3 is ineffective, since $p \neq u$. Consider therefore $\varLambda^3 = [(, \varDelta_1^3, \delta_{2k}', \varDelta_2^3, \varDelta_T^3], \varDelta_T^3 \neq \varLambda$.

POINT 5. There is a further effective path in S_3 only if $h^1/\varDelta_T^3 =)$. Such a path corresponds to one leading to point 6, where $p = [u, \varLambda] = u$. If $\varDelta^3 = [(, \varDelta_1^3, \delta_{2k}', \varDelta_2^3,)]$, the corresponding path in S_3 is effective, but $\varDelta^3$ is also clearly well-formed. It remains only to consider $\varDelta^3 = [(, \varDelta_1^3, \delta_{2k}', \varDelta_2^3,), \varDelta_T^3], \varDelta_T^3 \neq \varLambda$.

POINT 6. There is a further effective path in S_3 only if $h^1/\varDelta_T^3 =)$ or δ_{2k}'. Since $p = [u, \varLambda]$, (and δ_{2k}' in turn lead to ineffective paths by virtue of conditions (iii) and (iv) of Definition 13(b), respectively.

The conclusion is that for $i = 1$, $m_i = 1$, there is an effective path in S_3 only if $\varDelta^3 = [(, \varDelta_1^3, \delta_{2k}', \varDelta_2^3,)]$, namely only if $\varDelta^3$ is well-formed, provided that, at point 2, $h^1/\varDelta_T^3 \neq \delta_{1j}'$. It remains now to consider the case where $h^1/\varDelta_T^3 = \delta_{1j}'$ at point 2.

POINT 2 ($h^1/\varDelta_T = \delta_{1j}'$). Since $h^1/\varDelta_T^3 = \delta_{1j}'$, a path leads to point 7, where $p = [t, \delta_{1j}]$. If $\varDelta^3 = [(, \delta_{1j}']$, the corresponding path in S_3 is ineffective, since $p \neq u$. Consider therefore $\varDelta^3 = [(, \delta_{1j}', \varDelta_T^3], \varDelta_T^3 \neq \varLambda$.

It can easily be verified that the transitions from point 7 to points 8 and 9 are completely analogous to those from point 4 to points 5 and 6, and that, with obvious substitutions, identical arguments apply. This, together with the result for $L(\varDelta^3) = 1$, demonstrates that for $i = 1$, $m_i = 1$, $L(\varDelta^3) \geqq 1$, there is an effective path in S_3 only if $\varDelta^3$ is well-formed.

(B2) Consider now $i > 1$, $m_j \geqq 1$ for all $j \leqq i$, $\varDelta^3 \neq \varLambda$ arbitrary except $L(\varDelta^3) > 1$.

We note that termination of the formula at all points except 6 or 9 never corresponds to an effective path in S_3, since either $h^1/p \neq u$, or, if $h^1/p = u$, then $\bar{h}^1/p \neq \varLambda$, since $m_i \geqq 1$. Furthermore, since the path through S_3 for any given $c = h^1/x$ depends only on p, it is evident from Figure 6 that points 6 and 9 may be treated as equivalent.

Since $\varDelta^3$ is finite, it will have a rightmost left parenthesis, which may (a) lead to an ineffective path in S_3 and terminate the process; or (b) increase m_i, for a given i; or (c) increase i and set $m_i = 1$; or (d) be the head of a well-formed head of a tail $\varDelta_T^3$ of $\varDelta^3$. Case (a) obviously need not be considered further. In either case (b) or case (c) this left parenthesis leads to point 2. In case (d), one of the points 3, 5, or 8 will be reached from points 2, 4, or 7, respectively. Let k be the value of i at point 2 in cases (b) and (c), and at the immediately preceding passage through point 2 in case (d).

It can easily be verified, by arguments parallel to those in (B1), that paths leaving these points must either correspond to ineffective paths in S_3, or lead to point 6 (or 9), where $p = [u, v_{m_k-1}, \cdots, v_1, p_{k-1}]$. Since $p \neq u$, if $\varDelta^3$ is exhausted by the right parenthesis leading to point 6 (or 9), the corresponding path in S_3 cannot be effective. It remains only to consider the case where point 6 (or 9) is reached, but the remaining $\varDelta_T^3 \neq \varLambda$.

Assume that for $i = k - 1$, any path leaving point 6 (or 9) is effective only if $\varDelta^3 = [\varDelta_H^3, \varDelta_T^3]$ is well-formed, where $\varDelta_H^3$ is the head of $\varDelta^3$ processed by S_3, prior to arrival at point 6 (or 9) and $\varDelta_T^3 \neq \varLambda$ is the tail remaining to be processed by S_3.

If $m_k > 1$, then $m_k - 1 \geqq 1$. There is a further effective path in S_3 only if $h^1/\varDelta_T^3 =$) or δ_{2k}'. Since $m_k - 1 \geqq 1$,) leads to an ineffective path by virtue of condition (iii) of Definition 13(b). Note that except for a difference in the subscripts of v, point 3 and point 6 (or 9) have, in this case, equivalent configurations of p. An occurrence of δ_{2k}' therefore leads to point 4 with $p = [t, \delta_{2k}, v_{m_k-2}, \cdots, v_1, p_{k-1}]$. Since there are no further left parentheses by hypothesis, any path leaving point 4 either corresponds to an ineffective path in S_3, or leads to point 6 with $p = [u, v_{m_k-2}, \cdots, v_1, p_{k-1}]$. Repetition of this process, if feasible, must eventually lead back to point 6 with $p = [u, p_{k-1}] = [u, \delta_{ab}, v_{m_k-1}-1, \cdots, v_1, p_{(k-1)-1}]$. If $m_k = 1$, this condition is the original one at point 6 (or 9).

The condition $p = [u, \delta_{ab}, v_{m_k-1}-1, \cdots, v_1, p_{(k-1)-1}]$ is associated with point 5 if $\delta_{ab} = \delta_{2k}$ and with point 8 if $\delta_{ab} = \delta_{1j}$. There is a further effective path in S_3 only if $h^1/\varDelta_T^3 =$), corresponding to a transition to point 6 (or 9) where $p = [u, v_{m_k-1}-1, \cdots, v_1, p_{(k-1)-1}]$. By the induction hypothesis, any further path is effective only if $\varDelta^3$ is well-formed, which completes the proof.

THEOREM 10. *S_3 is strictly effective if and only if $\varDelta^3$ is well-formed or $\varDelta^3 = \varLambda$.*

The proof follows directly from Theorems 8 and 9, and Definition 13.

7. Some conclusions. The central role of Δ_M-theorems (Theorems 1 and 7) in translation both from L to P_3 and from P_3 to L is evident in §§5 and 6. Intuitively, this role may be explained by pointing out that any algorithm for which a Δ_M-theorem holds treats any nested well-formed subformula independently of the rest of the formula. As a consequence, such algorithms, if fail-safe, are fail-safe in a particularly satisfactory way: as one example, taken from natural languages, prepositional phrases or subordinate clauses can emerge unscathed, even though the sentence in which they are embedded may not be well-formed as a whole; as another example, taken from automatic programming, all the well-formed statements or subroutines of a program could be found at a single pass through a compiler, even though the program as a whole might not be well-formed. Debugging could therefore be considerably easier than it is in contemporary practice. Since L, P_1, P_2, and P_3 may all be regarded as representations of trees, the foregoing is equivalent to saying that any branch of a tree can be satisfactorily analyzed even if it has been broken off its parent branch.

In view of the underlying similarity of L and P_3 as tree representations, it may seem surprising that the proof of Theorem 9 for P_3 is so much less elegant than the proof of its counterpart for L, Theorem 5. There is, of course, the possibility that this may simply be due to a deficiency in the perception or ingenuity of the writer, who would gladly learn of a simpler proof. There may, however, be a deeper reason. The nonrecursive definition of well-formation or positiveness in L in terms of tail weight readily yields a nonrecursive definition of nonpositiveness, which is the essence of the proof of Theorem 5. An equally simple nonrecursive definition is lacking at present for P_3, hence the complexity of the proof of Theorem 9. In this light, it is gratifying that the complexity of S_3 is hardly greater than that of T_3.

Numerous extensions of the present study suggest themselves. For example, P_3 is a rather restrictive language for practical applications, and an extension to languages where parentheses may be omitted either in the presence of associative operators or in the presence of operators with a hierarchy, would be desirable. Such an extension has been given by Fischer [7] and turns out to be equivalent to that devised independently by Samelson and Bauer. In neither case has a check for well-formation been incorporated as yet, but the prospects for doing so are good. Samelson and Bauer have made it abundantly clear that the pushdown store technique, as they have applied it to the language ALGOL, is of unquestionable practical importance and, furthermore, that it can perform a great variety of functions not considered in the present paper. Their finding that "sequential treatment is not feasible in the case of certain optimizing processes such as recursive address calculation" is only one facet of the general problem of precisely characterizing the scope and the limitations of pushdown techniques, and of defining the place of these techniques in relation to syntactic theory, the theory of automata, algebra, and the topology of graphs.

The system described by Samelson and Bauer in Table 1 and Example 1 of their paper is essentially a translator from a parenthetic language with associative operators and an operator hierachy, feeding into an evaluator of the

BWW type. The control of transitions "by admissible state-symbol pairs" is not an essential feature of pushdown translators, since it is obviously absent in the algorithms of Figure 1 and 2; it is a feature introduced to account for operator hierarchy, much as state-symbol pairs are used to check for well-formation in the algorithm of Figure 3. Achievement of a deeper understanding of the rules whereby distinct pushdown algorithms may be combined and of the relation between the syntactic structures of languages and the features that algorithms must have to account for these structures is an important goal.

The development of a theory of pushdown algorithms should hopefully lead to systematic techniques for generating algorithms satisfying given requirements to replace the *ad hoc* invention of each new algorithm. It may be noted, for example, that Theorem 2 for T_3 applied to L has no equivalent for S_3 applied to P_3, due to the fact that the sequence ")(" is rejected by S_3. An appropriate theory would indicate, among other things, what modifications to S_3 should be made to accept the parenthetic equivalent of positive formulas in parenthesis-free notation. Such a theory would not only aid in devising appropriate algorithms for dealing with such languages as ALGOL, but also in the synthesis of languages which may be translated or analyzed by algorithms of the maximum simplicity and safe-failing characteristics consonant with other constraints such as the desired richness of expression and simplicity of the languages.

The results described in this paper provide a theoretical model that explains at least one essential feature of the predictive analysis technique for natural languages. Preliminary results obtained by Sherry suggest that this model can easily be extended to account for other important features of practical predictive analysis which, once fully understood, might find applications to the analysis and synthesis of artificial languages as well.

8. Acknowledgments. I am indebted for valuable criticisms and suggestions to my colleagues at the Computation Laboratory, to Professor V. H. Yngve of the Massachusetts Institute of Technology, and to several students in my course on Mathematical Linguistics, where much of the material in this paper was presented in the fall of 1959, especially to Patrick C. Fischer, who simplified an earlier version of T_3 essentially to the form given in §5.

BIBLIOGRAPHY

1. Y. Bar Hillel, *A quasi-arithmetical notation for syntactic description*, Language vol. 29, no. 1 (1953) pp. 47–58.

2. ————, *Some linguistic obstacles to machine translation*, Appendix II in "Report on the state of machine translation in the United States and Great Britain," Technical Report no. 1, Hebrew University, Jerusalem, 1959.

3. A. W. Burks, D. W. Warren, and J. B. Wright, *An analysis of a logical machine using parenthesis-free notation*, Mathematical tables and other aids to computation, vol. VIII, no. 46 (1954) pp. 53–57.

4. J. W. Carr, *Programming and coding*, Chapter 2 in E. M. Grabbe, S. Ramo, and D. E. Wooldridge, "Handbook of automation, computation, and control," vol. 2, New York, Wiley, 1959.

5. N. Chomsky, *Syntactic structures*, 's-Gravenhage, Mouton, 1957.

6. Dartmouth Mathematics Project, *Symbolic work on high speed computers*, Project Report no. 4, Dartmouth, New Hampshire, 1959.

7. P. C. Fischer, *A proposal for a term project for Applied Mathematics 205*, manuscript, 1959.

8. S. Gorn, *On the logical design of formal mixed languages*, Moore School of Electrical Engineering, University of Pennsylvania, Philadelphia, 1959.

9. P. Z. Ingerman, *A new algorithm for algebraic translation*, Preprints of papers presented at the 14th National Meeting of the Association for Computing Machinery, 1959, pp. 22-1-22-2.

10. K. E. Iverson, *The description of finite sequential processes*, "Theory of switching," Report no. BL-23, section III, Harvard Computation Laboratory, Cambridge, Massachusetts, 1959.

11. K. E. Iverson, and F. P. Brooks, Jr. *Automatic data processing*, draft manuscript (to be published by Wiley, New York, 1960).

12. Ju. I. Janov, *O logicheskix sxemax algoritmov*, "Problemy kibernetiki," no. 1, Gosudarstv. Izdat. Fiz.-Mat. Lit., Moscow (1958) pp. 75-127.

13. J. Kanner, *An algebraic translator*, Communications of the Association for Computing Machinery vol. 2 no. 10 (1959) pp. 19-22.

14. J. Lambek, *The mathematics of sentence structure*, Amer. Math. Monthly vol. 65 no. 3 (1958) pp. 154-170.

15. A. A. Ljapunov, *O logicheskix sxemax programm*, "Problemy kibernetiki," no. 1, Gosudarstv. Izdat. Fiz.-Mat. Lit., Moscow (1958) pp. 46-74.

16. W. Miehle, *Burroughs truth function evaluator*, Journal of the Association for Computing Machinery vol. 4, no. 2 (1957) pp. 189-192.

17. G. A. Miller, *Human memory and the storage of information*, I.R.E. Transactions on Information Theory vol. IT-2, no. 3 (1956) pp. 129-137.

18. A. G. Oettinger, *A new basic approach to automatic data processing*, Progress Report no. 3 by the Staff of the Computation Laboratory to the American Gas Association and Edison Electric Institute, section III, Harvard University, Cambridge, Massachusetts, 1956.

19. ———, *Current research on automatic translation at Harvard University*, National Symposium on Machine Translation, Los Angeles, February, 1960 (to appear in Proceedings of the Symposium).

20. ———, *A new theory of translation and its applications*, National Symposium on Machine Translation, Los Angeles, February, 1960 (to appear in Proceedings of the Symposium).

21. ———, *Automatic language translation: lexical and technical aspects*, Harvard Monographs in Applied Science, no. 8, Cambridge, Massachusetts, Harvard University Press, 1960.

22. I. Rhodes, *A new approach to the mechanical translation of Russian*, National Bureau of Standards, Washington, D. C., unpublished report, 1959.

23. ———, *A new approach to the mechanical syntactic analysis of Russian*, National Bureau of Standards, Washington, D. C., unpublished report, 1959.

24. ———, *The NBS method of syntactic integration*, National Symposium on Machine Translation, Los Angeles, February, 1960 (to appear in Proceedings of the Symposium).

25. J. Riguet, private communication, 1957.

26. P. Rosenbloom, *The elements of mathematical logic*, Dover, New York, 1950.

27. H. Rutishauser, *Automatische Rechenplanfertigung bei Programmgesteuerten Rechemaschinen*, Mitt. Inst. Angew. Math. Zürich, no. 3, Basel, Birkhaüser, 1952.

28. K. Samelson and F. L. Bauer, *Sequential formula translation*, Communications of the Association for Computing Machinery vol. 3, no. 2 (1960) pp. 76–83.

29. M. E. Sherry, *Predictive syntatic analysis*, National Symposium on Machine Translation, Los Angeles, February, 1960 (to appear in Proceedings of the Symposium).

30. R. Wells, *Immediate constituents*, Language vol. 23 (1947) pp. 81–117.

31. L. Wundheiler and A. Wundheiler, *Some logical concepts for syntax*, Chapter 13 in W. N. Locke and A. D. Booth, "Machine Translation of Languages," Cambridge, Massachusetts, Technology Press, and New York, Wiley, 1955.

32. V. H. Yngve, *Left-to-right sentence generation*, draft manuscript, 1959.

33. ————, *A model and an hypothesis for language structure*, draft manuscript, 1959 (to appear in Proc. Amer. Philos. Soc.).

HARVARD UNIVERSITY,
 CAMBRIDGE, MASSACHUSETTS

THE DEPTH HYPOTHESIS[1]

BY

VICTOR H. YNGVE

It is well known that there are striking contrasts as well as striking simi-larities between a natural language like English and the languages, or notation systems, of mathematics. We have, on the one hand, the wealth of complexi-ty of natural languages, particularly on the level of sentence structure, and, on the other hand, the simplicity and elegance of the mathematical notations. Some of the syntactic features found in English have the obvious function of role-marking and subordination, but it has not been clear why there is such a diversity of role-marking and subordinating devices in view of the fact that a single device can be used, as in the Łukasiewicz or Polish prefix notation. Then there is a long list of other complications in English syntax whose functions have been completely obscure. The many types of discontinuous constituents furnish examples of these syntactic devices with no obvious function.

In this paper, a "depth hypothesis" will be proposed as an explanation for many of these previously unexplained features of English syntax.[2] Psycholo-gists have measured what they call the span of immediate memory. We are able to memorize at a glance and repeat back correctly about seven random digits, about seven nonsense words, about seven items. This has been known for a long time, and has been summarized by George Miller[3] of Harvard. Apparently we have to live with this restriction when we talk. We can only remember about seven grammatical or syntactic constraints at one time. The depth hypothesis states that much of the syntactic complexity of English can be understood in terms of this memory restriction. The syntax of English contains many devices for automatically keeping utterances within the bounds of this restriction, and it contains many devices for effectively circumventing the restriction so as to regain the loss of expressive power that this restric-tion on immediate memory span would imply. The depth hypothesis predicts that *all* languages have extensive syntactic complications for the same pur-pose. This is subject to test.

A restriction on immediate memory span would not, however, be expected to have any influence on the structure of mathematical notations because they are written notations.

The way in which a limited memory can affect the syntactic structure of a language can be understood on the basis of a simple model of sentence

[1] This work was supported in part by the National Science Foundation, and in part by the U.S. Army (Signal Corps), the U.S. Air Force (Office of Scientific Research, Air Re-search and Development Command), and the U.S. Navy (Office of Naval Research).

[2] A more detailed and complete presentation is being published in the Proceedings of the American Philosophical Society.

[3] George A. Miller, *Human memory and the storage of information*, I.R.E. Transac-tions on Information Theory vol. IT–2, no. 3 (1956) pp. 129–137.

production. This model can be easily programmed on a computer. It was, in fact, designed for use in a mechanical translation system. The linguistically important features of the model can be understood on the basis of two assumptions. The first is that a phrase-structure or immediate constituent framework will be used for the description of the syntax of the language. But since such a description is static, it is necessary to introduce the aspect of time—the order in which the model does things—by a second assumption: that the words of a sentence are produced one at a time in their natural time sequence—that is, left-to-right according to conventional orthography— and that phrase-structure rules are applied by expansion—that is, from the top, down, in our diagrams.

$$S \longrightarrow NP + VP$$
$$NP \longrightarrow T + N$$
$$VP \longrightarrow V + NP$$
$$T \longrightarrow the$$
$$N \longrightarrow man$$
$$N \longrightarrow ball$$
$$V \longrightarrow hit$$

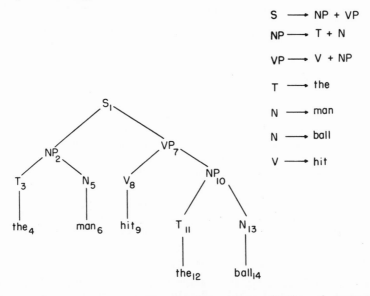

FIGURE 1. The production of a sentence involves the application of grammar rules like those shown on the right. The rules are applied by expansion and from left to right. The subscript numbers show the order in which the rules have been applied.

Figure 1 shows how these assumptions would work out in the actual production of sentences by the model. Somewhere in the memory of the device is stored a set of phrase-structure rules, like those listed on the right, that give the immediate constituents for every construction in the language. It is assumed that this list of rules is finite and that there is no linguistic significance to the order in which the rules are listed. Any order will do—an alphabetic order may be convenient. At the top of the tree is a symbol S for sentence. The first rule to be applied says to expand the symbol S into its immediate constituents: a subject noun phrase and a predicate verb phrase. Then the subject noun phrase is expanded into an article and a noun. And so on. The order in which the constructions are expanded into their constituents is given by the subscript numbers. This order involves always expanding the left-hand member of every construction first, and when reaching

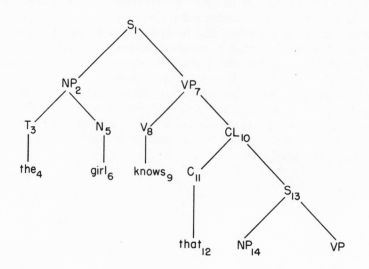

FIGURE 2. Indefinitely long sentences can be produced by reapplying certain rules. Here the rule $S \rightarrow NP + VP$ has been applied at node 1 and again at node 13.

the end of a branch, retracing to the next higher right-hand member. In this way the words are produced in their proper left-to-right order.

Although the grammar consists of a finite number of rules, it is a property of the device that it can produce any sentence chosen from an infinite set of sentences. It can do this by reapplying rules indefinitely to provide clauses within clauses within clauses. Figure 2 illustrates how the same rule can be applied twice. At the top, S is expanded into NP and VP, and at the right S is again expanded into NP and VP, in a dependent clause. This can go on without limit. "The girl knows that the papers reported that the woman said that the man," and so on.

The way in which a limited span of immediate memory comes into the picture can be seen from the following considerations. In producing a sentence, the device must remember somehow what it is committed to do next by the rules of the language. Having expanded S into a subject NP and a predicate VP, it goes on to expand the left-most constituent, NP. But somewhere in its memory it has to store the information that when it gets finished with all the branches hanging onto the NP, it is then committed to expand a VP, otherwise it will not have a grammatical English sentence. Similarly, after expanding NP into T and N, it must store away the N while it is expanding the T. In this way, every time the device goes down a left-hand branch, it must store in its temporary memory one symbol for each step taken down the branch. In the left diagram of Figure 3, the machine is working on node 5 of a sentence. It has stored away four node names, represented by the circles. In the diagram on the right, this same structure is shown at a later stage. The machine has finished with node 5, obtained

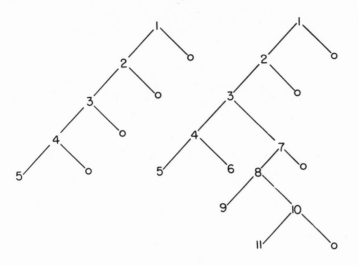

FIGURE 3. When rules are applied, symbols must be stored in a temporary memory to assure a grammatical completion of the sentence. The circles represent node names remaining in the temporary memory at these two stages in the production of a sentence. The numbers give the order in which rules have been applied.

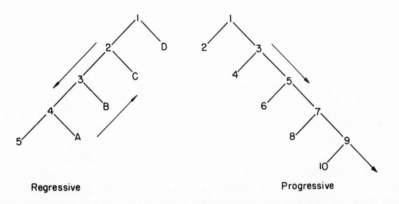

Regressive   Progressive

FIGURE 4. A regressive structure like the one on the left requires that an additional symbol be stored for each step down. This structure, which has a depth of four, requires that the four symbols A, B, C, and D be stored. A progressive structure like the one on the right can be extended indefinitely by using a temporary memory that can hold one symbol only.

nodes 6 and 7 from its memory and expanded them, and is now working on node 11. It still has four symbols stored away in its memory: two of the original ones and two new ones that resulted from the expansion of nodes 7 and 10. It will eventually have to return and expand them all.

If, according to the grammar, indefinitely long sentences can be produced (or equivalently, if the set of sentences is infinite), how much temporary

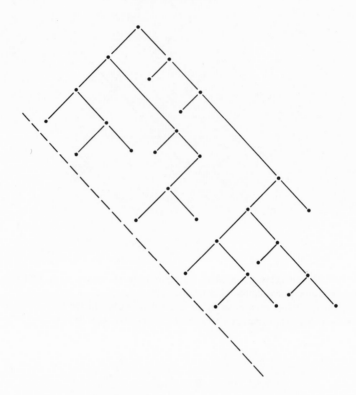

FIGURE 5. If the temporary memory can contain only three symbols, the structures it can produce are limited to a depth of three and can never penetrate the dotted line.

memory will have to be provided in the device? An unlimited amount? Let us examine this question. In Figure 4 on the left is shown a *regressive* struc- ture. We call it a regressive structure because the machine has to go down the stem expanding 1, 2, 3, 4, and 5, storing a number of symbols in its memory (here, four, because there are four unexpanded branches), then it has to go back up, expanding in turn the branches growing from A, B, C, and D. This regressive structure has a *depth* of four. The depth of a node is numerically equal to the number of symbols in temporary memory when that node is about to be expanded. On the right is shown a *progressive* structure. The machine can continue down the main stem, expanding as it goes, never retracing its steps, and it puts only one symbol away in its temporary memo- ry each time; and each time it takes it right out again and expands it. It is clear that as *regressive* structures grow longer they require more and more memory; but *progressive* structures do not. They can continue indefinitely with a minimum of memory.

There remains the picture illustrated in Figure 5. If the memory had room for only three symbols at one time, it could produce such a structure as is

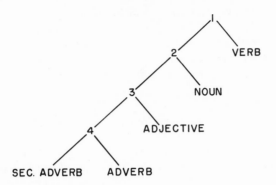

FIGURE 6. The part-of-speech hierarchy in English serves to count regressive steps and helps to prevent sentences from becoming too deep. English lacks such a counting system in the progressive direction.

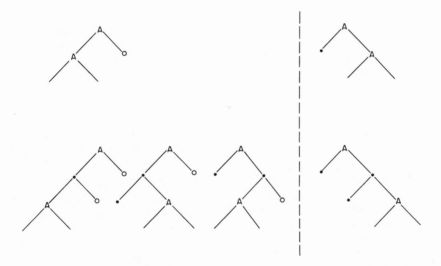

FIGURE 7. Indefinite reapplication of a rule A according to the patterns on the left would lead to structures exceeding any depth limit. They are ungrammatical. Indefinite reapplication according to the patterns on the right do not involve an unlimited increase in depth and are therefore safe.

shown here, but it would not be able to produce any structure that would penetrate the dotted line. We have noted that a person can remember only about seven items and repeat them back. It turns out that the sentences of English can be represented by trees that are limited, as if by a dotted line, to a depth of about seven. It can thus be seen that the structure of English is inherently *unsymmetrical* in the sense that there does not exist the same possibility of branching off to the left as to the right. It is interesting that the notations of mathematics and symbolic logic do not have this restriction. They are essentially written languages. The problem of remembering future commitments is solved by the mathematician by looking back at what he has written; he does not have to keep it all in his mind as he goes along. But in a spoken language one has to keep track of things in his head as he goes along, and one has the limitation, about seven items, on the span of immediate memory.

It is *not* the case that very deep structures are allowed in English but are just not used because of a memory limitation. It *is* the case that the grammar of English is so constructed that excessively deep constructions are actively prevented, and alternative constructions of lesser depth are provided. And it is this fact that accounts for much of the complexity of English over and above that of mathematical or symbolic logic notations.

One of the most striking features of English syntax is the coupling of a part-of-speech system with word-order rules. This is a case in point. Take, for example, the sentence "Very clearly projected pictures appeared." Here is a purely regressive structure with a depth of four.

Figure 6 shows how the sentence is organized. Counting down from the top we have first a verb—"appeared"—then a noun—"pictures"—then an adjective—"projected"—then an adverb—"clearly"—and finally a secondary adverb of a special limited class—"very." It is difficult to build much further in a regressive direction. The part-of-speech system provides a method of automatically counting down a regressive branch and stopping the construction before it gets over the depth limit. It is clear that this system is a counting scheme and is not tied to the meaning of the words, because it is often possible to shift the words up and down the ladder by making appropriate changes in part of speech. We can have "a very clear projection," where the participial adjective "projected" becomes the noun "projection" and the abverb "clearly" becomes the adjective "clear." The thing that remains constant is the part-of-speech labeling that serves to keep track of the extent of regression. It is characteristic of English that it lacks such a means for counting in the progressive direction.

There are many progressive constructions that can run on without limit. First of all there is co-ordination, as in a long string of co-ordinated noun phrases. This can go on without limit in the progressive direction. Then there is the accumulative pattern of modification of several adjectives before a noun. But when we get to subordinate clauses we have to look at the matter in a bit more detail.

In Figure 7, various structures are shown that involve reapplication of a rule labeled A. Those at the left of the dotted line would be ungrammatical because they imply the possibility of unlimited application of the rule A, and would lead to an unlimited increase in depth. They would trap a person into going too deep. Those at the right could occur and would cause no trouble. In English there are a number of structures involving subordinate clauses that can be iterated indefinitely. They have structures like those on the right. For example, the object clauses: "I watched him watch Mary watch the baby feed the kitten." Or, another type of object clause: "I imagined him hearing the announcer reporting Bill catching Tom stealing third base." A "that" clause: "John said that Paul said that Bill said that he had won the race." But a "that" clause can also be used before the verb as a subject clause, and it is a regressive construction. It cannot be iterated indefinitely. "That it is true is obvious." Now consider two "that" clauses: "That that it is true is obvious isn't clear." It is ungrammatical. It is the structure closest to the dotted line on the left in Figure 7. What is used, instead, is one of the typical complexities of English syntax, the anticipatory "it": "It isn't clear that it is obvious that it is true."

And now here is another progressive structure that can be extended indefinitely, an object "what" clause: "He knows what should have been included in what came with what he ordered." But if a "what" clause is placed in the subject position, it can only be done once. Here is an attempt at using three "what" clauses: "What what what he wanted cost would buy in Germany was amazing." It is ungrammatical. And it is a regressive structure. Instead, using three of the complications of grammar—a discontinuous constituent, a passive, and a nominalization—one can build a substitute progressive structure: "It was amazing what could be bought in Germany for the cost of what he wanted."

The discontinuous constituents in English seem to serve the purpose of postponing potentially deep structures to a point of lesser depth, by carrying structures from the left side of the tree over to the right side. An interesting example of this is shown by the following: If the passive is used to allow the subject of the active to remain unexpressed, a deep expression may be thrown into the subject position, where it starts with an initial tax of a depth of one. "In a recent paper, measurements of the effect of alloying on the superconductive critical temperature of tin were presented." Such structures have been called "top heavy" by grammarians. As an alternative, frequently the subject is split into discontinuous constituents: "In a recent paper, measurements (were presented) of the effect of alloying on the superconductive critical temperature of tin." Here, by a complication of syntax, the prepositional phrase modifier of the subject is postponed until after the predicate, so that we have the grammatical but "illogical" order of subject, predicate, modifiers of the subject. Time does not allow for more examples, but there are many.[2]

From the point of view advanced here, the sentences of English can be produced by a finite-state device. The syntax of English is not an endless catalog of whimsical complications, although it does contain some relics of the past. Neither does English appear to be an abstract formal system on a par with certain elegant mathematical notations. Instead, it is a particularly well engineered instrument of communication, with many ingenious innovations for adapting it to the capabilities of its users and to circumvent as much as possible the limitations of the human mind.

It remains to be seen how well the hypothesis applies to other languages. I hope that some of you will become interested in making such tests. Of course other languages are not the same as English. They will not have the same features as those that we can explain in English on the basis of the depth hypothesis. They may have just the opposite features to some of those explained in English—postpositions instead of prepositions, for example. But it is the over-all structure of the syntax of the language that should be judged in the light of the hypothesis, since it is usually the co-operation of a number of features that keeps any given sentence from becoming too deep. It is to be expected that all languages have methods of restricting regression, methods of conserving depth, and methods of circumventing the memory restriction so as to maintain expressive power.

The last part of the hypothesis proposes that depth phenomena be added to the list of already known factors that affect language change. A depth factor in language change should be easily observable if it exists, and it will probably show up quickly when grammatical sketches of different periods in the development of a language are compared.

MASSACHUSETTS INSTITUTE OF TECHNOLOGY,
    CAMBRIDGE, MASSACHUSETTS

FOUNDATIONS OF PHONEMIC THEORY[1]

BY

GORDON E. PETERSON AND FRANK HARARY

A *phonetic theory* is a description of the physiological formations which may be used in speech production, the transformations of these formations to acoustical speech waves, and the basic properties of the resulting acoustical waves. A general phonetic theory is basic to a phonemic theory. A *phonemic theory* specifies the organization of physiological time functions of speech into classes of basic linguistic elements. Such classes may be represented by discrete symbols.

The paper begins with a presentation of the essential relevant mathematical background which is to be applied to the definition of linguistic units. Both the theory of types and the theory of binary relations are involved. § 3 of the paper presents a general phonetic theory, in which speech parameters and phones are defined on a physiological basis. The basic requirements imposed upon the phonemic theory, and the theory of allophones, phonemes, and prosodemes are presented in § 4. The phonemicization and phonemic transcription of specific utterances within a dialect are discussed in § 5, and in § 6 the linearization of phoneme and prosodeme symbolization is developed. Applications of the theory to automatic speech recognition are discussed briefly in § 7, and future problems for phonemic research are considered in § 8. The paper concludes with a glossary in § 9 of the various definitions.

1. Introduction. There are a number of different conceptions of the province and problems of linguistic theory. Theories about the various aspects of language have, in fact, been developed in a number of different disciplines, but they will not be reviewed here.

In a field as complicated as phonemic theory, we do not consider, of course, that all of the basic issues can be resolved in a single paper, nor even that all of the basic problems can be identified. Thus we should like the ideas presented here to be considered preliminary rather than definitive.

Certain basic terms which are to be used throughout the paper should be defined. "Sign" is employed here as a behavioral term, and we shall assume from psychology the basis for its definition. When one stimulus becomes a substitute for another through conditioning (reflex or operant[2]), it has become a sign for the original stimulus. A *sign* is a conditional stimulus. A *code* is a set of discrete elements which may be combined in various ways to form signs. A *symbol* is an element of a code; when discrete elements are used to represent some portion or aspect of speech, they are usually called symbols.

---

[1] This research was supported by the Office of Scientific Research of the United States Air Force under contract AF 49 (638)–492. The authors are indebted to Miss J. E. Shoup for her many valuable suggestions.

[2] B. F. Skinner, *Verbal behavior*, New York, Appleton-Century-Crofts, 1957.

A *speech signal* is a pressure function of time which is generated by the human vocal mechanism and which functions as a set of one or more signs. In speech processing it is normally more convenient to analyze the pressure wave into a set of simultaneous acoustical parameters whose values may be expressed as individual time functions. An *utterance* is any combination of physiological formations, movements, and associated breath pressures which are produced by a single individual and which generate a speech signal.

We find the conversion from speech to printing (i.e., from continuous functions to a sequence of discrete symbols) to be an essential consideration in the development of linguistic theory. This results in part from the fact that the elements of a printed code have the properties of a mathematical representation of speech, in the sense that functions and relations may be symbolized by such a code in a rigorous manner. If mechanical procedures are to be prescribed for converting from either the physiological or the acoustical time functions of continuous speech to a discrete printed code, then the time functions and the properties of the discrete code must be specified systematically.

In §2 we present the essential relevant mathematical background which is to be applied to the definition of linguistic units. Both the theory of types and the theory of binary relations are involved.

A description of the basic physiological and acoustical characteristics of speech is fundamental to its discrete symbolic representation. Phonetic theory is concerned with the nature of the physiological formations of speech, the properties of acoustical speech waves, and the transformations from the physiological formations to speech acoustics. A complete phonetic theory is, of necessity, complicated in nature; the general basis for a phonetic theory, however, is outlined in §3.

A phonemic theory provides a basis for representing the physiological time functions of speech by discrete symbolic sequences. §4 presents a general phonemic theory. An essential part of this theory is the organization of the phone, a basic phonetic unit, into higher ordered sets of allophones and phonemes.

A phonemic description of the speech of a particular speaker is concerned with the representation of continuous time functions of that speech by the symbols of a discrete code. §5 discusses problems in developing such a phonemic description of speech, and in §6 a procedure is described for the linearization of phonemic and prosodemic transcriptions. The problems of mechanizing the transformation of speech to printing, once a code has been determined, are considered briefly in §7. Future problems for phonemic research are discussed in §8. The final §9 includes a summary of the definitions presented throughout the paper.

2. Mathematical foundations. According to the theory presented in later sections, phonemic units may be defined in terms of hierarchies of sets. A basis for these definitions lies in the mathematical theory of types and equivalence relations.

2.1. Russell's theory of types. The basic need for developing a consistent theory of types has been made evident by many paradoxes.[3] Russell succeeded in resolving all such paradoxes by introducing the theory of types. In this theory there is a given collection of elements called individuals; each individual is known as a *set of type* 0. A *set of type* 1 is defined as a collection of individuals: that is, as a set, each of whose elements is a set of type 0. Continuing, a *set of type* 2 is by definition a set of elements each of which is a set of type 1: in this case, a set of sets of individuals. In general, a *set of type* $(n + 1)$ is a set of sets of type n, etc. Accordingly, every set has a unique type peculiar to that set. The theory of types has been clearly expressed by Church.[4]

"As is well known, the simple theory of types may be described in the following terms. A particular domain to be called the domain of *individuals* is selected; this may be any domain within very wide limits, but in any particular system must be treated as fixed. Classes and relations (and functions, if the system provides for such) are then classified into a hierarchy of types. For simplicity in the description of this hierarchy it is convenient to think of relations (and functions) as defined in terms of classes—following a suggestion first made by Wiener in 1914. On this basis, the first type is composed of individuals, the second type of classes of individuals, the third type of classes of classes of individuals, and so on. The restriction imposed by the simple theory of types is that the members of a class which belong to the type $(n + 1)$ must all belong to the type n. There is no provision for classes which do not belong to a type: classes not obeying the restriction just stated are regarded as nonexistent, and names for such classes are excluded from the system."

Let $a_1 = \{a, b, c, \cdots\}$ be the set whose elements are $a, b, c, \cdots$. Each of its elements is a *representative* of a set a_1. In general, let $a_{n+1} = \{a_n, b_n, c_n, \cdots\}$ be a set of type $(n + 1)$, each of whose elements is a set of type n. The restriction imposed by the theory of types is that the members of a class of type $(n + 1)$ must all be of type n. Thus, in particular, a class cannot be a member of itself.

A *maximal set having a particular property* is a set with this property, which is not properly contained in any larger set with this property. Let $A = a_n$ and $B = b_n$ denote two sets of the same type. We say that A is a *subset* of B if each element of A also lies in B. Two sets A and B are *equal* if each is a subset of the other, i.e., they contain precisely the same elements.

The *difference* of two sets is the set of all elements which are in one but not in the other; $A - B$ is the set of all elements which are in A but not in B. The *intersection* $A \cap B$ is the set of all elements which lie in both A and B. The *union* $A \cup B$ is the set of all elements which are in $A - B$, $B - A$,

[3] R. L. Wilder, *Foundations of mathematics*, New York, John Wiley and Sons, 1956.

[4] A. Church, *Schröder's anticipation of the simple theory of types*, Reprinted for the members of the Fifth International Congress for the Unity of Science, 1939.

or $A \cap B$. The *symmetric difference* of two sets $A \oplus B$ is the set of all elements which are in the union of $A - B$ and $B - A$; symbolically $A \oplus B = (A - B) \cup (B - A)$. Thus $A \oplus B$ contains all elements which lie in exactly one of the two sets A and B. The *empty set* $\emptyset$ is the set which contains no elements. Two sets are called *disjoint* if their intersection is empty, i.e., there are no common elements to both sets.

2.2. Equivalence relations.

We have taken the elements of a particular set to be individuals or sets of type zero. We must now specify equivalence among these elements or among sets of these elements. Consider a set of elements which are related in certain aspects or properties. A *binary relation*, or briefly a *relation*,[5] is formally defined as a collection of ordered couples (or ordered pairs) of these elements. By an *ordered couple* is meant a collection of two elements, usually written (x, y), in which one is called first and the other is called second. If the ordered couple (x, y) is in relation R, we use the standard terminology that *x is in the relation R to y*, and write xRy.

A relation R is called *reflexive* if each element under consideration is in the relation to itself, i.e., (x, x) is in R for all elements x. A relation R is *symmetric* if whenever x is in the relation to y, then y is also in the relation to x; symbolically if (x, y) is in R, then (y, x) is also in R. Finally, a relation is *transitive* if whenever x is in the relation to y and y is in the relation to z, then x must also be in the relation to z. Symbolically, R is transitive if xRy and yRz imply that xRz.

An *equivalence relation* is one which is reflexive, symmetric, and transitive. For example, "has the same height as" is an equivalence relation on the set of all trees (or any other objects which have height).

The *domain* of a relation is defined as a collection of all first elements in the ordered couples belonging to the relation; its *range* is the set of all second elements. The *field* of a relation is the union of the domain with the range. Thus, if the relation is an equivalence relation, the domain, the range, and the field coincide.

The fundamental theorem on equivalence relations states that *an equivalence relation partitions its field*. This means that the field of an equivalence relation is divided or partitioned into subsets which are mutually exclusive (disjoint) and whose union is the entire field. Further, any pair of elements of the field is in the relation if and only if they lie in the same subset. These mutually exclusive subsets are called *equivalence classes*.

3. Phonetic theory.

A *phonetic theory* is a description of the physiological formations which may be used in speech production, the transformations of these formations to acoustical speech waves, and the basic properties of the resulting acoustical waves. A general phonetic theory is basic to a phonemic theory. Probably the best recognition of this fact is

---

[5] The theory of relations was also employed in the article: F. Harary and H. H. Paper, *Toward a general calculus of phonemic distribution*, Language vol. 33 (1957) pp. 143–169.

demonstrated by the writings of Pike[6,7]; it is also evident in the theory of Jakobson, Fant, and Halle,[8] a major portion of which is devoted to the development of a system of phonetic dichotomies.

Speech production involves several different types of complicated activities of the vocal mechanism. Rather than being quantized or discrete, most of these activities are continuously variable. Both the simultaneous and the sequential aspects of the activities must be considered.

Since speech is generated by a complex mechanical system, it seems reasonable that it should be organized in terms of the capabilities and the limitations of that system. Thus we find it essential to define the basic elements of speech in terms of physiological formations. While our first formulation[9] was in acoustical terms, the fact that speech is organized and coordinated according to the physiological mechanism is an essential fact which takes precedence over other considerations. Note that the innervation for speech must also be organized according to the nature and dynamics of the mechanical system it must control. The important role of the acoustical form of the speech signal is not to be disregarded, of course, in such operations as automatic speech recognition. While physiological production is more basic, the acoustical form of the speech signal is much more accessible and can be specified more conveniently. It follows that the essential problem in automatic speech recognition is the interpretation of the acoustical speech signal according to the organization and system of the physiological production of speech. An outstanding contribution to phonetics in the form of a detailed description of the transformations from speech production to speech waves has been presented by Fant.[10]

It is our objective to present the considerations basic to a complete phonetic theory of normal speech production. Although many of the concepts developed can be applied to defective speech, only normal speech production will be considered throughout the paper.

3.1. Speech production. In the production of speech, the vocal mechanism of a single individual may assume a large number of different configurations; in the production of speech by different individuals, however, an even greater number of sizes and shapes must be considered. While the acoustical waves of speech are the result of the physiological formations of speech production, each physiological variable does not have a single corresponding acoustical variable, nor is the converse true. Further, there is

[6] K. L. Pike, *Phonetics*, Ann Arbor, University of Michigan Press, 1943.

[7] K. L. Pike, *Phonemics*, Ann Arbor, University of Michigan Press, 1947.

[8] R. Jakobson, C. G. M. Fant, and M. Halle, *Preliminaries to speech analysis*, Massachusetts Institute of Technology Acoustics Laboratory Technical Report No. 13, January, 1953.

[9] G. E. Peterson and F. Harary, *A mathematical model for phonemic theory* (presented at the meeting of the Linguistic Society of America in New York City on December 30, 1958).

[10] C. G. M. Fant, *Acoustical theory of speech production*, Stockholm, Royal Institute of Technology, Division of Telegraphy-Telephony, Report No. 10, 1958.

not a one-to-one correspondence, but rather a many-to-one mapping from physiological formations to acoustical speech waves, for several physiological formations may map into the same acoustical time pattern. Clearly the induced binary relation on pairs of physiological formations is reflexive, symmetric, and transitive; it is therefore an equivalence relation. If two physiological formations map into the same acoustical time function they are *acoustically equivalent*.

There are various physiological mechanisms and processes involved in speech production. Those associated with vowel and consonant formations are here described as the vowel and consonant parameter classes, and are designated by the general headings shown in Figure 1. The individual subdivisions of the parameter classes are the vowel and consonant parameters. Each of the parameters within a given vowel or consonant parameter classes involves some special property which distinguishes it from its neighbors; these properties may be defined in terms of physical or physiological dimensions, but it seems unnecessary to elaborate these phonetic details here. It is assumed that in each case such a specification is possible. Some type of continuous range of variation may be observed within most of the parameters and there is a contiguity between many of the adjacent parameters. In some cases the boundaries between parameters cannot be clearly demarcated. Since our phonetic theory is expressed in physiological terms, however, specific boundaries can be defined arbitrarily where they are not otherwise clearly evident. Thus in the subsequent development we shall assume that all of the vowel and consonant parameters listed in Figure 1 can be appropriately defined. A *vowel or consonant parameter class* is a maximal set of related vowel or consonant parameters, respectively.

a. *Modifying vowel and consonant parameter classes.* Physiological vowel and consonant parameter classes which are associated with both vowel and consonant formations are air direction, laryngeal action, and secondary articulation. Each of these involves a set of parameters which are presented in an ordered sequence in Figure 1.

Thoracic egressive air provides the driving pressure for most speech production. Except where plosive consonant formations involve other air mechanisms, it is assumed that the driving air pressures for the vowel and consonant formations discussed below derive from the actions of the thorax. (The use of the esophagus as an air mechanism is here excluded as irrelevant to normal speech.)

Various types of laryngeal action may also be involved in both vowel and consonant formations. The entries in Figure 1 apply to vowels or consonants only and are designated (V) or (C), respectively.

The order of the individual categories under the parameter class of secondary articulation in Figure 1 is according to position along the vocal tract. While some of the parameters apply only to vowels or to consonants, many of them apply to both.

b. *Vowels.* On a phonetic basis, *vowels* are sounds which involve the following parameter classes of speech production: position of the hump of

VOWEL AND CONSONANT PARAMETERS

<u>Primary Vowel Parameter Classes</u>

Tongue Hump Relative to the Pharynx

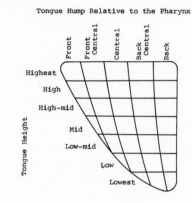

<u>Modifying Vowel and Consonant</u>
<u>Parameter Classes</u>

Air Direction
  Egressive
  Ingressive

Laryngeal Actions
  Whispered (V)
  Breathy (V)
  Clear (V)
  Laryngealized (V)
  Voiceless (C)
  Voiced (C)

<u>Primary Consonant Parameter Classes</u>

Place of Articulation

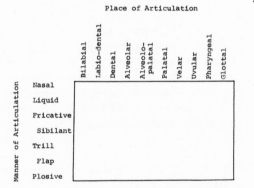

Secondary Articulations
  Spread
  Rounded (V)
  Labialized (C)
  Palatalized (C)
  Rilled (curled)
  Lateralized
  Retroflexed
  Velarized
  Nasalized
  Faucalized

PROSODIC PARAMETERS

Vowel and consonant duration
  V or C units (lexical quantity)
  V or C sequences (syntactic quantity)

Fundamental laryngeal frequency
  V or C units (tone)
  V or C sequences (intonation)

Speech production power
  V or C units (lexical stress)
  V or C sequences (syntactic stress)

FIGURE 1. The speech parameters.

the tongue relative to the palate (tongue height), position of the hump of the tongue relative to the posterior wall of the pharynx, air direction, laryngeal action, and (optionally) secondary articulation. The dimensions involved in the physiological formation of vowels have been considered in detail elsewhere.[11,12] The primary articulations of significance in the vocal tract shaping of vowels are symbolized in Figure 1 in a schematic which shows their approximate physiological positions. The back wall of the pharynx and the hard palate provide relatively fixed reference surfaces (approximating a right angle) toward which the tongue is humped in vowel formations. Degree of lip rounding is normally closely correlated with tongue height; thus it is unnecessary to indicate various degrees of lip rounding in the vowel chart, and rounding is shown as a secondary articulation in Figure 1. Variation in jaw separation may be very slight, and is so closely related to tongue height that it is here neglected.

The position of the hump of the tongue relative to the posterior wall of the pharynx and the position of the hump of the tongue relative to the palate (tongue height) are the *primary physiological vowel parameter classes*. Vowels are normally formed on egressive air, but they may be formed on ingressive air. In addition, vowels may involve certain of the laryngeal actions indicated in Figure 1. There are various secondary articulations which may be superimposed upon the primary vowel articulatory formations; these various secondary articulations (including lip rounding) are shown in Figure 1. The secondary articulations do not apply to all vowel formations indiscriminately, of course; for example, high-back vowels may already be considered velarized, high-front vowels cannot be retroflexed. The primary vowel parameter classes, air direction, laryngeal action, and secondary articulation are the *physiological vowel parameter classes*. The primary vowel parameter classes may be arbitrarily subdivided into parameters, as shown in Figure 1. It is desirable to separate each parameter class into a larger number of subdivisions than is normally found in language.

c. *Consonants* There is a long tradition in phonetics for specifying the consonants in terms of their basic physiological formations. On a phonetic basis, *consonants* are sounds which involve the following parameter classes of speech production: manner of articulation, place of articulation, air direction, laryngeal action, and (optionally) secondary articulation.

A description of the consonants according to their place of articulation and manner of articulation is basic. Such a description is given in Figure 1, which outlines the general possibilities of primary consonant formations. Place of articulation and manner of articutation are the *primary physiological consonant parameter classes*.

Some of the consonants may be formed on either egressive or ingressive air, and one of the two types of laryngeal action indicated is required for the formation of consonants. The secondary consonant articulations which may be superimposed upon the primary articulations are listed in Figure 1.

---

[11] G. E. Peterson, *The phonetic value of vowels*, Language vol. 27 (1951) pp. 541–553.

[12] A. S. House, and K. N. Stevens, *Auditory testing of a simplified description of vowel articulation*, J. Acoust Soc. Amer. vol. 27 (1955) pp. 882–887.

The term "liquid" refers to oral frictionless continuants in which the tongue apex forms the primary articulation (e.g., English [l], [r]). It will be noted that Figure 1 does not give a subclass of semivowels, since the concept of semivowel is based upon linguistic function rather than phonetic formation; basically, semivowels are vowel formations whose environments (to be defined later) resemble those of consonants within a particular language. Certain of the consonants involve a double place of articulation. For example, supralaryngeal clicks involve both an anterior and a posterior closure, and double plosives formed on egressive thoracic air have two positions of release. (Such double places of articulation may be indicated by inserting the same symbol in two different positions in the consonant chart of Figure 1.) There are several instances in the figure where it is clear that such a sound cannot be formed, but all of the categories given are necessary for the phonectic description of a general list of consonants. The primary consonant parameter classes, air direction, laryngeal action, and secondary articulation are the *physiological consonant parameter classes*. While distinctions among the various physiological consonant parameters are relatively clear, there are some instances in which relatively arbitrary boundaries must be drawn, as in the case of the primary physiological vowel parameters. There is a certain continuity in the parameter class of manner of articulation, however, which may not be immediately evident. A plosive may be continuously modified until it becomes a flap, which in turn may be doubled or tripled to form a trill; a flap or trill may be continuously modified to form a fricative; the degree of constriction for a voiced fricative may be continuously relaxed until a liquid is formed; etc.

d. *Vowel and consonant parameters.* Seven different classes of vowel (V) and consonant (C) parameters have now been identified.

(1) position of the hump of the tongue relative to the palate (tongue height) (V).

(2) position of the hump of the tongue relative to the back wall of the pharynx (V).

(3) manner of articulation (C).

(4) place of articulation (C).

(5) air direction (V, C).

(6) laryngeal action (V, C).

(7) secondary articulation (V, C).

e. *Prosodies.* Certain additional parameters are concurrent with vowel and consonant formations. Vowel and consonant duration, fundamental laryngeal frequency, and speech production power are the *physiological prosodic parameters*. A *prosody* is a set of functions of vowel and consonant duration, of fundamental laryngeal frequency, and of speech production power which are associated with a sequence of one or more vowel or consonant formations.

Duration. The duration of successive vowel and consonant formations may vary greatly. The duration of each vowel and consonant in a sequence is sometimes easily identified and sometimes is very difficult to determine. While much further research on duration in speech is needed, it seems appropriate to assume that the duration of each vowel and consonant has a discrete value, and thus a function of duration involves a series of discrete points plotted along a time base. Although vowel and consonant durations do not provide a continuous time function, and although time is a basic coordinate for all other parameters of speech, duration must be considered a basic prosodic parameter.

Fundamental laryngeal frequency. The frequency of laryngeal vibration is a basic property of both vowels and voiced consonants. This frequency is a continuous function and normally is directly represented in the periodicity of the acoustical speech wave. In special cases, such as breathy or laryngealized phonation, however, the rate may be difficult to specify. The following definition of fundamental laryngeal frequency as a basic physiological prosodic parameter is formulated to include such cases. Fundamental laryngeal frequency is the inverse of the dominant period of successive vocal cord cycles.

Speech production power. There are several different types of measurements which may be made of the energy dissipated in speech production. It may be that subglottal pressure is closely related to overall speech effort, but it seems probable that a phonetic parameter which will be more relevant to linguistic analysis is the power involved in speech production. Speech production power is here defined as a basic physiological prosodic parameter. *Speech production power* is the product of the total pressure and volume velocity of the air entering or being emitted from the vocal mechanism during speech. This definition agrees with the usual physical units in which power is energy per unit time, pressure is force per unit area, and volume velocity is volume per unit time. As in the case of the preceding parameters (except duration), speech production power may be considered a function of time for any specific utterance.

Vocal quality. Vocal quality is also sometimes considered to be a speech prosody. Individual speech patterns, often designated under the classification of vocal quality, are subsumed under the above physiological vowel, consonant, and prosodic parameters. Characteristic parameters, particularly of the secondary articulations, may determine individual voice identification.

f. *Speech targets.* As emphasized previously by Fairbanks,[13] the speech mechanism has the properties of a servosystem. There is, of course, an upper limit to the rate at which successive targets can be realized with such a system. In the case of speech production, the dynamics of the system are controlled primarily by the rates at which the larger physiological mechanisms can be moved. In the case of vowels the rate is controlled by the primary physiological vowel parameters and by the parameters of secondary articulation; in the case of consonants the rate is controlled by the parameters of place of articulation and of secondary articulation. These parameters are concerned with positional aspects of speech production, and during speech these positional aspects involve a sequence of approximations to steady-state values. The steady-state positions are often only approximated, and the transitions occupy

---

[13] G. Fairbanks, *A theory of the speech mechanism as a servosystem* (Part 1 of a symposium on Systematic Research in Experimental Phonetics), Journal of Speech and Hearing Disorders vol. 19 (1954) pp. 133–139.

most of the time between them. The physiological vowel, consonant, and prosodic parameters are the *physiological speech parameters*. A *speech target* is a speech formation which involves an approximation to a steady-state value or a characteristic rate of change (or movement) within a set of one or more concurrent physiological speech parameters. A *vowel target*, *consonant target*, or *prosodic target* is a speech target which involves physiological vowel, consonant, or prosodic parameters, respectively. Since the time constants of auditory perception are doubtlessly shorter than are those of some of the motor mechanisms of speech production, it is probable that the listener attends to the transitional portions of the signal as an aid to identifying the more sustained positions.[14] The extent to which speech is perceived in larger patterns is not clear at present. The relatively slow, hunting production of the child just learning to speak represents the acquisition of basic targets. These elements are perhaps integrated later into complete patterns which serve as the basic functional units of speech production.

g. *Phones.* The basic unit of a vowel or consonant formation may now be defined as a phone. A *phone* is a time segment of a set of concurrent (time) functions of physiological vowel or consonant parameters which contains an approximation to one and only one vowel or consonant target. *A phone is regarded as an individual, in the sense of type theory, and thus is a set of type 0.* The *empty phone* is a set containing no speech parameters. It should be noted that when the variation in the speech formation exceeds the particular parameter set in which the target occurs, the time boundary of the phone is thereby also exceeded. The targets of phones are of primary interest; in general, when utterances are segmented into sequences of phones, there is a residue in the time domain. Note, however, that the prosodies will form a different type of residue. Phones involve only the vowel and consonant formational aspects of utterances and are composed of physiological vowel or consonant parameters. In order to provide a basis for an analytical approach to additional concepts, sets of negative type may be introduced. *A segment of a specific time function of an individual physiological speech parameter is called a set of type* (−1).

h. *Phonetically similar phones.* Phones are regarded as sets of vowel or consonant parameters. *Phonetically similar phones* are composed of the same speech parameters. It should be noted that for two phones to be phonetically similar it is only required that they be composed of the same physiological parameters—not that they involve identical time functions of those parameters. Phonetic similarity is clearly an equivalence relation on phones, for it is reflexive, symmetric, and transitive. In the collection of all phones which could be produced by a single speaker, phonetic similarity partitions these phones into disjoint subsets whose union is the entire collection. Any pair of phones which are in the relation of phonetic similarity lie in the same subset. Phonetically nonsimilar phones are phones which are not composed of the same speech parameters.

---

[14] I. J. Hirsh, *Auditory perception of temporal order*, J. Acoust. Soc. Amer. vol. 31 (1959) pp. 759–765.

It should now be clear that an individual phonetic symbol may represent any set of phonetically similar phones, whether a single phone or a maximal set. A *phonetic symbol* represents a set of phonetically similar phones. The development of a complete description and symbolization for the various categories of Figure 1 will require a separate paper.

i. *Phonetic difference.* The necessity for comparing the phonetic properties of phones is well recognized in phonemic theory.[15] The phonetic difference between two vowel or two consonant phones obviously depends upon the difference in their physiological formations. It is irrelevant to specify an order of phonetic difference between a vowel phone and a consonant phone, since they not only involve different individual parameters, but also different

Table I.   Hierarchies of parameters for determining
order of phonetic difference.

For Vowels	*For Consonants*
1. Secondary articulation	1. Secondary articulation
.0 Spread	.0 Spread
.1 Rounded	.1 Labialized
.2 Rilled (curled)	.2 Palatalized
.3 Lateralized	.3 Rilled (curled)
.4 Retroflexed	.4 Lateralized
.5 Velarized	.5 Retroflexed
.6 Nasalized	.6 Velarized
.7 Faucalized	.7 Nasalized
2. Laryngeal action	.8 Faucalized
.0 Whispered	2. Laryngeal action
.1 Breathy	.0 Voiceless
.2 Clear	.1 Voiced
.3 Laryngealized	3. Air direction
3. Air direction	.0 Egressive
.0 Egressive	.1 Ingressive
.1 Ingressive	4. Place of articulation
4. Tongue hump relative to pharynx	.0 Bilabial
.0 Front	.1 Labio-dental
.1 Front central	.2 Dental
.2 Central	.3 Alveolar
.3 Back central	.4 Alveolo-palatal
.4 Back	.5 Palatal
5. Tongue height	.6 Velar
.0 Highest	.7 Uvular
.1 High	.8 Pharyngeal
.2 High-mid	.9 Glottal
.3 Mid	5. Manner of articulation
.4 Low-mid	.0 Nasal
.5 Low	.1 Liquid
.6 Lowest	.2 Fricative (sibilant)
	.3 Trill (flap)
	.4 Plosive

[15] W. A. Austin, *Criteria for phonetic similarity*, Language vol. 33 (1957) pp. 538-544.

parameter classes. We shall, however, provide a formula for determining a numerical value of the phonetic difference between two vowel or two consonant phones. This value is dependent upon the physiological vowel or consonant parameters by which the two phones differ.

We shall specify the phonetic difference in terms of three factors: (a) a hierarchy of parameter classes, (b) the number of parameters by which the two phones differ within each parameter class, and (c) the normalized difference between the various parameters by which the phones differ.

In Table I, separate hierarchies of vowel and consonant parameters are given for determining the phonetic difference between phones. The indices 1, 2, 3, 4, and 5 (in the left margin of each hierarchy) are the parameter class numbers, hereafter designated k. The decimal indices within each parameter class denote the individual parameters.

Let p and q be two vowel or two consonant phones, and let $S_1(p)$ be the set of parameters of the phone p in the first parameter class, $S_2(p)$ the set in the second parameter class, etc. The total number of parameters in a class k may be represented by n_k. For any set S, $n[S]$ denotes the total number of elements in the set S. The phonetic difference D_k between two phones p and q involving a particular vowel or consonant parameter class may now be formulated.

Let:

$$\varphi_k(p, q) = \begin{cases} 0 & \text{if} \quad S_k(p) = S_k(q), \\ 1 & \text{if} \quad S_k(p) \neq S_k(q), \end{cases}$$

$$\theta_k(p, q) = \begin{cases} 0 & \text{if} \quad S_k(p) = \varnothing \quad \text{or} \quad S_k(q) = \varnothing, \\ 1 & \text{if} \quad S_k(p) \neq \varnothing \quad \text{and} \quad S_k(q) \neq \varnothing \end{cases}$$

$$\text{(where } \varnothing \text{ is the empty set)}$$

and let $n[S_k(p) \oplus S_k(q)]$ be the number of parameters in the symmetric difference of $S_k(p)$ and $S_k(q)$, i.e., the number of parameters by which p and q differ in the kth parameter class. Let $|S_k(p) \oplus S_k(q)|$ be the sum of the absolute values of the differences between all pairs of decimal indices formed by parameters contained in phone p but not in phone q and all parameters contained in q but not in p. Let $T_k(p, q)$ be the number of difference terms for the parameter class k, i.e., the number of terms in $|S_k(p) \oplus S_k(q)|$. Thus:

$$T_k(p, q) = n[S_k(p) - S_k(q)] \cdot n[S_k(q) - S_k(p)].$$

We may now define:

$$D_k(p, q) = k\varphi_k(p, q) + \frac{n[S_k(p) \oplus S_k(q)]}{10} + \theta_k(p, q)\frac{|S_k(p) \oplus S_k(q)|}{10\, T_k(p, q)}.$$

Finally, the total phonetic difference $D(p, q)$ is the sum of the phonetic differences within each parameter class.

$$D(p, q) = \sum_{k=1}^{5} D_k(p, q).$$

The rather formidable defining equation for $D_k(p, q)$ actually expresses a simple number. The first term of the equation is an integer which is zero

Table II. Examples of calculations of phonetic differences between pairs of phones.

	p	b	t	d	k	g	f	v	s	z	l	r	m	n	ŋ	p̯k	ɟk	ʦ	t̃	ʧ
p	0.00	2.21	4.23	6.44	4.26	6.47	9.43	11.64	9.45	11.66	11.67	11.68	7.45	11.68	11.71	4.10	7.56	5.33	5.33	5.43
b	2.21	0.00	6.44	4.23	6.47	4.26	11.64	9.43	11.66	9.45	9.46	9.47	5.24	9.47	9.50	6.31	9.76	7.54	7.54	7.64
t	4.23	6.44	0.00	2.21	4.23	6.44	9.44	11.65	5.22	7.43	7.44	11.65	11.68	7.45	11.68	4.33	7.31	1.10	1.10	1.20
d	6.44	4.23	2.21	0.00	6.44	4.23	11.65	9.44	7.43	5.22	5.23	9.44	11.68	5.24	7.45	6.54	9.52	3.31	3.31	3.41
k	4.26	6.47	4.23	6.44	0.00	2.21	9.47	11.68	9.45	11.66	11.67	11.68	9.47	11.68	11.68	4.10	7.31	5.33	5.33	5.43
g	6.47	4.26	6.44	4.23	2.21	0.00	11.68	9.47	11.66	9.45	9.46	9.45	9.50	7.45	5.24	6.31	9.52	7.54	7.54	7.64
f	9.43	11.64	9.44	11.65	9.47	11.68	0.00	2.21	4.22	6.43	7.42	11.63	11.64	11.65	11.68	9.55	12.76	10.54	10.54	10.64
v	11.64	9.43	11.65	9.44	11.68	9.47	2.21	0.00	6.43	4.22	9.43	9.44	9.43	9.44	9.47	11.76	14.98	12.75	12.75	12.85
s	9.45	11.66	5.22	7.43	9.45	11.66	4.22	6.43	0.00	2.21	7.42	11.63	11.66	11.66	11.66	9.55	12.53	6.32	6.32	6.42
z	11.66	9.45	7.43	5.22	11.66	9.45	6.43	4.22	2.21	0.00	5.21	9.42	9.45	5.22	9.45	11.76	14.74	8.53	8.53	8.63
l	11.67	9.46	7.44	5.23	11.67	9.46	7.42	9.43	7.42	5.21	0.00	4.21	9.44	5.21	9.44	11.77	14.75	8.54	8.54	8.64
r	11.68	9.47	11.65	9.44	11.68	9.45	11.63	9.44	11.63	9.42	4.21	0.00	9.45	9.42	9.43	11.76	14.97	12.75	12.75	12.85
m	7.45	5.24	11.68	11.68	9.47	9.50	11.64	9.43	11.66	9.45	9.44	9.45	0.00	4.23	4.26	11.55	15.00	12.78	12.78	12.88
n	11.68	9.47	7.45	5.24	11.68	7.45	11.65	9.44	11.66	5.22	5.21	9.42	4.23	0.00	4.23	11.78	14.76	8.55	8.55	8.65
ŋ	11.71	9.50	11.68	7.45	11.68	5.24	11.68	9.47	11.66	9.45	9.44	9.43	4.26	4.23	0.00	11.55	14.76	12.78	12.78	12.88
p̯k	4.10	6.31	4.33	6.54	4.10	6.31	9.55	11.76	9.55	11.76	11.77	11.76	11.55	11.78	11.55	0.00	7.44	5.43	5.43	5.53
ɟk	7.56	9.76	7.31	9.52	7.31	9.52	12.76	14.98	12.53	14.74	14.75	14.97	15.00	14.76	14.76	7.44	0.00	8.41	8.41	8.51
ʦ	5.33	7.54	1.10	3.31	5.33	7.54	10.54	12.75	6.32	8.53	8.54	12.75	12.78	8.55	12.78	5.43	8.41	0.00	1.25	1.32
t̃	5.33	7.54	1.10	3.31	5.33	7.54	10.54	12.75	6.32	8.53	8.54	12.75	12.78	8.55	12.78	5.43	8.41	1.25	0.00	1.32
ʧ	5.43	7.64	1.20	3.41	5.43	7.64	10.64	12.85	6.42	8.63	8.64	12.85	12.88	8.65	12.88	5.53	8.51	1.32	1.32	0.00

if p and q do not differ in a parameter class and otherwise is the index number of the parameter class (as read from Table I). The digit in the tenths position in the value of $D_k(p, q)$ is determined by the second term in the equation and is the total number of parameters within the parameter class by which the two phones differ. The digit in the hundredths position (third term in the equation) is the sum of the differences, expressed as absolute magnitudes, between the indices for the parameters within a given class for which p and q differ, normalized by the number of differences. $D_k(p, q)$ will often be zero, whereas $D(p, q) = 0$ only for phonetically similar phones; thus phonetically similar phones have zero phonetic difference. Illustrative calculations of phonetic difference for a set of consonant phones are shown in Table II. Table III lists the correspondences among pairs with relatively small phonetic differences taken from Table II.

Table III. Illustrative pairs of phones having the same phonetic
difference as derived from Table II.

Phonetic difference	Pairs of phones
0.00	p-p, b-b, etc.
1.10	t-ţ, t-t̃
1.20	t-ţ̣
1.25	ţ-t̃
1.32	ţ-ţ̣, t̃-ţ̣
2.21	p-b, t-d, k-g, f-v, s-z
3.31	d-ţ, d-t̃
3.41	d-ţ̣
4.10	p-pk̬, k-pk̬
4.21	l-r
4.22	f-s, v-z
4.23	p-t, b-d, t-k, d-g, m-n, n-ŋ
4.26	p-k, b-g, m-ŋ
4.33	t-pk̬
5.21	l-n, l-z
5.22	t-s, d-z, n-z
5.23	l-d
5.24	b-m, d-n, g-ŋ
5.33	p-ţ, p-t̃, k-ţ, k-t̃
5.43	p-ţ̣, k-ţ̣, pk̬-ţ, pk̬-t̃
5.53	pk̬-ţ̣
6.31	pk̬-b, pk̬-g
6.32	s-ţ, s-t̃
6.42	s-ţ̣
6.43	f-z, v-s

j. *Phonetic environment.* The *phonetic environment of a phone* is a single ordered pair of phones, viz. the preceding phone and the following phone. *Two phones have phonetically similar environments* if their preceding phones are phonetically similar and their following phones are phonetically similar. (Obviously, the preceding and following phones of each environment need not be phonetically similar to each other.) Two phones have phonetically nonsimilar environments if their preceding phones or their following phones are phonetically nonsimilar. *Two utterances are phonetically similar* if each phone in the ordered sequence of one of the utterances is phonetically similar to the corresponding phone in the ordered sequence of the other utterance.

4. Phonemic theory. A phonemic theory specifies the organization of physiological time functions of speech into classes of phones and prosodies, classes of classes of phones, etc. Such classes may be mapped into discrete symbolic sequences, and conversely. The *analysis transformation* (printing) is a procedure for assigning time stretches of speech to sequences of symbols. Analysis is a many-one relation, and as such is properly identified as a transformation. The *synthesis process* (reading) is a set of instructions for pronouncing admissible sequences of discrete symbols to form natural speech. Synthesis is a one-many relation, for a given symbolic sequence can be implemented by more than one acoustic wave.

The synthesis process, in general, cannot regenerate specific time functions which occur in speech. Thus a theory which only provides a basis for speech synthesis (or the reading process) cannot be a general theory of speech. It only specifies the conditions for generating speech *from* a discrete code. The approach of speech analysis, however, subsumes any utterance which may occur within a certain restricted domain, whether it is generated in normal oral-oral communication or as a result of reading aloud. Thus the theory of speech analysis is more powerful than the theory of speech synthesis, and is the primary concern of the present paper. Once a theory of speech analysis has been developed, it is assumed that a statement of an inverse theory of speech synthesis is determined.

A phonemic theory specifies the general properties of the organization of speech time functions into classes. Obviously, then, a phonemic theory does not provide a means for discovering "phonemes"; it simply defines the sets of elements into which speech may be organized. Clearly, the definition of these sets will greatly influence the coherence and degree of success with which the speech of any given speaker can be represented in a discrete symbolization.

4.1. Requirements of the theory. We wish to develop a general phonemic theory which will provide the basis for a consistent (and mechanizable) symbolic representation of the speech of specific languages. For this purpose the following requirements of the theory are specified.

a. *Completeness.* Each aspect of speech production which serves as a sign must be included in its discrete symbolic representation.

b. *Linguistic independence.* The theory must be applicable to any particular language. It must not be restricted to English, French, or Chinese, or to languages in which stress, quantity, or tone are non-significant, etc.

c. *Speech-to-symbol correspondence.* For each vowel and consonant target in speech production, there must be a symbol in the discrete representation. Thus in the phonemic representation of an utterance, time sequences of vowel and consonant targets are not to be represented with a single symbol. This is a major restriction upon the phonemicization of a dialect of a language. It should be noted that the targets defined are physiological and not acoustical. Thus, for example, only a single symbol would be required to represent the controlled articulation of an unaspirated plosive, although a sequence of gap or voice-bar plus an impulsive release can be identified for such sounds in an acoustical analysis.

After the initial analysis transformation of an utterance, successive stages of rewriting may be carried out, of course, so that there is not a direct vowel or consonant target-to-symbol correspondence. Under the present theory, however, the resulting sequences after such rewriting do not form a phonemic representation of speech. Whether such sequences can be converted to natural speech by means of some synthesis process is irrelevant.

d. *Symbol recoverability.* It must be possible by analysis to reconstruct any admissible discrete symbolic sequence from speech which has been properly generated from that symbolic sequence; i.e., any utterance generated from a discrete symbolic sequences by synthesis must be convertible to the original symbolic sequences by analysis. As indicated above, many utterances can be mapped into the same symbolic sequence, but these same utterances cannot be recovered by synthesis. Under the requirement of symbol recoverability, however, all utterances which are generated from the same symbol sequence must be "phonemically equivalent."

The criterion of symbol recoverability provides a basis for defining the domain of utterances produced by various speakers which can be described by a given set of analysis transformations. All speakers within a given language, if they employ the same dialect, produce speech from admissible symbolic sequences which is convertible by analysis to the original symbolic sequences.

4.2. Definitions. It should be recalled that the vowel and consonant parameters were defined as individual categories of vowel and consonant formations. Any given speech parameter may assume many different values. A phone was defined as a time segment of concurrent functions of physiological vowel or consonant parameters containing an approximation to one and only one vowel or consonant target. The phonetic environment of a phone was defined as a single ordered pair of phones. The following definitions specify our phonemic theory.

a. *Semantically eqivalent utterances.* In any general linguistic theory it is necessary to specify an operational procedure for identifying utterances which are functionally equivalent. Some writers prefer to determine "linguistic equivalence" directly on the basis of native reactions of "same" and "different". The rigorous specification of such a procedure involves many difficulties, but these will not be analyzed here.

While the area of semantics has been subject to much controversy, we believe that adequate operational procedures can be specified for identifying utterances which are semantically equivalent. It should be recalled that a sign was defined in behavioral terms as a conditional stimulus. *Semantically equivalent utterances* are those which function as the same sign.

It is possible, of course, that a single utterance may belong to more than one semantic equivalence class, as in the case of homonyms. For example, consider the three utterances x, y, and z:

x. The rays of the sun meet.
y. The sun's rays meet.
   The sons raise meat.
z. Meat is raised by the sons.

If we denote the relation of semantic equivalence by E, it can be seen that E is reflexive and symmetric but not transitive. For xEx, yEy, etc.; and if xEy, then yEx; but the above well-known example shows that if xEy and and yEz, it does not follow that xEz. It will be observed that in the following development this lack of transitivity imposes no difficulty on the theory.

b. *Functionally similar phones.* *Two phones are functionally similar if they* have phonetically similar environments and occur in semantically equivalent utterances. Any set of phones is a set of type 1, for each of its elements is a set of type O. The *phonetic environment of a set of functionally similar* phones is a set of ordered pairs of phones, in which each pair is the phonetic environment of some phone in the set, and in which all of the preceding phones are phonetically similar and all of the following phones are phonetically similar. It will often occur that a phone is only functionally similar to phones to which it is also phonetically similar. Obviously, however, it is not necessary that two functionally similar phones be phonetically similar; examples are the use of either a voiceless [h] or a voiced [ĥ] in the word *ahead*, and the use of either [ɑ] or [ɔ] in the word *fog* by some speakers of midwestern American English. The relation of functional similarity on phones may be denoted by S, so that pSq indicates that phone p is in this relation to phone q. The relation S is both reflexive and symmetric. It is also transitive, for if pSq and qSr, then it must follow that pSr. Thus the relation of functional similarity is an equivalence relation. To clarify further, English [ɾ] may occur in either *latter* or *ladder*. Some instances of [ɾ] are functionally similar to [t] and some instances of [ɾ] are functionally similar to [d]. While a [ɾ] which is functionally similar to a [t] is phonetically similar to a [ɾ] which is functionally similar to a [d], the two instances of [ɾ] are not functionally similar to each other. An additional possibility is that an utterance in which [ɾ] occurs is ambiguous; i.e., [ɾ] may be functionally similar to either [t] or [d]. The instances of [ɾ] which occur under these circumstances are clearly different from those indicated above and thus they lie in a third set of functionally similar phones.

In any procedural test for determining semantically equivalent utterances a certain variation in human response to phones near the border of a functionally related set must be anticipated. Thus functionally similar phones could be specified more precisely in terms of distribution functions, rather than by disjoint sets. Such a specification would require the statistical procedures of psychophysics.

It should be noted that the relation of functional similarity on phones automatically prescribes the dialect or field of utterances encompassed by the theory. Thus what has preceded and what follows is not restricted to the speech of a single speaker.

c. *Allophone.* A *phonetically related set* is a set of phones obtained by taking the union of a maximal set of phonetically similar phones and all sets of functionally similar phones which contain a member of that set. Thus a phonetically related set is uniquely determined by a maximal set of phonetically similar phones and may be said to be "generated" by it. However, some phonetically related sets may be properly contained in the union of one or more other phonetically related sets. We are interested only in uncovered phonetically related sets. An *uncovered phonetically related set* is a phonetically related set which is not contained in the union of one or more other phonetically related sets. In order that the requirements of the theory be satisfied, however, certain phones must be excluded from an uncovered phonetically related set. A *primary phonetically related set* is an uncovered phonetically related set excluding those phones which lie in sets which generate other uncovered phonetically related sets. An *allophone* is the set of phones contained in the intersection of a maximal set of phonetically similar phones and a primary phonetically related set of phones. *Any allophone is a set of type 1.* In many instances, a primary phonetically related set is composed of a single allophone; some primary phonetically related sets may contain more than one allophone. A *canonical allophone* is a maximal set of phonetically similar phones which generates a primary phonetically related set. The *phonetic difference between two allophones* is the phonetic difference between any phone in the first allophone and any phone in the second allophone. *Two allophones have a minimal phonetic difference* if there is a smaller phonetic difference between them than between either of these allophones and any other allophone. We have set off phonetically similar phones by [ ]; we shall set off allophones by ( ).

d. *Phoneme.* If the intersection of two primary phonetically related sets is not empty, all of the phones contained in this intersection lie in functionally similar sets. It is now necessary to establish the conditions under which primary phonetically related sets have nonsimilar phonetic environments. *Two primary phonetically related sets have nonsimilar phonetic environments* if all of those phones from one of the sets which do not lie in the intersection of the two sets have phonetic environments which are nonsimilar to the environments of all of those phones from the other set which do not lie in the intersection. Symbolically, if A and B are two primary phonetically related sets, then the two sets have nonsimilar phonetic environments if all of the phones in $A - B$ have phonetic environments which are nonsimilar to all of the phones in $B - A$. A *phoneme* is the set of all allophones which lie in primary phonetically related sets having nonsimilar phonetic environments, and which have canonical allophones with pairwise minimal phonetic differences (not to exceed some specific upper limit). The upper limit of phonetic difference between canonical allophones which are involved in the union of primary phonetically related sets is arbitrary. Since all sets of allophones are sets of type 2, *a phoneme is a set of type 2.*

Table IV presents a hypothetical illustration of the union of allophones to form phonemes. The numbered columns represent six different environments, and functionally similar sets of phones are grouped together within each column. The allophones contained in each phoneme are listed at the bottom of the table.

Table IV. A hypothetical illustration of the union of allophones to form phonemes. The numbered columns represent six different environments and functionally similar sets of phones are contained within the intersections of the lettered subdivisions and the columns.

	1.	2.	3.	4.	5.	6.
A.	p	p	p	p	p	p
	ꝑ		b	ꝑ	t	
			ḅ	ḅ		
B.	t	t		t	t	t
		ɾ		ṭ	p	d
C.	d	d	d̠		d	d
	d̰	ɾ	d̦			t
D.	k	k	k	g	g	g
	ḵ		ḵ	g̣	g̡	
	k̰				g̰	

Phonemes	Allophones
/p/	(p, ꝑ, b, ḅ)
/t/	(t, ɾ, ṭ)
/d/	(d, d̠, ɾ, d̦)
/k/	(k, ḵ, k̰, g, g̡, g̰)

Two allophones are *co-phonemic* if they both lie in the same phoneme. The co-phonemic relation for allophones is reflexive, symmetric, and transitive; thus the co-phonemic relation is an equivalence relation. Phonetically similar allophones may lie in different phonemes. In accordance with the above example, an allophone $(ɾ)_1$ in such words as *latter, knotted* represents a different phoneme than another allophone $(ɾ)_2$ in *ladder, nodded.* Thus, higher ordered linguistic information (morphology, etc.) is required to resolve certain phonemic ambiguities, i.e., on the basis of phonetic data alone it is not always possible to identify the phoneme to which an allophone belongs.

According to the criterion of symbol recoverability, it must be possible by analysis to reconstruct any admissible discrete symbolic sequence from speech which has been properly generated from that symbolic sequence; i.e., any utterance generated from a discrete symbolic sequence by synthesis must be convertible to the original symbolic sequences by analysis. Symbol recoverability may be achieved if each ambiguous allophone is simultaneously symbolized by the various phonemes which it may represent. In the above example, [ɾ] of *latter* or *ladder* may be written

$$\frac{/t/}{/d/}$$

to indicate phonemic uncertainty. This symbol pair may be taken to specify the pronunciation [ɾ], thus preserving symbol recoverability. Here we have followed the convention of setting off phonemic symbols by / /. It should be noted that writing

$$\frac{/t/}{/d/}$$

to indicate phonemic ambiguity is different from specifying an additional phoneme

$$\left/\frac{t}{d}\right/ \quad \text{or} \quad /ɾ/ .$$

It will be noted that the phoneme has been specified without reference to "contrast" and that circular references to environment are not involved. While it is possible to define functionally contrastive allophones in terms of the basic theory presented here, the concept of contrast appears to be more relevant to applied procedures in the identification of the phonemes of a language than to linguistic theory. The relation of functional contrast among allophones, incidentally, is not reflexive, but it is symmetric and transitive.

e. *Prosodemes.* It is generally recognized that the physiological prosodic parameters are not independent in language. An excellent example is the judgment of what is often called "stress" in English, which is known to involve vowel and consonant duration, fundamental laryngeal frequency, and speech production power. A prosody was previously defined as a set of functions of vowel and consonant durations, of fundamental laryngeal frequency, and of speech production power which are associated with a sequence of one or more vowel and consonant formations. An *alloprosody* is a maximal set of prosodies which occur in phonetically similar and semantically equivalent utterances. Since we consider a prosody to be a set of type 0, *an alloprosody is a set of type 1.* We assume that in any given alloprosody one particular prosodic parameter is dominant; i.e., within a set of phonetically similar utterances some particular prosodic parameter primarily controls the semantic equivalence class to which any given utterance within the set belongs. The specification of the dominant prosodic parameter within an alloprosody is clearly an empirical problem requiring experimental investigation. Four different classes of alloprosodies are normally identified (tone, intonation, quantity, and stress) depending upon the dominant parameters involved.

An *alloprosody level or degree* (i.e., tone level, intonation level, degree of quantity, degree of stress) is the relative order of magnitude of a prosodic target within the dominant physiological prosodic parameter of an alloprosody. A *prosodeme* is a set of alloprosodies having the same dominant prosodic parameter and the same sequence of alloprosody levels or degrees. *A prosodeme is a set of type 2.* A *prosodeme level or degree* is the corresponding level or degree within an alloprosody which lies in the prosodeme. To illustrate, if a sequence of digits is used to represent a prosodeme of intonation, each individual digit represents the relative order of magnitude of a target (including the case of a characteristic rate of change) of fundamental laryngeal frequency within an alloporosody of the prosodeme. It must not be assumed, of course, that the individual digits represent fixed values of fundamental frequency. Utterances which represent the same sequence of prosodeme levels or degrees are *prosodemically similar*. Prosodemes whose alloprosody levels are derived from alloprosodies which have the same dominant prosodic parameter are *prosodemes of the same class*. Altogether, six possible classes of prosodemes may be defined, depending upon the dominant physiological prosodic parameter of the alloprosodies involved, and upon whether the prosodeme is normally associated with individual vowels and consonants or with sequences of vowels and consonants. These are:

lexical quantity	syntactic quantity
tone	intonation
lexical stress	syntactic stress

While the actual measurement of the individual physiological prosodic parameters is still technically difficult, their definition is reasonably unambiguous. The functional specification of prosodemes of tone, intonation, stress, and quantity in individual languages, however, is often difficult. It appears that in the past there have been many vague uses of the terms in describing various languages.

f. *Dialect.* When semantically equivalent utterances, produced by different speakers, are also both phonetically similar and prosodemically similar, the speakers speak the same *dialect*.

5. Phonemicization. Vowel and consonant phones represent allophones of phonemes which may be represented by discrete symbols. A *phonemicization* of a dialect is the specification and discrete symbolic representation of the phonemes and prosodemes employed by speakers of that dialect. A *phonemic transcription* of an utterance is a discrete symbolization of the phonemes and prosodemes represented by the utterance according to a particular phonemicization.

It should be emphasized that the definitions of phone, allophone, phoneme, prosody, alloprosody, and prosodeme do not provide the details of a procedure for determining the phonemes and prosodemes of the speech of a given speaker or dialect. They do, however, provide a set of criteria which in our opinion the phonemic description of the speech of a particular speaker should meet. Thus the appropriateness of individual elements within a phonemicization may be evaluated in terms of such a theory.

According to the theory presented above there is at least one phone in every allophone, and at least one allophone in every phoneme. Thus for every phonemic symbol in the transcription of an utterance there must be an identifiable vowel or consonant phone. In determining the phonemes and prosodemes involved in the speech of a particular speaker, or in determining the transcription of specific utterances, the analyst is obligated to make a careful investigation of the phonetic properties of the speech. An essential objective is a specification of the physiological speech parameters involved in the speech. The instrumentation and procedures of physiological phonetics are directly relevant. The methodology of acoustical phonetics may be even more valuable, however, because of the convenience with which the acoustical speech signal may be analyzed, and because a great deal is now known about the interpretation of physiological productions from acoustical analyses of the speech signal.

The selection of letters to represent individual phonemes and prosodemes is arbitrary, of course. Thus the isomorphic mapping from one alphabet to another is only a change in notation. By selecting multiple letters to represent a given phoneme or by representing different phonemes with the same letter, it is possible, of course, to represent a given phonemic sequence by a larger or smaller number of letters. In one extreme, by identification (reiteration) of letters, the alphabet may be reduced to a binary code. According to the above theory, the alphabets involved would not be phonemic alphabets. It may be noted that only in certain cases would symbol recoverability be possible, i.e., would it be possible to generate speech from the symbolic sequences which upon analysis would consistently yield the same sequence.

A chart similar to that of Figure 1 may be used to identify the physiological parameters involved in the allophone classes and prosodemes of a particular dialect.

6. Phoneme and prosodeme linearization.

In a phonemic transcription it is desirable, of course, to represent both phonemes and prosodemes. If different types of notation for vowel and consonant phonemes, and for prosodemes of tone, intonation, lexical stress, etc. are employed, then a linearization of the transcription can readily be achieved. Such a linearization is accomplished by assigning a priority to the prosodemes relative to the vowels and consonants: in English, for example, in the order of consonants, intonation, lexical stress, syntactic stress, and vowels. Table V should make the process evident.

Table V. An example of a phonemic and prosodemic linearized transcription.

Consonants:			f	ð		z	h		m
Vowels:		ɑ		ɝ	I			o	U
Intonation:			3	2	2			3	ɬ
Lexical stress:									
Syntactic stress:									

f3′ɑð2⌣ðɪzh3˙oɬUm "Father is home" is a linearization of the above phonemic-prosodemic matrix.

7. Automatic speech recognition. It is our basic thesis that speech is primarily organized according to the capabilities and constraints of the production mechanism. For routine analysis, however, the physiological mechanism is essentially inaccessible. Also, when speech is carefully formed in an acoustical environment which is relatively free of distortions and noise, very high intelligibility can be achieved from the acoustical form of the signal. Thus for the practical purposes of automatic speech recognition, the operations should be based primarily upon the acoustical speech wave.

The theory described above provides a basis for the transformation from *speech production* to its symbolization by a discrete code representing *phonemes and prosodemes*. We may symbolize this transformation by $S \rightarrow P$, and the transformation from *speech production* to *speech acoustics* by $S \rightarrow A$. In automatic speech recognition, the objective is not to perform the complicated inverse transformation from acoustical parameters to physiological speech formation, $A \rightarrow S$, for the result of such a transformation must also be symbolized. Rather, the essential problem is to perform logical operations upon the acoustical speech parameters to achieve a direct transformation to phonemic and prosodemic symbols, $A \rightarrow P$.

The experiments of Ladefoged and Broadbent[16] have suggested that the same phone may belong to different allophones which are members of different phonemes. They showed that identical phones may be judged differently by the same listeners when the acoustical properties of the utterances in which the phones occur are varied in a particular manner. The experiments were conducted with a speech synthesizer, and whether such effects can be demonstrated in human speech (by systematic changes in physiological production) is yet to be determined. If speech style and the domain of speakers is sufficiently restricted, however, it may be assumed that any given phone will represent only one allophone of one phoneme.

Automatic speech recognition should be much more successful if the identification of phonemes from acoustical parameters is regarded as an optimization procedure. In such a procedure tentative phonemic and prosodemic sequences are established for referral to stored information about the speech system under analysis. Essential considerations in automatic speech recognition are the nature of the linguistic information to be stored and the details of the symbolization desired at the output.

8. Phonemic research. Important empirical problems of phonemics are the development of operational procedures for determining semantic equivalence between utterances and phonetic difference between phones.

Probably the essential problem for future phonemic research is the rigorous application of systematically formulated phonemic theory to the analysis of dialects of individual languages. The recent description of Russian by Halle is a commendable experiment toward such an objective.[17]

Intereffects among phonemes and prosodemes probably exist in speech, and

[16] P. Ladefoged and D. E. Broadbent, *Information conveyed by vowels*, J. Acoust. Soc. Amer. vol. 29 (1957) pp. 98–104.

[17] M. Halle, *The sound patterns of Russian*, 's-Gravenhage, Mouton and Co., 1959.

are an essential problem for future phonemic theory. At the experimental level there are innumerable questions about the relation of speech physiology and speech acoustics to its perception. Answers appear to be most valuable when the questions are expressed in terms of coherent phonemic formulations.

After a phonemicization has been achieved, the mechanistic reduction of specific utterances to consistent linear phoneme and prosodeme level sequences is, of course, a severe test of any theory of phonemic analysis.

9. Summary. This paper has been primarily concerned with the transformation from continuous speech to its discrete symbolic representation. The paper begins with an analysis of the phonetic properties of speech and proceeds to a statement of the linearization of phonemic and prosodemic sequences. The basic theory is formulated in terms of the physiological parameters of speech production. The following definitions represent the essential development of the paper.

(1) A *sign* is a conditional stimulus.

(2) A *code* is a set of discrete elements which may be combined in various ways to form signs.

(3) A *symbol* is an element of a code.

(4) A *speech signal* is a pressure function of time which is generated by the human vocal mechanism and which functions as a set of one or more signs.

(5) An *utterance* is any combination of physiological formations, movements, and associated breath pressures which are produced by a single individual and which generate a speech signal.

(6) A *phonetic theory* is a description of the physiological formations which may be used in speech production, the transformations of those formations to acoustical speech waves, and the basic properties of the resulting acoustical waves.

(7) If two physiological formations map into the same acoustical time function, they are *acoustically equivalent*.

(8) On a phonetic basis, *vowels* are sounds which involve the following classes of parameters of speech production: position of the hump of the tongue relative to the palate (tongue height), position of the hump of the tongue relative to the posterior wall of the pharynx, air direction, laryngeal action, and secondary articulation.

(9) The position of the hump of the tongue relative to the palate and the position of the hump of the tongue relative to the back wall of the pharynx are the *primary physiological vowel parameter classes*.

(10) The primary vowel parameter classes, laryngeal action, air direction, and secondary articulation are the *physiological vowel parameter classes*.

(11) On a phonetic basis, *consonants* are speech sounds which involve the following classes of parameters of speech production: manner of articulation, place of articulation, air direction, laryngeal action, and secondary articulation.

(12) Manner of articulation and place of articulation are the *primary physiological consonant parameter classes*.

(13) The primary consonant parameter classes, laryngeal action, air direc-

tion, and secondary articulation are the *physiological consonant parameter classes*.

(14)   Vowel and consonant duration, fundamental laryngeal frequency, and speech production power are the *physiological prosodic parameters*.

(15)   A *prosody* is a set of functions of vowel and consonant duration, of fundamental laryngeal frequency, and of speech production power which are associated with a sequence of one or more vowel or consonant formations.

(16)   The physiological vowel, consonant, and prosodic parameters are the *physiological speech parameters*.

(17)   A *speech target* is a speech formation which involves an approximation to a steady-state value or a characteristic rate of change (or movement) within a set of one or more physiological speech parameters.

(18)   A *vowel target, consonant target*, or *prosodic target* is a speech target which involves physiological vowel, consonant, or prosodic parameters, respectively.

(19)   A *phone* is a time segment of a set of concurrent (time) functions of physiological vowel or consonant parameters which contains an approximation to one and only one vowel or consonant target.

(20)   *Phonetically similar phones* are phones which are composed of the same speech parameters.

(21)   The *phonetic environment of a phone* is a single ordered pair of phones, viz. the preceding phone and the following phone.

(22)   *Two phones have phonetically similar environments* if the preceding phones are phonetically similar and the following phones are phonetically similar.

(23)   *Two utterances are phonetically similar* if each phone in the ordered sequence of one of the utterances is phonetically similar to the corresponding phone in the ordered sequence of the other utterance.

(24)   A *phonemic theory* specifies the organization of physiological time functions of speech into classes of basic linguistic elements.

(25)   The *analysis transformation* (printing) is a procedure for assigning time stretches of speech to sequences of symbols.

(26)   The *synthesis process* (reading) is a set of instructions for pronouncing admissible sequences of discrete symbols to form natural speech.

(27)   *Semantically equivalent utterances* are those which function as the same sign.

(28)   *Two phones are functionally similar* if they have phonetically similar environments and occur in semantically equivalent utterances.

(29)   The *phonetic environment of a set of functionally similar phones* is a set of ordered pairs of phones, in which each pair is the phonetic environment of some phone in the set, and in which all of the preceding phones are phonetically similar and all of the following phones are phonetically similar.

(30)   A *phonetically related set* is a set of phones obtained by taking the union of a maximal set of phonetically similar phones and all sets of functionally similar phones which contain a member of that set.

(31)   An *uncovered phonetically related set* is a phonetically related set which is not contained in the union of one or more other phonetically related sets.

(32) A *primary phonetically related set* is an uncovered phonetically related set excluding those phones which lie in sets which generate other uncovered phonetically related sets.

(33) An *allophone* is the set of phones contained in the intersection of a maximal set of phonetically similar phones and a primary phonetically related set of phones.

(34) A *canonical allophone* is a maximal set of phonetically similar phones which generates a primary phonetically related set.

(35) The *phonetic difference between two allophones* is the phonetic difference between any phone in the first allophone and any phone in the second allophone.

(36) *Two allophones have a minimal phonetic difference* if there is a smaller phonetic difference between them than between either of these allophones and any other allophone.

(37) *Two primary phonetically related sets have nonsimilar phonetic environments* if all of those phones from one of the sets which do not lie in the intersection of the two sets have phonetic environments which are nonsimilar to the environments of all of those phones from the other set which do not lie in the intersection.

(38) A *phoneme* is the set of allophones which lie in primary phonetically related sets having nonsimilar phonetic environments, and which have canonical allophones with pairwise minimal phonetic differences (not to exceed some specified upper limit).

(39) Two allophones are *co-phonemic* if they both lie in the same phoneme.

(40) An *alloprosody* is a maximal set of prosodies which occur in phonetically similar and semantically equivalent utterances.

(41) An *alloprosody level or degree* (i.e., tone level, intonation level, degree of quantity, degree of stress) is the relative order of magnitude of a prosodic target within the dominant physiological prosodic parameter of an alloprosody.

(42) A *prosodeme* is a set of alloprosodies having the same dominant prosodic parameter and the same sequence of alloprosody levels or degrees.

(43) A *prosodeme level or degree* is the corresponding level or degree within an alloprosody which lies in the prosodeme.

(44) Utterances which represent the same sequence of prosodeme levels or degrees are *prosodemically similar*.

(45) Prosodemes whose alloprosody levels are derived from alloprosodies which have the same dominant prosodic parameter are *prosodemes of the same class*.

(46) When semantically equivalent utterances, produced by different speakers, are phonetically similar and prosodemically similar, the speakers speak the same *dialect*.

(47) A *phonemicization* of a dialect is the specification and the discrete symbolic representation of the phonemes and prosodemes employed by speakers of that dialect.

(48) A *phonemic transcription* of an utterance is a discrete symbolization of the phonemes and prosodemes represented by the utterance according to a particular phonemicization.

THE UNIVERSITY OF MICHIGAN,
ANN ARBOR, MICHIGAN

ON THE CALCULUS OF SYNTACTIC TYPES[1]

BY

JOACHIM LAMBEK

In classical physics it was possible to decide whether an equation was grammatically correct by comparing the "dimensions" of the two sides of the equation. These dimensions formed an abelian group with three generators L, M and T, admitting fractional exponents.[2]

One may ask whether it is similarly possible to assign "grammatical types" to the words of English in such a way that the grammatical correctness of a sentence can be determined by a computation on these types. As long as "John loves Jane" fails to imply "Jane loves John" one cannot expect these types to form an abelian group. Probably they should not form a group at all.

Some time ago [3] I suggested a group-like mathematical system, which I called the "syntactic calculus". For reasons that will appear later, it would have been better to call it the "associative syntactic calculus". My method was closely related to an earlier syntactic method by Bar-Hillel, which in turn goes back to the "semantic types" of Ajdukiewicz, Leśniewski and ultimately Husserl. Independent type theories were also developed by Church and Curry,[3] who calls his types "functional characters".

My proposal was briefly this: We start by assigning certain primitive types to words and strings of words. Thus all well-formed statements have type s, all names have type n, all intransitive infinitives have type i, etc. From these primitive types compound types are built up by three formal operations: multiplication, left division and right division. The following examples will illustrate the general method. We write $X \to x$ to indicate that the string X has type x.

$$John \to n$$
$$John\ works \to s$$
$$works \to n\backslash s$$
$$must\ work \to n\backslash s$$
$$work \to i$$
$$must \to (n\backslash s)/i$$
$$John\ work \to ni$$

Given the method of assigning compound types implicit in the foregoing examples, one can prove that the following rules are universally valid [see **3**, § 7]:

(1) $$x \to x$$

---

[1] This paper was written while the author held a grant from the Canada Council.

[2] In the language of modern algebra, this group is a three-dimensional vector-space over the field of rational numbers.

[3] See [3] for detailed references.

(2) $(xy)z \rightarrow x(yz)$ (2′) $x(yz) \rightarrow (xy)z$

(3) $$\frac{xy \rightarrow z}{x \rightarrow z/y}$$ (3′) $$\frac{xy \rightarrow z}{y \rightarrow x\backslash z}$$

(4) $$\frac{x \rightarrow z/y}{xy \rightarrow z}$$ (4′) $$\frac{y \rightarrow x\backslash z}{xy \rightarrow z}$$

(5) $$\frac{x \rightarrow y \quad y \rightarrow z}{x \rightarrow z} .$$

Here $x \rightarrow y$ means that all strings of type x also have type y. The horizontal line is meant to indicate that the "conclusion" below it follows from the "premise" or "premises" above it.

The free algebraic system or deductive system with axiom schemes (1), (2) and (2′) and rules of inference (3) to (5) may be called the associative calculus of types. Surprisingly, this system has no obvious decision procedure: While the provable formula $(x/y)y \rightarrow x$ suggests a method of simplifying expressions by decreasing their length, the provable formulas $x \rightarrow (xy)/y$ and $x \rightarrow y/(x\backslash y)$ contradict this. Nonetheless, it turned out [3] that a method first proposed by Gentzen for the intuitionistic propositional calculus also works here.[4]

Let us turn to the linguistic applications of the associative syntactic calculus.[5] It soon became apparent that, unless elaborate precautions were taken, the most natural assignments of types to English words tempted one to admit many pseudo-sentences as grammatical, e.g.

(*) *John is poor sad. John likes poor him.   Who works and John rests?*

Now I have been unable to find any agreement among modern linguists as to what constitutes a grammatical sentence. At one extreme there are those who call every utterance a sentence, that is any string of words ever mouthed by poet or peasant. At the other extreme there are those who would declare cannibalism ungrammatical on the grounds that *man* does not belong to the class of food-nouns.

My own standard of grammaticalness will sound equally absurd. I have regarded as grammatical

John works today today, John works yesterday today,

simply because I was unable to state a simple procedure which would rule out these expressions without at the same time ruling out

John works today at lunch, John works at lunch today,

both of which seem acceptable to me.

However the pseudo-sentences (*) could be systematically ascribed to one cause, namely the fact that types had been assigned to unstructured strings of words. Suppose we assign types not to strings, but to *phrases*, that is bracketed strings of words or perhaps morphemes. Better still, let us avoid

[4] In fact, it works more neatly here, since Gentzen's "structural" rules completely disappear.

[5] See Appendix II for other applications in mathematics.

the difficult question of identifying the *atomic* phrases and define as follows:[6]
All atomic phrases are phrases.
If A and B are phrases so is (AB).
Types are introduced by a similar recursive definition:[7]
All primitive types are types.
If x and y are types so are (xy), (x/y) and $(x\backslash y)$.
It is understood that types are assigned to phrases in accordance with the following rules:
If A has type a and B has type b then (AB) has type (ab).
If (AB) has type c for all B of type b then A has type (c/b).
If (AB) has type c for all A of type a then B has type $(a\backslash c)$.
Again the types give rise to a formal calculus. Rules (1), (3), (3'), (4), (4') and (5) are still valid, but the associativity rules (2) and (2') fail to hold. In particular, the following consequences of the associative law must be dropped:

$$(x\backslash y)/z \rightleftarrows x\backslash(y/z) , \quad (x/y)/z \rightleftarrows x/(zy) , \quad (x/y)(y/z) \rightarrow x/z .$$

The last of these goes back to Ajdukiewicz.

A careful investigation shows that the decision procedure for the associative calculus can be adapted to the non-associative calculus. A sketch of the modified decision procedure will be found in Appendix I.

Previous papers have elaborated the claim that the syntactic calculus can be used to transfer many grammatical rules from the grammar to the dictionary. Let me illustrate this by the sentence "John must work". A phrase-structure analysis of this sentence looks like this:

$$\underbrace{John \underbrace{(must\ work)}_{\underbrace{m \qquad i}_{v}}}_{s}$$

This analysis presumes that we are given a dictionary with the type assignments

$$John \rightarrow n , \quad must \rightarrow m , \quad work \rightarrow i$$

and a list of grammatical rules containing

$$mi \rightarrow v , \quad nv \rightarrow s .$$

Using the syntactic calculus, we can re-write the last two rules thus:

$$m \rightarrow v/i , \quad v \rightarrow n\backslash s .$$

These give rise to the single rule

$$m \rightarrow (n\backslash s)/i .$$

We may now revise the dictionary thus:

---

[6] Juxtaposition denotes concatenation and brackets denote themselves. As usual with recursive definitions it is understood that the class of all phrases is the smallest class satisfying the stated conditions. According to the usual convention, brackets on the outside of a complete phrase may be omitted.

[7] See the preceding footnote. Read "(x/y)" as "x over y" and "$(x\backslash y)$" as "x under y".

$$John \rightarrow n, \quad must \rightarrow (n\backslash s)/i, \quad work \rightarrow i.$$

Without any further grammatical rules we may then analyse the same sentence as follows:

$$\begin{array}{ccc} John & (must & work) \\ n & (n\backslash s)/i & i \end{array}$$
$$\underbrace{\qquad\qquad}_{n\backslash s}$$
$$\underbrace{\qquad\qquad\qquad}_{s}$$

Suppose we have replaced all grammatical rules of a language by suitable type assignments in the dictionary. It is then possible to parse a given string of words in a purely mechanical fashion: First we turn the string into a phrase X by bracketing and write under each word one of the types assigned to it by the dictionary. Let x be the compound type of the whole phrase. If $x \rightarrow s$ is a provable formula of the syntactic calculus, X is a statement. If $x \rightarrow i$ is provable, X may be one kind of request, and so on. This process is repeated for all other bracketings and type assignments. Of course a given string may possess syntactic ambiguity. For example, the string *time flies* may be parsed as a statement or as a request [3, §5].

Since mechanical parsing of sentences is not only of conceptual but also of practical importance (in connection with mechanical translation of languages), it becomes of interest to know for which languages it is possible to replace all grammatical rules by type assignments in the dictionary. This is certainly the case for the formal languages of mathematical logic, at least for all those that I have looked at [3, §4]. With a view of investigating this problem for natural languages such as English, we shall look at some phrase structure and transformational grammars. It has been pointed out by several people that these grammars possess a mechanical parsing procedure anyway, as long as one avoids elliptical transformation rules. Nonetheless, it is of some interest to determine the extent and limitations of the present methods.

For our purpose it will be convenient to think of a phrase structure grammar as follows: The dictionary assigns to each atomic phrase a finite number of primitive types. The grammar consists of a finite number of rules of the form $p_i p_j \rightarrow p_k$ where the p_i are primitive types.[8]

While it seems unlikely that the elimination of grammatical rules in favour of dictionary entries can be carried out for every phrase structure grammar in this sense (without making the dictionary infinite), this can be done in many examples (in fact all that I have tried).

Take for instance Chomsky's language L_2 [2, p. 151]. The sentences of this language are all strings of the form XX^*, where X is a string of A's and H's and X^* is the mirror image of X. One easily verifies that this language is completely described by the dictionary:

$$A \rightarrow a, \quad s/a, \quad (s/a)/s$$
$$H \rightarrow h, \quad s/h, \quad (s/h)/s.$$

[8] In Chomsky's hierarchy of grammars [2], this is essentially a type 2 grammar. See his discussion of his Theorem 5 on page 150. His arrow is the reverse of ours.

The informal comma separating the different types assigned to one word in the dictionary can be replaced by a formal connective $\cap$. Thus, in the last example, we could write

$$A \rightarrow (a \cap (s/a)) \cap ((s/a)/s) ,$$

where the right hand side represents a compound type in an enlarged syntactic calculus. We would have to adjoin two new axioms

$$x \cap y \rightarrow x , \quad x \cap y \rightarrow y$$

and one new rule of inference

$$\frac{t \rightarrow x \quad t \rightarrow y}{t \rightarrow x \cap y}$$

to our formal system. It would not be difficult to extend our decision procedure to this enlarged system, but we shall desist from doing so.[9]

It may happen that type assignments in a dictionary are in a sense stronger than the explicit rules of a phrase structure grammar. Let me illustrate this by an example.

I have previously [3, §6] suggested that the pronoun *he* be given the type $s/(n\backslash s)$. This means that *he* when followed by any phrase of type $n\backslash s$ (e.g. *must work*) yields a phrase of type s, that is a statement. In other words, the type assignment

$$he \rightarrow s/(n\backslash s)$$

is equivalent to the transformation rule

$$\frac{nX \rightarrow s}{he\ X \rightarrow s} .$$

Such a rule may indeed be implied by the totality of rules and type assignments of a phrase structure grammar, but it is clearly not one of these rules.[10]

We have here a transformation rule which can be conveniently replaced by a type assignment in the dictionary. A similar example is the rule

$$\frac{nX \rightarrow s}{who\ X \rightarrow (?)}$$

where (?) is the type of well-formed questions. This is equivalent to the dictionary entry

$$who \rightarrow (?)/(n\backslash s) .$$

Again the transformation rule

$$\frac{n(must\ i) \rightarrow s}{(must\ n)i \rightarrow (?)}$$

_____

[9] In the application to ideal theory mentioned in Appendix II, $A \cap B$ is of course the intersection of the ideals A and B. A dual connective to form the sum of two ideals also plays a role.

[10] It won't do to enter "$he \rightarrow n$" into the dictionary, for then the non-sentence "John must like he" would obtain type s.

could be handled by supplementing the original dictionary entry

(1) $must \rightarrow (n \backslash s)/i$

by the further assignment

(2) $must \rightarrow ((?)/i)/n$.

Unfortunately, this won't allow us to derive the sentence "Must he work?". Let $\hat{n} = s/(n \backslash s)$ be the type of *he* considered above; then we really want the type assignment

(3) $must \rightarrow ((?)/i)/\hat{n}$.

It is not necessary for the dictionary to carry both (2) and (3). (3) alone will do, since

$$((?)/i)/\hat{n} \rightarrow ((?)/i)/n$$

is a derivable formula in the syntactic calculus. Instead of proving this rule, let us parse the sentence "Must John work?" using (3) and the provable formula[11]

$$n \rightarrow \hat{n} = s/(n \backslash s) .$$

Thus

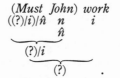

Incidentally, we have here a simple example of a sentence analysis, in which the types need not get "shorter" as we go from top to bottom, i.e., in the direction of the arrow.[12]

Unfortunately there seems to be a limit to this sort of thing. I have not succeeded in handling the interrogative *whom*, without some rather artificial devices.

Consider for instance the sentence

Whom must John call today?

According to Chomsky [1], this is derived from the pseudo-sentence

*Him must John call today,

which in turn is derived from

Must John call him today?

The easiest way to account for this sequence of transformations by type assignments is to assume that **him* and *whom* consist of two atomic phrases

---

[11] A proof of the dual formula $x \rightarrow (y/x) \backslash y$ appears in Appendix I.

[12] A similar example was given in [3, § 6]. Unfortunately this example was marred by a repeated misprint. In [3, p. 163, lines 1 and 4] all occurrences of the type symbol "s" should be replaced by occurrences of the type symbol "n^*".

each, say

$$*him = * + h'm$$
$$s/i \quad (i/(i/n))/((?)/i)$$
$$whom = w + h'm$$
$$(?)/i \quad (i/(i/n))/((?)/i) \,.$$

The reader will have no difficulty in verifying that the *whom*-sentence under consideration now receives type (?) as it should.

Some other type-assignments to *whom* will work equally well. Unfortunately they all have one defect in common: Certain non-sentences such as

Whom must John call and resign his job?

also receive type (?). If I am not mistaken, Chomsky can avoid the derivation of this non-sentence from

Must John call him and resign his job?

by stipulating that the transformation which introduces *and* must come after the transformation which introduces *whom*.

If we ignore the order of succession of transformation rules we would make this entry into our dictionary:

$$whom \rightarrow ((?)/i) + ((i/(i/n))/((?)/i)) \,.$$

The purpose of the plus sign is to indicate that the place occupied by it may be a phrase boundary.

But even if such clumsy type-assignments are admitted, there are still the "elliptical" transformation rules which cause difficulty, as for example the rule which allows us to drop the relative pronoun *whom* in *the man (whom) John must call today* $\cdots$. I don't see how such a rule could be incorporated into the dictionary, unless the first dictionary entry was a blank with the type of the relative pronoun *whom* assigned to it. The presence of such a blank in the dictionary would play havoc with our procedure for deciding whether a given string of English words can be bracketed to be a phrase of prescribed type.

I must confess that I am still in two minds about the usefulness of the syntactic calculus for the study of grammars of natural languages. I shall therefore let the above examples speak for themselves and refrain from drawing any conclusion.

Appendix I

We present the non-associative syntactic calculus as a deductive system Σ, beginning with the usual inventory.

Variables: $v_1, v_2, \cdots$.

Terms: All variables are terms.

If x and y are terms so are $(x \cdot y)$, $(x \backslash y)$, (x/y).
We shall make the usual convention for omitting brackets on the outside. Also we shall write xy for $x \cdot y$.

Formulas: $x \rightarrow y$, where x and y are terms.

Axiom scheme: $x \to x$.
Rules of inference:

$$\frac{xy \to z}{x \to z/y} \qquad\qquad \frac{xy \to z}{y \to x\backslash z}$$

$$\frac{x \to z/y}{xy \to z} \qquad\qquad \frac{y \to x\backslash z}{xy \to z}$$

$$\frac{x \to y \quad y \to x}{x \to z} \;.$$

For the purpose of describing a decision procedure for Σ we introduce a related system Σ_G which contains Σ. The terms of Σ_G will be called G-terms, to distinguish them from the terms of Σ.

G-terms: All terms are G-terms.

If X and Y are G-terms so is (X, Y).

G-formulas:[13] $X \to y$, X a G-term, y a term.

G-rules of inference:

$$\frac{T, y \to x}{T \to x/y} \qquad\qquad \frac{y, T \to x}{T \to y\backslash x}$$

$$\frac{T \to y \quad F(x) \to z}{F((x/y),\, T) \to z} \qquad\qquad \frac{T \to y \quad F(x) \to z}{F(T,\, (y\backslash x)) \to z}$$

$$\frac{P \to x \quad Q \to y}{P, Q \to xy} \;.$$

Cut-rule:

$$\frac{T \to x \quad F(x) \to y}{F(T) \to y} \;.$$

Here T, P, Q are arbitrary G-term. $F(X)$ represents a G-term in which X appears as a factor. By this we mean that $F(X) = X$ or $F(X) = G(X, T)$ or $F(X) = G(T, X)$ where $G(X)$ is a shorter G-term containing X as a factor.

With every G-term X there is associated a term x obtained from it by deleting all commas. Thus if X is $((v_1/v_2), v_2)$ then x is $((v_1/v_2)v_2)$. It is not difficult to prove the following:

METATHEOREM 1. $X \to y$ *is provable in* Σ_G *if and only* $x \to y$ *is provable in* Σ.

This is an fact an immediate consequence of the lemmas:

LEMMA 1.   *If all commas are deleted in any G-rule, including the cut-rule, we obtain a derived rule of inference of* Σ.

LEMMA 2.   *Every rule of inference in* Σ *is a derived rule of inference in* Σ_G.

The proofs of these two lemmas are much like the argument in [3, § 8]. The reader will easily supply the details.

COROLLARY. $x \to y$ *is provable in* Σ *if and only if it is provable in* Σ_G.

---

[13] The G-formulas are the non-associative analogues of the so-called "sequents" (*Folgen*) of Gentzen.

Here, for example are proofs of the formula $x \to (y/x)\backslash y$ in Σ and Σ_G:

$$\frac{\dfrac{y/x \to y/x}{(y/x)x \to y}}{x \to (y/x)\backslash y} \qquad\qquad \frac{x \to x \quad y \to y}{\dfrac{y/x,\, x \to y}{x \to (y/x)\backslash y}} \; .$$

By the *degree* of a G-term or G-formula we mean the total number of occurrences of the connectives $\cdot$, $/$ and $\backslash$ in it. Occurrences of the comma are not counted. Thus $((v_1/v_2)v_2)$ has degree 2, but $((v_1/v_2), v_2)$ has degree 1.

A glance at the G-rules other than the cut-rule shows that each such rule introduces an occurrence of one of the connectives $\cdot$, $/$, $\backslash$ into the conclusion and that the degree of the conclusion is larger than the sum of the degrees of the premises. It is now easily seen that we have a decision procedure for Σ_G without cut-rule, namely the method of seeking proofs by working backward from the conclusion.

METATHEOREM 2. *Any G-formula provable with cut-rule is also provable without cut-rule.*

To show this, we define the degree of a cut (instance of the cut-rule) as the sum of the degrees of $F(T)$, x and y. The result then follows from the lemma:

LEMMA 3. *In any cut whose premises have been proved without cut, the conclusion is either identical with one of the premises, or else the cut can be replaced by one or two cuts of smaller degree.*

To prove this we must investigate a large number of cases and subcases as in [3, §9]. In fact, the argument there goes over to the non-associative situation with minor changes. For example, let us consider Case 6 of [3, §9]: The last steps in the proofs of both premises introduce the main connective of $x = x'/x''$. It follows that $F(x)$ has the form $G(x, U)$ and we have:

$$\frac{\dfrac{T, x'' \to x'}{T \to x'/x''} \qquad \dfrac{U \to x'' \quad G(x') \to y}{G(x'/x'', U) \to y}}{G(T, U) \to y} \; .$$

This derivation may be replaced by

$$\frac{\dfrac{T, x'' \to x' \quad G(x') \to y}{U \to x'' \quad G(T, x'') \to y}}{G(T, U) \to y}$$

where both new cuts have smaller degree than the old cut.

COROLLARY 1. *Σ_G has a decision procedure.*

COROLLARY 2. *Σ has a decision procedure.*

This follows from Corollary 1 and Metatheorem 1.

Appendix II

The associative syntactic calculus also has application in mathematics. In multiplicative ideal theory AB, A/B and $B\backslash A$ may be interpreted as the product, right residual quotient and left residual quotient of the ideals A and B respectively. More interesting perhaps is the application to bimodules worked out by G. D. Findlay and the present author in 1956. Here is a necessarily abbreviated report of our work, which has never been published.

The idea is briefly this: Each proof of a formula in the associative syntactic calculus may be used to construct a canonical mapping between functors of bimodules built up from $\otimes$ and Hom. For example the proof of the formula $C/(AB) \to (C/B)/A$ from postulates (1) to (5) gives an explicit construction for the canonical mapping of $\mathrm{Hom}_T(A \otimes_S B, C)$ into $\mathrm{Hom}_S(A, \mathrm{Hom}_T(B, C))$, where $_RA_S$, $_SB_T$ and $_RC_T$ are given bimodules. The decision procedure for the associative syntactic calculus can then be used to find all canonical mappings from one functor into another.

It is convenient to assign a number to each proof in the associative syntactic calculus as follows. We recall that the axioms and rules of inference were labelled 1, 2, 2′, 3, 3′, 4, 4′ and 5. For the present purpose we shall replace the labels 2′, 3′ and 4′ by 20, 30 and 40 respectively.

(i)   The proof of an axiom (m), where $m = 1, 2$ or 20, has number m.

(ii)   If a formula is derived from a formula whose proof has number n by rule (m), where $m = 3, 30, 4$ or 40, the resulting proof has number mn.

(iii)   If a formula is derived by rule (5) from formulas whose proofs have numbers m and n, the resulting proof has number $5mn$.

For example, if t is short for $(x\backslash y)/z$, we have the following derivation

$$(5) \quad \cfrac{(20) \quad \cfrac{}{(xt)z \to x(tz)} \qquad (40) \quad \cfrac{(4) \quad \cfrac{(1) \quad \cfrac{}{t \to (x\backslash y)/z}}{tz \to x\backslash y}}{x(tz) \to y}}{(3) \quad \cfrac{(xt)z \to y}{(30) \quad \cfrac{xt \to y/z}{t \to x\backslash(y/z)}}}$$

The number of this proof is 3035204041.

Given the final conclusion of a proof, the number of the proof almost completely describes the proof, but not quite: Every time rule (5) is used, the so-called middle term y must be specified. This shortcoming disappears when we work with the associative analogue of Σ_G and avoid the cut-rule,

If $_RA_S$, $_SB_T$ and $_RC_T$ are bimodules, R, S and T being associative rings, we write

$$AB = A \otimes_S B, \quad C/B = \mathrm{Hom}_T(B, C), \quad A\backslash C = \mathrm{Hom}_R(A, C).$$

AB is an R-T-bimodule, C/B is an R-S-bimodule and $A\backslash C$ is an S-T-bimodule, in a natural fashion.

For expository purposes we shall from now on only consider R-R-bimodules, where R is fixed once and for all. If A and B are such, then so are AB,

A/B and $B\backslash A$. Note that the traditional notation fails to distinguish between A/B and $B\backslash A$. The class of canonical mappings is defined recursively as follows. We assume that $a \in A$, $b \in B$, $c \in C$.

$$\phi_1 : A \to A$$
$$\phi_1 a = a$$

$\phi_2 : (AB)C \to A(BC)$ $\qquad$ $\phi_{20} : A(BC) \to (AB)C$

$\phi_2 \Sigma(a \otimes b) \otimes c = \Sigma a \otimes (b \otimes c)$ $\qquad$ $\phi_{20} \Sigma a \otimes (b \otimes c) = \Sigma(a \otimes b) \otimes c$

If $\phi_n : AB \to C$ $\qquad\qquad\qquad$ If $\phi_n : AB \to C$

then $\phi_{3n} : A \to C/B$ $\qquad\qquad$ then $\phi_{30n} : B \to A\backslash C$

$(\phi_{3n}a)b = \phi_n(a \otimes b)$ $\qquad\qquad$ $a(\phi_{30n}b) = \phi_n(a \otimes b)$

If $\phi_n : A \to C/B$ $\qquad\qquad\quad$ If $\phi_n : B \to A\backslash C$

then $\phi_{4n} : AB \to C$ $\qquad\qquad$ then $\phi_{40n} : AB \to C$

$\phi_{4n} \Sigma a \otimes b = \Sigma(\phi_n a)b$ $\qquad\qquad$ $\phi_{40n} \Sigma a \otimes b = \Sigma a(\phi_{40n}b)$

If $\phi_m : A \to B$ and $\phi_n : B \to C$

then $\phi_{5mn} : A \to C$

$$\phi_{5mn} a = \phi_n(\phi_m a) .$$

This notation is not entirely unambiguous, e.g. the identity map of B into itself is also denoted by ϕ_1, but it will do.

It is now apparent that if n is the number of a proof of a formula $x \to y$ in the associative syntactic calculus, there is a corresponding canonical mapping $\phi_n : X \to Y$. One example should make this clear: We found that the formula $(x\backslash y)/z \to x\backslash(y/z)$ has a proof with number $n = 3035204041$. Consequently we should have a canonical mapping

$$\phi_n : (A\backslash B)/C \to A\backslash(B/C) .$$

Let $f \in (A\backslash B)/C$; then we compute

$$
\begin{aligned}
(a(\phi_{3035204041} f))c &= (\phi_{35204041}(a \otimes f))c \\
&= \phi_{5204041}((a \otimes f) \otimes c) \\
&= \phi_{4041}(\phi_{20}((a \otimes f) \otimes c)) \\
&= \phi_{4041}(a \otimes (f \otimes c)) \\
&= a(\phi_{41}(f \otimes c)) \\
&= a((\phi_1 f)c) \\
&= a(fc) .
\end{aligned}
$$

To see the meaning of this, let us return to the classical notation. Assume we have bimodules ${}_R A_S$, ${}_R B_T$ and ${}_U C_T$. (It is important that the subscripts match as indicated.) We have shown that there is a canonical mapping

$$\phi_n : \mathrm{Hom}_T(C, \mathrm{Hom}_R(A, B)) \to \mathrm{Hom}_R(A, \mathrm{Hom}_T(C, B))$$

given by

$$(a(\phi_n f))c = a(fc) .$$

This is of course what one would have expected.

The decision procedure for the associative syntactic calculus given in [3] can be used to find all canonical mappings (according to our recursive definition of "canonical") from one functor into another. However, this decision procedure operates not on formulas $x \to y$ but on "sequents" $x_1, x_2, \cdots, x_n \to y$. These are the associative analogues of the G-formulas of Appendix I. The suggested method for finding canonical mappings therefore does not deal with mappings $\phi : A \to B$ directly but with multilinear mappings $\emptyset : A_1 \times A_2 \times \cdots \times A_n \to B$. It has already been observed by Bourbaki[14] that linear mappings of the kind we are interested in are best defined with the help of multilinear mappings. The details are too technical to be given here, but an example may help the interested reader to reconstruct the general method.

A proof of the formula $(a\backslash b)/c \to a\backslash(b/c)$ using the decision procedure of [3] looks like this:

$$
\frac{\dfrac{a \to a \quad b \to b}{a, a\backslash b \to b} \qquad c \to c}{\dfrac{a, (a\backslash b)/c, c \to b}{\dfrac{a, (a\backslash b)/c \to b/c}{(a\backslash b)/c \to a\backslash(b/c)}}} \quad .
$$

We interpret this proof in terms of mappings:

1. From the identity mappings $A \to A$ and $B \to B$ one derives the multilinear mapping

$$\emptyset : A \times \mathrm{Hom}_R(A, B) \to B$$

defined by

$$\emptyset(a, g) = ag ,$$

where $a \in A$ and $g \in \mathrm{Hom}_R(A, B)$.

2. From this and the identity mapping $C \to C$ one derives the multilinear mapping

$$\emptyset' : A \times \mathrm{Hom}_T(C, \mathrm{Hom}_R(A, B)) \times C \to B ,$$

where

$$\emptyset'(a, f, c) = \emptyset(a, fc) = a(fc) ,$$

for $c \in C$, $f \in \mathrm{Hom}_T(C, \mathrm{Hom}_R(A, B))$.

3. From this one derives

$$\emptyset'' : A \times \mathrm{Hom}_T(C, \mathrm{Hom}_R(A, B)) \to \mathrm{Hom}_T(C, B) ,$$

defined by

$$(\emptyset''(a, f))c = \emptyset'(a, f, c) = a(fc) .$$

4. From this one derives the mapping

$$\phi : \mathrm{Hom}_T(C, \mathrm{Hom}_R(A, B)) \to \mathrm{Hom}_R(A, \mathrm{Hom}_T(C, B))$$

defined by

$$a((\phi f)c) = (\emptyset''(a, f))c = a(fc) .$$

ϕ is the canonical mapping we were expecting.

[14] See N. Bourbaki, *Algèbre multilinéaire*, Paris, Hermann, 1948.

REFERENCES[15]

1. N. Chomsky, *Syntactic structures*, The Hague, Mouton and Company, 1957.

2. ———, *On certain formal properties of grammars*, Information and Control vol. 2 (1959) pp. 137–167.

3. J. Lambek, *The mathematics of sentence structure*, Amer. Math. Monthly vol. 65 (1958) pp. 154–169.

4. ———, *Contributions to a mathematical analysis of the English verb-phrase*, J. Canad. Ling. Assoc. vol. 5 (1959) pp. 83–89.

INSTITUTE FOR ADVANCED STUDY,
PRINCETON, NEW JERSEY

---

[15] Further references may be found in [3].

GENETIC RELATIONSHIP AMONG LANGUAGES[1]

BY

H. A. GLEASON, JR.

That certain pairs of languages show relationships has long been known. Comparative linguistics arose to explain and exploit these relationships. It has developed methods of some power and achieved some important results. However, comparative linguistics has been characterized in recent years by rather scant discussion of theoretical and methodological questions. In the meantime demand for its results is increasing rapidly (e. g. by anthropologists) and the possibility of new departures in method has arisen. I propose to formulate a part of its basic theory in such a way that it can be tied in intimately with certain developing methods which may fall within the purview of this symposium.

1. We can assume that resemblances between languages can be of at least four origins: 1. They may be reflections of certain *language universals*. Thus it is commonly assumed that the rather frequent occurrence of items like [mama] for 'mother' may be conditioned in some way by some general feature of the process of language learning. 2. They may be *analytic artifacts*. That both Latin and English are considered to have a present tense may be due to the fact that Latin provided the model for English grammar. The English "present tense" was established on a scant basis under the strong stimulus of the model. Field linguists aim at describing a language in terms of its own structure. They never quite succeed, and occasionally they fail miserably. Similarities in their results can be mere reflections of their methods or their prejudices. 3. Resemblances may be the result of mere *chance*. 4. Similarities may result from *historic connections* between the languages. Linguists commonly distinguish, sometimes rather too sharply, between two subtypes: inheritance and borrowing. Thus the similarity between English *father* and Latin *pater* is an inheritance similarity, since both are assumed to have a direct and continuous descent from a generally similar word in the ancient language (proto-Indo-European) from which English and Latin both descend. *Paternity* and *paternitas* show a borrowing similarity, since we know that the English word is derived directly from the Latin.

The interest and usefulness of these four classes of resemblances are quite different, and the first task of the comparativist must be to distinguish them as clearly as possible and assign observed resemblances to the proper type. Resemblances rooted in language universals are of great interest in developing a general theory of language, but of little specific historical significance. Analytic artifacts are of little or no linguistic interest, but their control is of crucial importance in any careful comparative work. This can be accomplished by critique of sources, which, though commonly neglected and seldom discussed, is one of the essential techniques of comparative linguistics.

[1] This work is supported in part by the National Science Foundation.

Chance resemblances are of no interest, except as the linguist wishes to learn better how to recognize them and to exclude them from further consideration. Since they may bulk large, statistical techniques may be of considerable importance. Similarities due to historic connection are of great interest, since they can yield evidence from which historical reconstructions can be made. In practice, comparative linguistics restricts itself largely to attempting to identify and interpret similarites due to historic connection. It therefore marches closely on historical linguistics, and these commonly become almost indistinguishable.

2. Comparative linguistic work normally starts with vocabulary. This is most simply done by matching word lists on the basis of glosses for the several items in some third language. Thus we might compare Lamba[2] *iŋgoma* with Ganda *eŋŋoma* on the basis that they occur in the word lists opposite the English gloss 'drum'. In any pair of word lists some word pairs may be resemblant, as that just cited. But there will also always be non-resemblant pairs at Lamba *inyati*, Ganda *embogo* 'buffalo'. Comparative linguistics, in the preliminary stages, concerns itself only with those word-pairs that are in some sense resemblant.

Linguists have commonly been uneasy about relying on vocabulary. They consider vocabulary to be the least significant part of a language. It may be very unstable and vary widely from speaker to speaker and situation to situation. Phonology and grammar are more central. Yet there are certain crucial advantages of vocabulary over other sectors of language for comparative work. 1. Vocabulary items are relatively easily found and easily stated. 2. There can readily be obtained a sizeable sample of word pairs (or glosses that will produce word pairs) which come close to being independent of each other. This is possible because the vocabulary of a language is only partially structured. It is rather easy to avoid items likely to be structurally connected, or to detect and discard them when they do appear. Other sectors of language are more tightly structured, and the connections are sometimes less easily seen, so that statistically usable samples are very much harder to obtain. This either immensely complicates statistical reasoning or renders it impossible. Hence it is difficult to detect chance resemblances in other more central sectors of language. 3. Gloss lists can be selected in such a way as to bias our results in certain desirable ways. For example, word resemblances due to language universals are particularly common in a few specific meanings (e. g. child words for parents) and apparently negligible elsewhere. By eliminating such glosses, this source of resemblances can be minimized to the point of insignificance, and hence be safely overlooked in preliminary comparative work. Or again, the balance in frequency between similarities due to inheritance and those due to borrowing can be quite different in different sectors of the vocabulary. A list of glosses likely to produce a maximum proportion of inheritance similarities and a minimum of borrowing

---

[2] Lamba and Ganda forms are from: C. M. Doke, *English-Lamba vocabulary*, 1933; E. O. Ashton, E. M. K. Mulira, E. G. M. Ndawula and A. N. Tucker, *A luGanda grammar*, 1954.

similarities is known as the "basic vocabulary." This is the result of no mystic property of any otherwise definable set of items, but merely a statement of cumulated past experience. Using such a gloss list, the finding of pairs similar by inheritance is greatly facilitated. Using a strongly "non-basic vocabulary," the other type may emerge more clearly. Using the two contrastively may differentiate the two types quite sharply.[3]

3. Starting with a set of word-pairs drawn largely from the "basic vocabulary," the linguist attempts to sort out word-pairs that seem likely to be resemblant because of inheritance. He does this by attempting to find a set of criteria of similarity which is of the appropriate kind and so tight that it will pass relatively few word-pairs showing merely chance similarity, but which will, nevertheless, pass a considerable number of word-pairs. If this can be found it is said to define the word-pairs as *cognates*. The criteria themselves are stateable in terms of a set of equations known as *correspondences*. A correspondence is a statement that in a certain environment a given phoneme in one language will correspond—if the words are cognate—to a stated phoneme in another language. Thus Lamba *o* corresponds under most conditions to Ganda *o*. Lamba *g* corresponds to Ganda ŋ when and only when it follows ŋ and precedes some nasal (e. g. *m*) later in the same word. Lamba *iŋgoma* is said to be cognate with Ganda *eŋʒoma* because every phoneme in each matches a phoneme in the other by some such rule, the order being preserved. (In other instances the order may be deformed in some regular and stateable manner.) Lamba *inyati* and Ganda *embogo* are not cognate because for most of the phonemes no such correspondences can be established.

The first step in comparative linguistics, then, after a sample of word-pairs has been obtained is to find in it a set of cognates and a set of correspondences, each characterizing and defining the other. Traditionally this has been done by inspection and re-inspection, guess and check, by a competent and experienced linguist. The work may be tedious and exacting.

4. Operational criteria used in discovering correspondences and cognates are manifold, but most fall into two general types. The first of these may be called *phonetic plausibility*. In some cases this means nothing more than merely sounding alike. For example, anyone who knows both English and German is inevitably aware of certain word-pairs which sound much alike. Such are possible cognates, and on further investigation some, but not all, pairs will prove actually to be cognates. On a more sophisticated level, phonetic plausibility may also serve to identify certain pairs of sounds as possible correspondences which are not phonetically similar. There are many known cases of *k* (i.e., *k* in some proto-language) becoming by regular change č, š, *s* or *g*, or remaining *k*. Any two of these resultant sounds might, as a matter of phonetic plausibility, be considered as a possible correspondence since they might be derivable from *k*. Occasionally, cases that an experienced linguist would call phonetically plausible seem to the layman quite unlikely.

---

[3] An excellent discussion of a closely related problem can be found in: I. Dyen, *The Ngaju-Dayak 'Old Speech Stratum'*, Lg. 32: 83–87, 1956.

Thus Nyoro[4] -*gita* and Sotho -*fura* 'fat, oil', I would judge to be phonetically plausible, however unlike they may seem to the average observer.

In any but the most superficial type, phonetic plausibility may be a very complex matter. It is in essence a distillation of the linguist's experience, personal and second hand, with a wide variety of languages. In the case just cited, it includes a certain amount of knowledge not only of language in general, but also of Bantu languages in particular: that *f* may correspond to velar stops, that *i* and *u* may interchange in the situations in which *f* does so correspond, that in some languages voice is historically of no significance where the next syllable has *t*, and that *t* and *r* may correspond. It follows that any precise formulation of phonetic plausibility may be quite difficult, though certain gross features may be so stated. The fullest use of the criteria of phonetic plausibility must, for some time, remain the function of a trained, experienced and imaginative linguist.

5.   The second general type of criterion is that of *recurrence*. Traditionally this has not been handled particularly well. The usual procedure is to go through a pair of word lists and select all those word-pairs which look interesting. These are selected in part on the basis of phonetic plausibility, and in part on the basis of recurrence of phoneme-pairs. After this subjectively selected sample has been gathered, it is then examined carefully for recurrences, and those which are found are considered as tentative correspondences. These are checked by another, more complex type of recurrence which can be designated as *co-occurrence*. If such tentative correspondences are found together in the same word-pairs in such a way that they account for all or nearly all of the phonemes of the words, they are considered established. This is a rather stringent requirement, and only this stringency saves much traditional comparative work from being seriously misled.

Both types of recurrence can be used in a more satisfactory way. But this will require the examination of samples of word-pairs which are statistically acceptable. This means, at least, that they must not be selected on the basis of what phoneme-pairs they contain. Criteria of recurrence should, therefore, be applied *before* rather than *after* criteria of phonetic plausibility. Since this application is basically a matter of counting within a sample and some rather elementary calculation, the criteria of recurrence can be applied by machine. There is thus the possibility that at least a major segment of the work of finding the cognates and correspondences can be programmed onto computers. To do so may expedite the work. But more important, such programming may make better use of certain criteria and thus actually improve the reliability of the procedures. In any case it will render parts, at least, of the work easily checkable.

6.   In 1954 I found myself maneuvered into arguing that comparative reconstruction could be done by machine. This was a bit against my better judgment, but nevertheless it led me to make some tentative experiments.

---

[4] Nyoro and Sotho forms are from: M. B. Davis, *A lu Nyoro-lu Nyankole-English and English-lu Nyoro-lu Nyankole dictionary*, 1952, A. Mabille and H. Dieterlen, *Southern Sotho-English dictionary*, rev. ed., 1950.

The first of these was rather elaborately designed and involved a great deal of statistical calculation. It worked, but chiefly it indicated that a much simpler procedure would suffice. After five experiments, the first report was given before the Yale Linguistics Club in 1955.[5] Since that time the method has been applied to a number of other pairs of languages. Certain complications have been found, and some of them successfully met, and the technique has been improved in a number of details. These experiments were not restricted to one group of languages, but have involved, so far, Mayan, Bantu, Dravidian, Indic, and Romance languages.

All of the experiments have been done by hand-sorting. But throughout, the aim has been to design a procedure which can be fully programmed in advance, and which will, therefore, meet at least one requirement for a machine. Actual machine programming is probably now feasible, and presumably will soon be attempted.

As it now stands, the procedure does not do reconstruction, but it does do a major part of the work of finding cognates and correspondences. The input is a number (preferably over 500) of word-pairs matched by having similar glosses. The process sorts these word-pairs into three sets. One of these consists of word-pairs with extremely high probability of being cognates and establishing a set of correspondences of similar very high probability. Typically, this set is defined by having *every* phoneme in *every* word-pair accounted for in terms of one of the correspondences, and *every* correspondence recurring at least three times in the set. This is an extremely strong condition. As a result the set can be considered so thoroughly established that it requires no further attention until a very much later stage of the comparison. Even then the expectation is that very little emendation will be required. A second set consists of word pairs showing so little prospect of being historically connected as to warrant no expenditure of effort until a very much later stage in the comparison. Even then it is highly unlikely that more than a very few pairs will ever be of any historical interest. The third set consists of word-pairs which show some evidence of being interesting, but which fall short of being established as cognates by the very stringent criteria through which the first set was selected. (Most match in part by the same correspondences as define the first set, but do not match throughout.) These need and warrant the attention of an experienced linguist. He will ordinarily be able to justify treating many of them as cognates with little trouble, since he can apply to them additional criteria not easily built into the machine program. Of those which cannot immediately be shown to be cognates, many will present problems of potentially great interest.

One experiment[6] will serve as an example. This started with 329 word-pairs in Jacaltec and Tzutuhil, two Mayan languages of Guatemala. The procedure divided this sample into three sets: 1.59 word-pairs, each of which

<hr />

[5] H. A. Gleason, Jr. *A procedural technique for comparative reconstruction.* This paper has recently been duplicated and is available for limited distribution.

[6] This is the experiment reported on at the Yale Linguistics Club. The languages are quite closely related; otherwise a starting sample of only 329 word-pairs might not have been adequate.

matched throughout in terms of 25 correspondences. Each correspondence was found in at least 3 word-pairs in the 59. One of these was ṣanab šaxap' 'sandal'. The correspondence ṣ š occurs in 5 word-pairs in the set; a a in 32; n x in 5; b p' in 6. These cognates and correspondences form a core of firmly established items for any further work.   2. A set of word-pairs which largely match by these established correspondences, but not entirely.   Among them was q'ab q'aʔ 'arm', included because q' q' and a a were both firmly established by recurrence in the first set (in 10 and 32 word-pairs respectively), but b ʔ was found in only two otherwise acceptable word-pairs. This, and many others, the linguist will feel adequately justified in accepting as cognates, even though they fall outside the definitions set up for the mechanical procedures.   It also includes some word-pairs like ṣil šilšil 'cricket', in which ṣil šil would be totally matched. The linguist will have to judge whether the process of reduplication can appropriately be inserted into the rules relating cognates in these two languages.   3. A set of word-pairs approximately two-thirds of the original sample, in which none of these established correspondences are found, or where only one or two are found, and which accordingly show very little prospect of being cognate.   Included are items such as ṣoç t'ot' 'snail' and xolom waʔ 'head'.

What the mechanical procedure accomplishes, then, is to organize the raw data into such a form as to allow maximum efficiency in the utilization of trained linguistic manpower.   It is not wasted by being applied to pairs which can be firmly established without it, or which show no prospects of being established by it, but can be concentrated on those only which show the sort of problems which require its special abilities.

7. The procedure operates by tabulating phoneme pairs at some position (usually initial) from the whole sample of word-pairs in a contingency table. Those phoneme-pairs in which observed frequency exceeds expected frequency are taken to indicate the possible presence of cognates, and all word-pairs showing them are selected.   The process is repeated within this smaller sample using the phoneme-pairs in some other position (say post-initial). After a number of such selections (three seems in most cases the most feasible), all pairs in the selected sample are checked, and the rejected part of the sample is gone through for word-pairs that partially match.   The correspondences are thus set up by recurrence in the same word-pairs.

An example[7] will show the effect of this.   A set of word-pairs from Tamil and Kannada was put through the process.   Afterwards every word-pair was checked by a Dravidian specialist who gave a judgment on each.   He labeled 27% as cognates without complications, 12% as cognate with complications, 10% as loans (mostly from Sanskrit), 50% as unrelated, and 1% as unassignable.   In the experiment the disposition of each pair at each step had been noted.   This permitted an analysis of the effect of each selection:

---

[7] This experiment was reported on in full before the Linguistic Summer School at Dehra Dun, India in 1957. I am indebted to Dr. Bh. Krishnamurti of Andhra University for the classification of the word-pairs.

	Number in sample	Simple Cognates	Unrelated
Original	714	27%	50%
After 1st sorting	360	50	17
After 2nd sorting	263	57	6
After 3rd sorting	143	79	0
After checking	100	95	0

Each step raised the percentage of simple cognates and lowered that of unrelated words. When the final selection was reached, all unrelated words had been excluded, but five non-cognates remained. These were common loans from Sanskrit which had been borrowed so early as to have undergone all applicable phonologic changes in the two languages. They, therefore, showed exactly the same relationship to their matches as inherited native words. For this reason they could be identified as loans only by certain additional information not provided to the machine (i.e., a knowledge of Sanskrit), and the machine would, therefore, be entirely correct in accepting them as cognates. We may consider the experiment a success. The remaining simple cognates (48% of those in the original sample), the complicated cognates, and the remaining loans, were mostly in the set selected to receive the linguist's attention. The finally rejected set consisted almost wholly of unrelated word-pairs.

8. The traditional approach starts with a more or less random searching for interesting-looking word-pairs. An experienced linguist can make effective use of any sort of dictionary, or any sort of word-list, matching a French gloss in one with a German gloss in another, or matching more or less synonymous but different glosses. He can detect similarities of part of one word with part of another, leaving the justification of this to a later step. The mechanical procedure starts by matching two word-lists. This is efficient only when there is a considerable amount of standardization in the glosses and their arrangement. In many languages, it is of utmost importance that affixes have been removed, and the forms of entry standardized. Much of the raw material usable under traditional procedures cannot be used in the mechanical technique except after rather laborious preparation. This is at the present time a very serious bottle-neck.

The second difficulty is that the procedure will not, at present, operate in all the situations in which it might be desirable. Since the program I have been using makes no use of phonetic plausibility, and since it applies the criteria of recurrence more strictly than traditional procedures, it is not surprising that it will not handle languages very remote from one another—languages where the evidence of relationship is rather scant and unobvious. Some will consider this a serious defect, but to do so is to be too severe. There is a tremenduous quantity of such low-level work which needs to be done, and any small increase in efficiency may be decidedly worthwhile. This is particularly true in larger language families, since the labor of list preparation increases arithmetically with the number of languages, but the labor of comparison geometrically. Moreover, the present limitations of the method are not necessarily permanent. Certain types of phonetic plausibility could be built in—particularly those dealing with simple phonetic similarities, or with symmetries. Some more complex matching procedures can be developed.

9. Each cognate and each correspondence can be assumed to be of some evidential value for past language conditions in the group. Some at least of these features will contribute to the reconstruction of certain parts of a proto-language from which all the languages of the group may be assumed to have been descended. This immediately transforms the nature of the investigation from a synchronic comparison of languages to a diachronic reconstruction of history. Such reconstruction is generally the first objective beyond the mere finding of cognates and correspondences. However, another operation, usually left implicit, must intervene before successful reconstruction can proceed.

10. Reconstruction implies some framework within which to operate. Two models of language development are commonly contrasted. One, the *Wave hypothesis*, envisions any period in the history of a language family in terms of an array of contiguous speech forms subject to various mutual influences by which innovations anywhere in the whole area may diffuse, but only in stateable ways. The reconstruction of history would then be the reconstruction of one or more of these earlier stages and, from examination of the results of diffusion, the analysis of the relationships between the speech forms that controlled those processes. Such a model seems to have a very considerable similarity to empiric reality. But it provides us with no very clear operating procedures for the initial stages of reconstruction. The factors are too many and too complex. It seems very nearly impossible to derive results which are not, in most instances, highly ambiguous, and inaccessible to procedural checks.

11. A second model, the *Stammbaum hypothesis*, envisions the history of a language family as involving a number of splits. These are generally dichotomous, and have the effect of replacing one language by two, each of which is a continuation of the one replaced, and each of which thereafter proceeds to develop independently. This is certainly the less obvious of the two models. Sharp separations are rarely observed, and total independence of adjacent languages seems almost inconceivable. But in spite of these difficulties, it is this model which provides operational procedures for the initial stages of reconstruction that prove workable and productive. Perhaps this paradox stems from the fact that in the preliminary stages of historical reconstruction we deal only with selected segments of language—precisely those segments which do work most nearly in the Stammbaum way—though on general examination of any language situation we are impressed most easily by the segments of languages which operate most nearly in the Wave hypothesis way. In any case, it does not seem that the two hypotheses are ultimately contradictory, since in actual practice each seems inevitably to require correction by the other.

12. The Stammbaum hypothesis is, then, the best basis—possibly the only

workable basis—for the earliest stage of historical reconstruction. It provides a clear basis for my statement above that *some* cognate pairs may be of evidential value in reconstructing a proto-language behind any language group. The Stammbaum model sets up a language family in terms of a series of branchings, preferably dichotomous. Just beneath each branching is a proto-language. This proto-language is accessible to the linguist in two ways: By comparison of languages in each of the two branches above it, and by comparison of a language above it with a language (necessarily a proto-language) below it. Every cognate pair in the ultimate languages is evidence for some proto-language, but direct evidence for only one, i.e., that at the convergence point of the two branches. Only certain ones are therefore of evidential value for the deepest proto-language. False reconstruction can only be avoided by assigning each pair of cognates to the correct proto-language. This can in turn be done if a workable Stammbaum is found, and the processes of finding that Stammbaum and making the assignments are practically synonymous.

It follows that the reconstruction of a proto-language is not, as it is commonly formulated to be, the next step after finding cognates. Rather the next step must be the finding of a most probable genetic tree. Comparative linguistics needs procedures for this task. It is interesting to note that there has probably been less publication on this subject and less discussion in textbooks or linguistics courses of this process that any of the other steps in reconstruction. This has been the most poorly understood and least adequately-handled stage in the work.

13. The evidence for selecting a suitable Stammbaum might reasonably be looked for in the same place that the evidence for over-all relationship is found: in comparable word-lists. The requirements are the same as mentioned above. In particular, we want an appreciable sample, the individual items of which show considerable statistical independence. Much of the work has, in fact, traditionally been done with vocabulary, often by superficial inspection. It can be made more precise by counting and some elementary calculation. All such methods—there are several of them—can be designated as *lexicostatistical*.

The simplest, of course, is simply to count similarities and differences. The assumption seems natural that the common proto-language will be later for two languages with more similarities than for two languages with less. In some instances this may suffice to draw a Stammbaum. Recently the assumption has been advanced that with a certain section of the "basic vocabulary" there is a reasonable constant and empirically determinable change rate. This is the method of *glottochronology*.[8] It merely adds an approximate temporal dimensioning to the Stammbaum. The method was suggested by an analogy to C_{14} dating. But this analogy is not correct. The decay rate for each C_{14} atom may be considered identical with the average for all such

---

[8] Glottochronology was first developed by Morris Swadesh on the basis of suggestions going back to Edward Sapir. The history and theory are now conveniently summarized, with a full bibliography, in: D. H. Hymes, *Lexicostatistics so far*, Current Anthropology 1: 5–44, 1960.

atoms. But the decay rates of different items in the basic vocabulary vary widely.[9] The rate for the whole is an arithmetic average. It cannot be handled simply in an exponential equation. Glottochronologic dates tend to heavy errors (underestimations) when the time is appreciably greater than that (about a millenium) for which the device was calibrated. But this can presumably be corrected. The technique needs a great deal more careful testing,[10] and particularly a better theoretic undergirding than it has had. It seems, however, certainly to have sufficient merit to warrant this work.

14. In a recent paper[11] I suggested two additional lexicostatistical methods. One of these may be nothing more than a convenient rule of thumb procedure. The other, however, is of some interest. It consists of counting, for any pair of languages, those instances where a word-pair is not cognate but where each has a cognate outside the pair. A minimum is taken to indicate immediate relationship (i.e., connection through one tri-junction only). Given four languages, it does not distinguish between the following five genetic trees:

On examination it is found that these are topologically equivalent, and collectively represent one of three ways to connect four labeled end-points through tri-junctions:

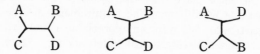

There are $1 \cdot 3 \cdot 5 \cdots (2n - 5)$ such distinct ways of connecting any n languages, and the technique selects one of these. Each represents $2n - 3$ genetic trees in the more familiar sense. The genetic trees in each such set differ only in the point at which the proto-language connects. From a linguistic point of view, this may be a crucial difference, of course. But generally speaking other methods will suffice to make this distinction clearly.

That this method should produce a totally non-metric result suggests a re-examination of the assumptions on which it operates. It turns out that not only is there no assumption about rate, but there is none about time in

[9] M. Swadesh, *Towards greater accuracy in lexicostatistical dating*, IJAL 21: 121–137, 1955.

[10] D. D. Thomas, *Basic vocabulary in some Mon-Khmer languages.* Anthropological Linguistics 2 (3): 7–11, 1960. This represents the first attempt to broaden the basis of calibration beyond the limited number of cases where an ancestral language is available. More of this sort of work is urgently required.

[11] H. A. Gleason, Jr. *Counting and calculating for historical reconstruction*, Anthoropological Linguistics 1 (2): 22–32, 1959.

any form. The widespread criticism of glottochronology has centered about the assumption of a constant rate of change. With this criticism in the background it is interesting to note that rate assumptions are not at all universal in lexicostatistics. Those methods other than glottochronology which do have some assumption of rate of change have generally rather weak assumptions. It follows lexicostatistics as a whole will not fall if glottochronology should prove to be untenable.

In actual practice it is comparatively simple to tabulate for all the pairs in a moderate-sized language family the information from which these several types of lexicostatistical calculations can be made. With a suitable machine it would be entirely feasible even for large language families. Actual experiments have been rather limited so for, but it does seem that all three lexicostatistical methods are of value. They have not been found to give contradictory results. Under certain circumstances one will give a clear answer where the others are ambiguous.

15. In the sequence of procedures running from an input of suitable word-lists to an output of reasonably firm first reconstruction, two important steps can be programmed onto computers. There remain steps which must be handled in more traditional ways, but even these are greatly expedited by better organization of the material. There is a possibility that the programmable portions of total procedure may be expanded somewhat, and that they may be made more powerful. It seems, now, in principle possible to greatly increase the production of certain kinds of historical linguistic results. Various details of the operation remain to be designed or improved but this seems clearly possible. If the challenge of making available sufficient data of suitable quality and form can be met, we may have a greatly improved tool for the uncovering of history.

HARTFORD SEMINARY FOUNDATION,
    HARTFORD, CONNECTICUT

ON THE THEORY OF WORD FREQUENCIES AND ON RELATED MARKOVIAN MODELS OF DISCOURSE

BY

BENOIT MANDELBROT

Abstract. This paper is principally devoted to a variety of topics related to our model for the law of word frequencies of Estoup and Zipf. Earlier synchronic interpretations of the model will only be sketched, for purposes of easy reference. More space will be devoted to showing that the model can also be reworded in diachronic terms and these considerations will be emphasized by being treated first, although the synchronic approaches seem preferable.

We shall then devote a section to a criticism of certain attempts to apply the lognormal probability distribution to data on word frequencies. The final section will be devoted to a discussion of the scope of the term "linguistics", with special emphasis being placed upon the role of statistical laws and of other enumerational laws, such as Willis' species-genera relationship.

0. Introduction. It is well-known how easily a simple and economic theory may transform an empirical law from something quite amazing and difficult to believe into something almost obvious, within the framework of some more general set of scientific considerations. It seems that such is already the fate of certain laws of what we have proposed to call "macro-linguistics": the *statistical relationship between "rank" and frequency* for natural words in ordinary discourse, and the *relationship between species and genera* in natural taxonomies. Let us recall that these laws were discovered by J. Estoup [3] and J. Willis [18], respectively, but (together with many similar considerations) were made well-known by the publications of G. Zipf [20]. Our own models for these laws were published since 1951 and their essentially final form was given before 1957,[1] but was not fully published at that time.

The present paper will be principally devoted to a variety of new topics relative to the rank-frequency relationship, that is, the relationship which exists between the frequency of a word and the rank it occupies in the ordering of all the words in a sample by decreasing frequencies. Let W_r be the

---

[1] Naturally, the term "final form" applies only to our own contribution to this problem. We do not want to exclude the possibility of entirely different explanations, other than further reinterpretations of one of our central arguments. However, we do not believe that the model suggested by H. A. Simon provides a useful alternative to ours (see references [17; 8], and a further paper to appear soon in Information and Control).

A nonmathematical account of our theory, incomplete but only slightly outdated otherwise, has appeared in reference [6]. That paper also gives a bibliography of our mathematical publications on the law of Estoup-Zipf; unfortunately these articles are unaccessible and mostly out of date. At the present time, a pretty complete picture of our work on word frequencies is provided by the present paper together with reference [7] and Chapter 2 of reference [6]. Concerning our theory of the law of Willis, see reference [5] and Chapter 3 of reference [6]. We regret that the pressure of time did not allow us to polish the present paper into a more definitive form.

190

word which occupies the rth position in this ordering and let $p(r)$ be its frequency of occurrence in a long sample of discourse. The most surprising fact is of course that a relation between r and $p(r)$ exists at all. It is not quite a universal relationship, in that it depends upon a few parameters; but, if these parameters are known, one may predict the value of $p(r)$, without knowing which word actually occupies the rth rank in the sample being investigated: one has $p(r) = (B-1)V^{B-1}(r+V)^{-B}$, where B and V are constants.

Our earlier models of the $p(r)$ law were synchronic, that is, were relative to samples of discourse long enough to allow one to speak of probabilities as limits of frequencies and short enough to allow one to assume that these probabilities have not changed between the beginning and the end of the sample. One must assume that these requirements are satisfied with samples of the usually available length (the same thing must be assumed for grammatical laws). The form of the law $p(r)$ must then be explained on the basis of some "instantaneous" properties of the mechanism generating the words. Indeed, the rank-frequency relationship was shown (broadly speaking) to be very closely linked with the so-called "finite-state" model of discourse, which is itself essentially the same thing as a finite Markov chain, that is, mainly a sequence of events ruled by chance in which the after-effects of events die out rapidly. Several authors have pointed out how curious it is that this stochastic scheme was precisely first introduced by Markov as a model of natural linguistic discourse. However, it then went into a long period of oblivion as such, until it was revived by Claude Shannon in his *Information theory* [16] and applied by us to the present linguistic problem.

In the simplest markovian scheme, a text is regarded as being a sequence of words obtained by successive independent drawings from a population characterized by the fixed set of probabilities $p(r)$. Suppose moreover that letters (which include "space": this is a very important feature) are themselves generated by a simple markovian mechanism: for example, suppose that successive letters are chosen independently from each other or that the letter which occupies a given position in the text is chosen by a chance mechanism which depends at most upon the letters (already known) which occupy the few preceding positions. *Then, the law $p(r)$ relative to the words will take the form required by the law of Estoup-Zipf.* There are many formally equivalent ways of expressing the same property, as we shall recall in § 3.

However, stated in such terms, the "finite-state" model appears as rather shocking because of the well-known existence of some long-range influences in discourse, such as those studied by grammar. There are two principal ways out of this difficulty. One is to destroy all properties not linked to the law $p(r)$ by considering only every tenth word (say) of a long continuing sample. The other way out conforms more closely to actual grammatical structure, by acknowledging that the "degree of validity" of the finite state model (whatever this means, exactly) decreases as the "wealth" of grammatical structure increases. For example, in texts of children and of some psychopaths, there is little or no long-range grammatical constraint; it is then not at all surprising that the predictions of the finite-state model could be satisfied. As the degree of grammatical constraint increases, the quality of the predictions of a finite state model becomes a little better than was really expected. Finally, in cases where there is a very strong long-range structure (which may be grammatical but is more likely to refer to the metric of poetry), one has no reason to expect that the predictions of a finite state model have any validity. However, it seems difficult to construct reasonable stochastic models to take account of effects that are synchronic but go beyond interactions between immediately neighboring symbols.

Besides the grammatical constraints, there are at least two additional reasons why the stationary time series model cannot be strictly true. First of all, the frequencies of those words, which express the topic discussed in a text, undergo fluctuations that surely exceed those predicted by the laws of stationary processes. But such words are sufficiently few to be used by H. P. Luhn as a manageable summary of the concept of "topic", for purposes of mechanical abstraction of scientific articles. Besides, data are non-existent on this account, and we shall have to neglect this difficulty. (See Appendix B.)

On the other hand, any set of rules, whether grammatical, or statistical, may appear to be in a steady state when observed on a short enough time scale and hence appear to be in equilibrium and properly constitute a "system". But, when it is observed during a longer time period, one may find that it changes as a result of influences which were already initially present. The best of all possible words would prevail, insofar as statistical laws are concerned, if they satisfied the synchronic criteria and in the same time were invariant with respect to the laws of diachronic change. We have been able to achieve such a compatible combination of synchronic and diachronic models. In fact, these models are all entirely equivalent, from the formal mathematical point of view, so that they involve exactly equally strong assumptions. However, they appeal to quite different kinds of "intuition" or of "feeling of reasonableness", and we have no doubt that different readers will choose different models as being the most "explicative". We are well beyond the stage where we could express a preference. (We can only stress the fact that the "diachrony" which we shall study still corresponds to periods during which the parameter B, as defined below, remains invariant.)

Under the circumstances, a great deal of the original great interest in "Zipf's laws" is bound to be transferred to the examination of the possible discrepancies between the actually observed empirical facts and the predictions of the theories. This amounts to the examination of the validity of the markovian model used in this context. Such a conclusion may seem disappointing to many, because Zipf's laws are essentially the only kind of undisputable enumerational property of discourse and one had hopes of drawing more far-reaching conclusions from them.

As things stand, one of the most striking features of these laws refers to method rather than to content. They can be explained by following the time-honored procedure of physical models: one starts from assumptions having the following features: a) they are not absurd or unbelievable but are obviously simplifying so that they can be manipulated analytically, and b) they seem to have far less content than the actual properties of discourse but are not so devoid of content as to be true in any case (one can easily draw counter-examples to these assumptions). From such a point of departure, one finally arrives to the prediction of entirely non-obvious properties of discourse. Disappointingly, we know of very few other examples of applications of this method in linguistics.[2]

The question then arises very sharply of the place of the finite-state model and of other information-theoretical considerations, within the broader framework of linguistics. This actually amounts to the examination of the meaning of the term "linguistics" itself, which we shall discuss in § 5. In § 1 we shall give a theory of the relationship which exists between the "cost" of a word, identified to the logarithm of its probability, and the "rank" of this word in the ordering of all words by decreasing probabilities. Several details of this section are published for the first time. § 2 will be devoted to new diachronic considerations. § 3 will sketch, for the sake of reference, some of our previously published synchronic models. § 4 will be devoted to the lognormal distribution of probability, which it is unadvisable (in our opinion) to attempt to apply in the present context.

1. The theory of the relation between cost and rank for natural words. The main tool of our theory is the following relationship:

$$C = -\log_2 p \,,$$

where p is the probability of occurrence of some signal in a message and C is the "cost" of transmitting this signal in some optimal binary code. This relationship is extremely familiar in information theory. It may be obtained under a wide variety of definitions of "optimality", from the viewpoint of efficiency in the utilization of error-free binary communication symbols; but the same result may also be reduced to mathematically quite equivalent conditions of randomness and in § 2.1 we shall show that it can be explained by diachronic considerations. We shall postpone to § 3 a summary of several well-known synchronic ways of reducing this relationship to more fundamental concepts. Further, we shall not restrict ourselves to binary codes, and shall write:

---

[2] We would like to add a few words on the subject of rigor in models in social science. In the crude present state of the different fields of that area, it is quite useless to search for the kind of mathematical rigor which one now expects in the models of physics (and even those often lack full mathematical precision). No theory should leave the data too far behind it. Hence, the only reasonable procedure, in describing the results of research of the type under discussion here, seems to be the following. One should strive to treat one or more crucial simple cases with full rigor (one may take as example the Moivre-Laplace case of the "ordinary" central limit theorem of probability). It is quite likely that identical conclusions could be reached from other hypotheses, but practically utilisable necessary and sufficient conditions for the validity of a result are very seldom available. Therefore, all that one can do is to somehow circumscribe the range of wider hypotheses under which one thinks that one's result remains true. This part of a theory is bound to be subjective to a degree, but the central core must be perfectly rigorous. We very much hope that we did not too often fail to follow the above prescriptions.

The present paper is predominantly devoted to the study of that core theory. For extensions, see reference [7].

$(C p)$ $$\beta C = -\log_e p ,$$

where β is a factor which depends upon the scale chosen for C.

Let us apply the relationship $(C p)$ to the words of natural discourse. Each word will be labeled by the rank which it occupies in a list of all words, arranged by order of decreasing probability in a given text of total length k; that is, $r = 1$ designates the most frequent word (W_1), $r = 2$ designates the second most frequent word (W_2), etc.; the number of words more frequent than a word of frequency p will be $r(p) - 1$. Then, Zipf's empirical result is that, for large samples k and for words other than the most frequent ones one has, whichever the language in which a text was written:

$(p r)$ $$p(r) = P r^{-B}$$

where P and B are some constants. As we shall see at the end of this section, $B \geq 1$, except in some special cases. If $B > 1$, one may assume that r is unbounded, that is, the rank R of the least frequent word may be assumed infinite. (For $B \leq 1$, R must be finite, to insure that $\sum_1^R p(r) = 1$.) If $B > 1$ and $R = \infty$, one can easily show that there is no danger in identifying the ranks r relative to the sample frequencies and to the population probabilities[3] (it is unfortunate that, in the past, we did not stress this point in print). By combining the relations $(p r)$ and $(C p)$, we obtain:

$$\beta C = -\log P + B \log r ,$$

$$\log r = \frac{\log P}{B} + \frac{\beta}{B} C = \log K + \beta' C ,$$

(by definition of K and β'). Finally, the following relation must hold:

$(r C)$ $$r = K \exp [\beta' C] .$$

At this point, the status of our argument is the following: we have shown that the empirical law of word frequencies would be "explained", if one could interpret the concept of "cost" in such a fashion that the relations $(C p)$ and $(r C)$ be satisfied. The second of these relations implies a kind of model of the "morphological" structure of the words. In the present paper, we wish to emphasize the wide variety of methods available to explain the relation $(C p)$; it seems therefore appropriate to avoid the complications which accompany the most general definition of "cost" and to work everything out in the simplest case exclusively. Let us therefore be content here with mentioning that the best interpretation of "cost", that we know of, considers it as equal to the time required to read a word (see p. 50 of [6]). It is perfectly

---

[3] One can easily show the following: Let $B > 1$, $R = \infty$ and average the ranks of the different words which all appear the same number of times, i, in a sample of k. Then, if the sample of k is drawn from a population characterized by a set of $p(r)$ given by the law $(p r)$, one has:

$$E[r] = (i/kP)^{-1/B}$$

(except for small values of i). Hence, although the sample rankings may be different from text to text, it remains true on the average that the same rank-frequency law holds for sample and for population ranks (see Appendix A for more details).

obvious that words are *not* read letter by letter and, even if they were, the "costs" of different letters would be different. However, to simplify matters, we shall carry out the arguments in the very crude approximation implied in the last sentence. That is, we shall consider that a "word" is any sequence of letters bounded by successive occurrences of some (improper) letter called the "space"; we shall also consider that the "cost" of a word is equal to the number of proper letters which it contains, plus the cost of "space", which will be designated by C_0. The relation (Cp) then becomes

(np) $$p(W_r) = p_r = \exp\left[-(n_r + C_0)\right] = P' \exp\left(-n_r\right).$$

Further, let the number of different proper letters be M. Then,

there is   1   word of cost C_0

there are M words of cost $C_0 + 1$

there are M^2 words of cost $C_0 + 2$, etc.;

adding, one finds that:

there are $\dfrac{M^n - 1}{M - 1}$ words of cost less than $C = C_0 + n$.

For large n, this gives

$$r = K'M^{C-C_0} = K \exp\left[C \log M\right]$$

which is of the form required to explain Zipf's data on word frequency for large r. Note that $\beta' = \log M$.

It is unfortunate that the simplest case above cannot be generalized to other examples without formal difficulties. However, it turns out that the same result (rC) can be obtained under wider, more realistic and mathematically more convenient conditions, *as long as a word is a sequence of letters contained between two successive spaces and as long as there is "little interaction" between successive proper letters.* (See reference [7].)

A closer examination of the cost of coding for small values of r suggests, in the case $B > 1, R = \infty$, the following improvement of the law (pr), which then becomes valid for all r:

(prV) $$p(r) = (B - 1)V^{B-1}(r + V)^{-B}.$$

V is a second coefficient. This further approximation turns out to be experimentally excellent, which means that the deviations between the empirical and theoretical $p(r)$ nicely add to zero, for some V. But one should note that there is nothing mysterious about this convenient fact. The asymptotic theory yields $p(r) \sim Pr^{-B}$, together with the values of the constants B and P. It turns out, however, that in typical examples of the theory, $P^{-1} < \sum_{1}^{\infty} r^{-B}$, so that P is too large to allow the law (pr) to apply to all values of r. On the other hand, the values of $p(r)$ observed for small r are also typically smaller than predicted by the asymptotic formula. Hence, the most natural procedure is to write the coefficient P^{-1} as $P^{-1} = \sum_{V}^{\infty} r^{-B} = \sum_{1}^{\infty} (r + V)^{-B}$. Thus, V is determined by P. One can show that this procedure is actually entirely justifiable under a wide variety of different conditions; but sometimes one needs more complicated corrections which involve more new parameters.

Moreover, the empirical deviations from (prV), for small r, are hardly at all due to fluctuations of frequency between different finite samples; they are mostly due to the still unsmoothed-out details of the costs of letters of the alphabet and of their interaction. This fact has very important consequences from the viewpoint of the *estimation of the value of the fundamental parameter B*. Because of the essential contribution of Zipf to the establishment of the "Estoup-Zipf" law, it would have been natural to trust his estimates for B. Unfortunately, it is not at all clear how they were achieved and it seems that Zipf relied upon the interpolation of the empirical data on $\log [f(r)]$, by the linear function $\log P - B \log r$ which results from the law (pr); it also seems that fitting by "least squares" was used, which would imply that the deviations between the law (pr) and the data were attributed, for all r, to chance exclusively. Whichever the case, Zipf's values for B are grossly underestimated, as compared with values obtained when the first few most frequent words are disregarded. As a result, Zipf finds that the observed values of B are close to 1 and even less than 1, while we find that the values of B are not less than 1, except in the following cases: Palestinian Hebrew around 1935, the abstracted loan words in Notker's mixed prose and in Pennsylvania Dutch the "holophrases" (not the words) in Plains Cree and Nootka and one or two poets. The cases where B is very close to 1 correspond to extremely "wealthy" vocabularies typical of many literary materpieces (see also §2.4); it is convenient to treat these cases *as if B* were *slightly* greater than 1. For nonliterary discourse, B may very much exceed 1; see also Appendix B.

It should be remarked that the smallness of the number of cases known to us, for which $B < 1$, is no reason for not explaining these data. But it is not at all unreasonable to find that the variety of models available for the case $B > 1$ is greater than the variety of those applying to $B < 1$: the simplest model of the relation (Cp), given in § 3.1, yields only $B > 1$.

The above estimation procedure, involving as it does the seemingly unjustified elimination of some data (the validity of which is unquestioned), may appear as being "unscientific", as compared with the "objective" least squares method. But actually, things are very similar to what happens if one raises the problem of estimating the temperature T of a gas from sample values of the volume v and of the pressure p, with the help of Boyle's law, "$T = v \cdot p$". One could of course try to fit a straight line of slope -1 to the curve of $\log p$ as a function of $\log v$ and note the position of this line. But this would also take into account the data relative to the region in which the gas is not perfect and the Boyle law fails. It is therefore clear that one must fit the straight line only to those data for which the straightness of the empirical curve is unquestionable. Of course, this complicates things somewhat. (The comparison between our linguistic problem and the above physical example is not at all arbitrary; the way we derive the word frequency law for large r and small $B-1$ is very similar to the derivation of the law of perfect gases.)

Further, since we are on the subject of estimation of B, we may as well compare our method, based upon the empirical frequencies as approximations to the $p(r)$, with two other methods. *One* is based upon the empirical data upon the function $f(i, k)$, which gives the number of different words, each of which appears i times in a sample of k. This function is easily deduced from $p(r)$, by a kind of "differentiation" procedure; as a result, the effects of chance fluctuation are less well compensated and the estimation of B is more influenced by chance. The *other* alternative method for the estimation of B is based on the contrary upon an "integral" of $p(r)$, the function which gives $d(k)$, the number of different words in a sample of k. This is the educators' "type-token" function and a considerable body of data have been processed to give only $d(k)$, and not $p(r)$. From (pr), it follows that $E[d(k)] = $ constant $k^{1/B}$ (if $B > 1$ and $R = \infty$; see Appendix A) and this is a very good representation of the data indeed, granting that B may be close to 1.

2. Diachronic considerations

2.1. A random walk which generates the relation between cost and probability.

In the present section, the ranking of words by decreasing probability will not remain constant in time, so that we shall label them with the help of an arbitrary index, h. Our aim is to give a diachronic model of the relation

$$(np) \qquad\qquad p(W_h) = P' \exp(-\beta n_h)$$

which we would like to exist between the probability of the word W_h, and n_h, the number of proper letters which are required to code it. For that, we assume the existence of finite periods of time, such that it can be reasonably postulated that diachronic change occurs only at the boundary points between successive periods. We then construct a diachronic transformation, called "simplest random walk" of n, which leaves the above law $p(W_h)$ invariant and which also yields the law $p(W_h)$ as a limit distribution, irrespectively of the initial conditions of the process.

For that, let q', *independent of n and of t*, be the probability that the length n of a word increase by one letter between the time periods t and $t + 1$, and let q'' be the probability that this length decrease by one letter; the remaining $1 - q' - q''$ is then the probability that the length remain invariant.

The law of decrease cannot, however, apply irrespectively of the original n, because n must remain ≥ 0. Technically, the simplest is then to postulate that q'' is independent of n, as long as n is positive, but that, for the most frequent word ($n = 0$), the length can only increase (with probability q') or remain invariant (with probability $1 - q'$). The corresponding stochastic process is what is called the *"simplest random walk"* of the number of letters in a word, with a *lower* reflecting barrier. If $R < \infty$, which is necessarily the case if $B < 1$, we also require a second barrier, which may also be reflecting, but from above. There is no clear justification for such a barrier, other than the fact that it is required in order to obtain $p(W_h)$ as a limit distribution independent of initial conditions.

A random walk is a markovian process. Naturally, the markovian assumption applies here between successive periods of diachronic change of the set of $p(h)$, whereas in the finite-state model it applied to successive letters or words. But, despite these deep differences, the formal mathematics will turn out to be essentially the same.

To this simple process, one can of course object that the number of words containing n proper letters must remain equal to M^n, whereas the best that the above random walk can guarantee is that the *expected* number of words be equal to M^n. There are two ways out of this difficulty. One may argue that the existence of synonyms and homonyms destroys somewhat the strict relation between a code and the word which it represents; this is very reasonable but raises all kinds of complicated questions. The other method is to replace the independent changes of length of the different words by a kind of game of "musical chairs", in which words exchange codes among themselves so that if one word is considered, independently of all others, it has the above probabilities q' and q'' of getting a longer or a shorter code.

However, this formal complication may be disregarded in this paper. The essential thing is that the repeated application of the random walk mechanism of variation of the length of words will eventually lead to an exponential steady-state distribution of $p(W_r)$, but only if the barriers provide the appropriate limit conditions. Specifically, if $q' < q''$, and in the absence of barriers, $n(h, t)$ would eventually become negative and unbounded in absolute value, whichever h; however, this is always prevented by the requirement that $n \geq 0$ and one can show that a steady-state is indeed attained if $q' < q''$. If $q' > q''$, and in the absence of barriers, $n(h, t)$ would on the contrary eventually become unboundedly large and positive, whichever h; this can be prevented only by imposing an additional upper barrier, for example another reflecting barrier (see however the last lines of this section); its motivation is far less obvious than that of the barrier at $n = 0$ and one must recall that such a barrier implies that the number R of different words is finite.

Now, assuming that a steady-state exists, let us write one necessary condition: the equality between the expected number of words which go from length $n + 1$ to length n, and the expected number of words which go the other way:

$$q'' \cdot \text{Prob (a word of length } n + 1) \cdot M^{n+1} = q' \cdot \text{Prob (a word of length } n) \cdot M^n.$$

Hence, and by definition of β,

$$\frac{\text{Prob (a word of length } n + 1)}{\text{Prob (a word of length } n)} = \frac{q'}{q''M} = \exp(-\beta) .$$

recalling the notations $\beta' = \log M$ and $B = \beta/\beta'$, this can also be written as

$$q'/q'' = \exp(\beta' - \beta) = \exp[\beta'(1 - B)] .$$

To sum up, a steady-state always exists under the condition $q' < q''$ which leads to $B > 1$, but, under the condition $q' > q''$ which would lead to $B < 1$, one must moreover assume that r is bounded by some number R and n is bounded by $\log_M R$.

Let us return to the reflecting character of the barriers at $n = 0$ and $n = \log_M R$. When one deals with such barriers, another technically simple assumption is that they are "absorbing". In that case, whenever the length of a word attains the value corresponding to the barrier, this word vanishes from the system. Of course, in order to preserve a constant total number of words, one will have to combine an absorbing barrier with "immigration" of new words, at exactly the same (constant) rate. One may also have a partially absorbing barrier with a correspondingly smaller immigration. It is clear that the combination of absorption and immigration is not at all appropriate for the barrier at $n = 0$, because the most frequent words are the most permanent members of the vocabulary. But this combination is not a priori absurd in the case of the barrier corresponding to the least frequent word. Under these conditions, the number of different words ever used, from period 0 to the current period t, will increase linearly with t, irrespectively of the sign of $B - 1$. (However, one may also argue that "old" words may come back eventually into the vocabulary; then the number of different words would increase less than linearly; but any assumption as to its rate of increase would be quite foreign to the present model.)

It can be noted that the random walk of this section is very similar to a process which is used as a model of physical brownian motion. There it is classically known that the steady-state can also be characterized as being the "most probable" or the "expected" state at every instant of time, when the average of n is fixed (this average has a concrete meaning, because one can add the numbers of letters). These specifications being "synchronic", they will be treated in §3; they will establish the complete formal equivalence between the above diachronic model for the law of Estoup-Zipf and several of our older synchronic models.

2.2. Restatement of the random walk model in terms which no longer refer to the concept of cost and to the relation (Cp). (We do not think that this restatement has any particular virtue, and it will have several kinds of drawbacks. Hopefully, it may facilitate the comparison of our family of mathematically equivalent models, with models due to other authors. However, the reader can proceed immediately to §2.4, without any loss of continuity.)

Let $f(i, t)$ be the (random) number of different words, each of which occurs exactly i times in the sample of discourse which corresponds to the time period t. Designate by $k(t)$ the total number of words in the time period t. One has $k(t) = \sum if(i, t)$, so that $k(t)$ is also a random variable. In the model which we shall sketch in this section, the distribution of $k(t)$ will be stationary, that is, dependent upon the past, but independent from the value of t. (We may note that it would appear as more logical, a priori, to choose as parameter the number of words since some time origin; however, this would introduce some unneccessary but serious technical complications, as we shall see soon.)

Let $i(h, t)$ be the number of occurrences, during the period t, of the word arbitrarily designated by the symbol h. In §2.1, we have assumed that the k words in a time period are chosen independently of each other, with *probabilities* which vary from one period to the next, according to a markovian scheme. Now assume that the *sample frequencies* in a period will depend upon the sample frequencies during the immediately past period and, in order to simplify and to stick close to § 2.1, assume that the number $i(h, t + 1)$ can only take the value $i(h, t)$ or the values $\exp(\beta)i(h, t)$ or $\exp(-\beta)i(h, t)$, with the respective probabilities $1 - q' - q''$, q'' and q'; then $\log i(h, t)$ will perform a simple random walk (it might also have performed a more complicated diffusion, in which $\log i$ might have varied by smaller steps; this would not have changed the essential features of the present model). The resemblance of this model with a random walk of $p(h)$ is obvious but not complete, because $p(h)$ may be approximated by $i(h)/k$, where k is the same for all words during the time period t, but is not the same during successive time periods. Note that, precisely because k is not fixed, there are no "musical chairs" complications in this model. However, one may wonder how the $i(h, t)$ occurrences of W_h are scattered among the k words in the period t; we shall not enter into this question here.

The above conjecture about the behavior of $i(h, t)$ does not at all refer to any coding procedure. Hence, it may seem that the model which we shall develop from this basis will imply weaker hypotheses than the model of § 2.1. But actually such is not at all the case: the only thing is that, *if the multiplicative behavior of i is not justified by other considerations (such as considerations of coding), it just becomes a special ad-hoc assumption, not reduced to any more fundamental concept.* (Similarly, in the theory of the Pareto income distribution, in economics, things become very simple if one assumes that, from year to next, $\log$ (income) performs a random walk. But, although $\log$ (income) has been hallowed by long history, its use continues to imply a special kind of assumption, the law of random proportionate effect; see our references [9; 10].)

Note also that the sum and the average of a set of expressions $\log(i)$ have no concrete meaning, so that one cannot even speak of the most-probable or of the expected synchronic state given the average of $\log(i)$. Hence, the model of this section cannot be reinterpreted in synchronic terms analogous to the models of §§ 3.2 and 3.3. (The lack of synchronic version does not condemn a model, but shows it to be very much less versatile—on top of its other drawbacks. Similarly, the Pareto income distribution cannot be considered as being the most probable—although some authors have attempted to do so—because the average of $\log$ (income) has no concrete meaning.)

Let us now return to boundary conditions. Just like in § 2.1, the random walk of $\log(i)$ may have to be modified and/or constrained by barriers, for large and/or for small values of i. Let us however postpone these questions and assume even, to simplify, that in the intermediate zone, i must take the form $S' \exp(-\beta n)$, where n is an integer. One can then show that, if a steady-state exists for the distribution of i, the number of different words in the "frequency bracket" n must take the form $S'' \exp(\beta' n)$, with $q'/q'' = \exp(\beta' - \beta)$. If the problem of high and low values of i did not lead to any difficulty, the continuation of this argument would yield the Estoup-Zipf law, with $B = \beta/\beta'$. Unfortunately, the high and low values of i do indeed lead to awkward complications.

For rare words (small i) one cannot assume that $i = S' \exp(-\beta n)$ with an integral n and the simple random walk of $\log i$ must be modified accordingly. However, this can be done without influencing the steady-state distribution for the middle range of values of i. Further, the random walk of $\log i$, as modified for small i, must involve a barrier, because i cannot become less than 1. This barrier can be reflecting or it can be a combination of an absorbing barrier and of immigration of new words, at a constant rate as measured on the scale of the t. (One may also suppose, just as in § 2.1, that a word may be dropped after one time period and recovered sometime later. But such a problem remains foreign to the present setup.)

Let us now consider what happens to frequent words and in particular to the most frequent one. If a barrier prevented words from occurring more than a certain number of times in each time period, things would be very similar to what happened in § 2.1. But actually, an upper reflecting barrier is not at all indispensable and a steady-state distribution of i may exist without it for any value of B.

In the cases which lead to $B < 1$, one further finds that the mean value of i is finite. This mean is the expected value of the number k of words uttered during the period t. Hence, the rate of addition of words to a sample will be roughly proportional to the rate of flow of time, as measured by the parameter t. (However, if $B > \frac{1}{2}$, the variance of k will be infinite, so that the "fluctuations" of the difference between k and $E(k)$ will be quite unusual by the standards of intuition established by the gaussian distribution.)

Note that, under the conditions which lead to $B < 1$,

$$E\{i(h, t + 1) \,|\, i(t, h)\} = Qi(h, t)$$

with $Q = q' \exp(-\beta) + q'' \exp(\beta) + (1 - q' - q'') < 1$. However, this regression of i towards $i = 1$ has of course nothing to do with the need to leave space for new immigrant words at that level; immigration and autoregression are two altogether distinct things.

Consider now the random walks which lead to $B > 1$; now the mean value of i, and the expected value of k, will be infinite. Moreover,

$$E\{i(h, t + 1) \,|\, i(h, t)\} = Qi(h, t)$$

where $Q > 1$; the regression goes towards infinity, not towards 1 as when $B < 1$. But nothing blows up. Random variables with infinite expectation are quite foreign to the usual probabilistic "intuition", but there is nothing unproper about them. For example, a well-known case of such a variable is provided by the time which it takes, in fair coin tossing between "Peter" and "Paul" (assumed both to have an infinite wealth), before the gain of Peter reaches any prescribed value. The fluctuation of the number of words k per time period is now enormous, although the k relative to each period is finite and although the percentage of periods during which k exceeds some finite but large value may be very small. We cannot enter here into the rather long calculations which this problem involves. Note however the following.

Suppose that the k of successive periods have the same distribution as the one found here, but are otherwise independent random variables; then the number of time periods, starting at $t = 0$, required to accumulate m words, will increase like $m^{1/B}$, that is, far less than linearly. (See reference [5].)

COROLLARY. *Suppose that the barrier at $i = 1$ is partially or totally absorbing, with an additional immigration at a constant rate—measured in terms of the variable t—and suppose that the words dropped once never return; then, the rate of additional new words—measured in terms of the total number of words, m, since the period $t = 0$—will be of the form $\alpha_0 m^{-1+1/B}$, where α_0 can vary between 0 (included) and a maximum corresponding to perfect absorption and hence to maximum immigration.*

We shall not study this model any further; its main drawback seems to be that it predicts that, when $B > 1$, the law of Estoup-Zipf should hold best for frequent words; as we have mentioned, this is certainly not the case (the law of Estoup-Zipf would not apply very well to very rare words, either, because of the effects of the barrier and of the corresponding changes in the model; but this correction would apply to words which occur only a few times during periods of stationarity of the ratio i/k and such words can hardly ever be expected to appear in the very much smaller samples which are usually available). The second drawback of this model concerns the value of the ratio i/k for the word which happens to be the most frequent during the time period t; the prediction is that this ratio depends very much upon the value of the number k corresponding to the tth period: if k is very large, i/k will be very close to one (for the sake of comparison, recall that, if the sum k of the random variables $i(h)$ were gaussian, the contribution to k of the largest of the variables i would have been negligible for all k); if k is small, the i/k of the most frequent word would be far from 1. All these predictions are quite natural in the case of the Willis species-genera problem, but certainly not here.

2.3. A markovian model, in which the "memory" reaches back to some origin of time. The markovian processes of §§ 2.1 and 2.2 share the features that "time" is divided into successive periods, containing a fixed or a random number of words, and that the statistical properties of discourse during one period depend only upon chance and upon the statistical properties during the preceding period. This markovian hypothesis is of course an extreme idealization of the facts, in at least two ways. First, one would think that the periods during which there is no diachronic change must correspond to very large numbers of words; call them "years". Then the assumptions of §§ 2.1 and 2.2 amount to the claim that the statistical current properties of discourse depend upon chance, conditioned by the properties of discourse during the preceding full calendar year. It would be more reasonable to assume that the conditioning segment of past discourse is constituted by the 365 days just preceding today. Actually, one will not consider that this difficulty is serious, if one assumes (as we do, after all) that it is better to consider that the Estoup-Zipf distribution is established by the synchronic recurrence of space in a markovian sequence of letters and of spaces, so that the diachronic models are only ways of showing how this distribution can be maintained. Even if one hesitates to adopt our current attitude, one will not expect much change to come from the above-mentioned "moving sample" answer to this objection and one will hesitate to tackle the unnecessary formal difficulties of such an approach.

A *second* objection is that one would think that the far-away past of a sample of discourse maintains *some* influence *forever*, in a more active fashion than implied by the markovian assumption.

There is a way of answering this second objection simply, by introducing the directly opposite kind of idealization. Consider again a sequence of time periods and suppose that the properties of discourse during period t depend upon chance, conditioned exclusively upon its cumulated properties during *all* t preceding periods. That is, a markovian process will now be performed by the function $j(h, t)$, which gives the number of occurrences of the word W_h, from time period 0 to period t. This is a rather unlikely modification of the process of §2.2 and there are obvious difficulties in choosing the stochastic matrix of the Markov process and in defining a steady-state solution. As to immigration, it is still not necessary, because one may assume, like in §§2.1 and 2.2, that all the words were already present in the sample corresponding to the first time period (recall that these are periods of synchronic stationarity of discourse, and must be so long that the words which occur only a few times in such periods have a very small chance of ever being observed in the samples of the usual size). However, immigration is not contradictory with the general conceptual set-up of the problem and, in order to preserve the idea which one has of a steady-state of $j(h, t)$, the best is to assume that the addition of new words has a uniform rate as measured on the scale of the time periods t. When this rate is measured on the scale of the cumulated number of words, m, it either is uniform, α_0 (if $B < 1$) or has the form $\alpha_0 m^{-1+1/B}$ (if $B > 1$); in either case, α_0 and B are independent.

As we have mentioned, we think that in the problem of word frequencies, it is better to apply the markovian assumption to successive time periods, rather than to the cumulated numbers $j(h, t)$ from some arbitrary and far removed time origin. However, in the species-genera problem of J. C. Willis, G. Yule [19] has successfully applied the markovian assumption to $j(h, t)$ and has thus explained the law of Willis as if it represented the result of the evolution of species. This diachronic model can be contrasted with our own synchronic explanations,[1] in which the distribution of species among genera is taken to be a linguistic device, conditioned by the needs of some types of communication.[4]

---

[4] This seems to be the best place to give some more precise indications about the relationship which exists between Simon's 1955 models of the law of Estoup-Zipf, our own 1951 model (as reworded in a diachronic fashion in §2.1), Yule's 1924 model (which was slightly modified and translated, rather unconvincingly, into word frequency terms is §2.3), and Champernowne's 1953 model (which referred to income, but on which our §2.2 was very closely patterned). The most characteristic feature of Simon's method, which is preserved in all the variants which he has offered so far, is that he chooses to follow the gradual unfolding of a text, word by word. In many mays, this would a priori seem to be preferable to our use of the auxiliary parameter t. Let us however consider things in closer detail.

2.4. A relation between the Estoup-Zipf and the Willis problems.
Let us now approach the variation of the probabilities $p(h)$ in time in a different way. Consider two equal samples of discourse, which may belong to the same author at different times, but will rather belong to different authors. It is extremely unlikely that the numbers of occurrences i' and i'' of the same word in the two samples be independent random variables. But let us see what would happen if they were; more precisely, assume that both samples are characterized by the same parameter B, but that the way in which the same vocabulary is ranked in the two samples are totally independent, so that i' and i'' are independent random variables. Then, the following striking thing is true: the total number of occurrences of a word in the combined sample, $i' + i''$, still substantially follows the same law as either i' or i''. More precisely, for large i, this statement holds best if $V = 0$ and it never holds very closely for small i. This kind of invariance has been used extensively by us in our theory of Willis categories ([5] and Chapter 3 of [6]), where it is very relevant to the problem. In the present context, the independence between i' and i'' is just too far reaching an assumption. But it indicates why, if the law of Estoup-Zipf (pr) is satisfied by the parts of a mixture of texts, it may be satisfied by the whole; it was obvious that this result holds for different samples from the same population; in § 2.2, the proof was given under conditions of "small" dissimilarity between the parts, and the present section referred to a case of extreme dissimilarity between the parts. It is likely (see footnote 2) that the results hold more generally, as they should in order to explain the available data on mixed texts of different authors, or even the available data on samples of one author which are so long that they cannot any longer be considered as homogeneous, and which do not correspond to successive periods of time.

3. Synchronic considerations on the relation between cost and probability. In § 1, in order to identify $\log r$ to the number of letters in a word, we had to make a "morphological" hypothesis, concerning the way in which letters are made into words. Now, we shall need a syntactical hypothesis, concerning the way in which words are made into sentences. In this section, every sequence of words will be considered to be a possible sentence, and the

---

First assume $B < 1$. Then there is little difference between the methods using the parameters k or t, which are roughly speaking proportional. But certain special features of the original Simon's model introduce a relationship between the rate of addition of new words, α, and the parameter B (called $1/\rho$ in Simon's papers and in our criticism of these papers); this relationship is not preserved in other variants and of course it does not appear in either of the models of our § 2; we think that one should not obtain any such relationship. Besides, the predicted behavior of i/k in time appears to be incorrect.

Assume now $B > 1$. Then, Simon's approach is decidedly inferior. Its main drawback is that it requires a special postulate concerning the rate of addition of new words, as we have explained in our [8].

Of course, this whole §2, as well as §3.1, is proof that we have no objection to a "stochastic" approach, as such. Besides, Simon's model appears as being most useful indeed, in other possible fields of its application and it has served to point out many important features of the linguistic application.

reordering of the words in a sentence will be assumed to lead to a new one. We shall call this the "Maxwell-Boltzmann" syntax. (See Appendix B.)

It would have been extremely interesting to be able to check whether the same results hold under wider and more realistic syntactical assumptions. So far, we have been able only to check that such is indeed the case for the so-called "Bose-Einstein" syntax, in which the reordering or permutation of the words of a sentence does not change its meaning (see reference [7]).

We may point out that the different synchronic considerations which we shall now sketch are entirely equivalent from the viewpoint of the formal mathematics. See in particular the comments upon "teleology" in § 3.4.

3.1. The discourse as a random sequence of independent and equiprobable letters, cut into words by the recurrence of the improper letter "space".

(It then follows that the discourse is a random sequence of independent words, but not conversely.) Let p_0 be the probability of "space" and $(1 - p_0)/M$ be the probability of any one of the other letters. The probability of a word containing n proper letters will then be:

$$p_0\left[\frac{1 - p_0}{M}\right]^n = p_0 \exp\left\{-n \log\left[M/(1 - p_0)\right]\right\} = P' \exp\left(-\beta n\right).$$

This is precisely the relationship (np), which we set out to explain. The values of the different constants are the following: $P' = p_0$, $\beta = \log\left[M/(1 - p_0)\right]$ and hence $\exp\left(-\beta\right)$ is the probability of each proper letter. Note also the important facts that the number of different words is unbounded and that

$$B = \beta/\beta' = \beta/\log M = 1 + \left|\frac{\log(1 - p_0)}{\log M}\right| > 1.$$

It will be noted that, when sentences are thus generated as random sequences of both letters or words, one cannot a priori force the number of letters in the sentence to have a predetermined value, but one can fix the number N of words in the sentence; it is sufficient to decide to stop after the Nth recurrence of space. To distinguish this situation from those of §§ 3.2 and 3.3, we shall refer to sentences of N words as "canonical sentences".

DISCUSSION. The above model makes very little difference between the proper letters and space. As a result, if this model could be taken entirely seriously, the same rank-frequency law would hold for the "pseudo-words", defined by successive recurrences of some proper letter. G. A. Miller and E. Newman [13] have checked this prediction for the pseudo-words of natural language defined by the letter "e"; they find that pseudo-words *do not* follow the (pr) law with $B > 1$, as they should if the model of random generation were entirely true; they seem rather close to the (pr) law with $B < 1$. In other terms, the properties of the recurrence of "space" seem more intrinsic in some ways than those of the recurrence of any proper letter. This also seems supported by even the crudest psychological experiments which suggest that the reading of written discourse (or the perception of speech signals) is not performed letter by letter and is closer to being performed word by word. If so, it would be more natural to consider that randomness applies to the sequence of some more abstract cerebral coding elements, rather than to letters. The only element common to all coding systems would be the space, so that the (pr) relationship for the ordinary words would provide the only conceivable check of the randomness of the higher coding elements. However more evidence concerning "e-words" is needed to elaborate this conjecture.

3.2. Mean word frequencies when the discourse is considered as a random sequence of independent and equiprobable Maxwell-Boltzmann sentences, with predetermined numbers for both the natural words and the letters.

These will be called "*microcanonical sentences*"; their definition is made possible by the fact that one can meaningfully add "costs", when they are interpreted as numbers of letters corresponding to successive words.

Let N be the number of words (and of spaces) in a sentence and a, the number of proper letters. All sentence configurations are equiprobable; hence the number $E(N_r)$, or expected number of occurrences of a word made of n_r proper letters, is the ratio of the number of "favorable cases" to the total number of "cases"; that is, it is the ratio

$$\frac{\text{number of sentences of } N-1 \text{ words and } a-n_r \text{ proper letters}}{\text{number of sentences of } N \text{ words and } a \text{ proper letters}} = E(N_r).$$

The numerator is easily derived from the denominator. One notes that a sentence of N words and a proper letters may be obtained by first ordering the letters in all possible ways, and then mixing in the $N-1$ spaces (other than the last space, which is necessarily at the end of the sentence). The first operation leads to M^a combinations, the second one to

$$\binom{N+a-1}{a} = \frac{(N+a-1)!}{(N-1)!a!}.$$

Hence

$$E(N_r) = M^{-n_r} \cdot \left[\frac{(N-1+a-n_r-1)!}{(N+a-1)!}\right] \cdot \left[\frac{a!}{(a-n_r)!}\right] \cdot (N-1).$$

For large N and a, this becomes:

$$E(N_r) = \frac{N-1}{N+a-1} \cdot M^{-n_r} \cdot \left(\frac{a}{N+a-2}\right)^{n_r}$$

which is the result obtained in § 3.1, granting that

$$\beta = \log\left[M / \left(\frac{a}{N+a-2}\right)\right]$$

and therefore that

$$a/(N+a-2) \sim a/(N+a) = 1 - p_0$$

where p_0 is the proportion of spaces in a sentence, that is, roughly, the "probability of space". Further, $\exp(-\beta)$ is the probability of any proper letter.

(If one considers a finite discourse, there is no difference between its statistical properties when it is a segment of an infinite canonical discourse, and when it is a segment of a microcanonical discourse with very large N and a.)

3.3. The set of word frequencies which is "most likely" under the conditions of § 3.2. Instead of the average values $E(N_r)$, let us now consider the set $E'(N_r)$ of values of N_r, which is encountered in the greatest possible number of different sentences, obtained from each other only by permutation of words. We again take the length of a word to be unbounded.

The set $E(N_r)$ maximizes the number $\dfrac{N!}{E'(W_1)!E'(W_2)!\cdots}$ under the two restrictions:

that the total number of words is fixed, that is, $\sum E'(N_r) = N$

and that the total number of proper letters is fixed, that is, $\sum n_r E'(N_r) = a$.

Suppose that N and a are both extremely large, so that one can apply the Stirling approximation to $N!$ (actually, if the number of different words is infinite, and $p(r) \to 0$ as $r \to \infty$, this approximation can never hold for all r; but the range of r in which it holds tends to ∞, as N and $a \to \infty$).

The problem now becomes that of maximizing:

$$-N\sum \frac{E'(N_r)}{N} \log \frac{E'(N_r)}{N}$$

subject to the requirements

$$\text{that } \sum \frac{E'(N_r)}{N} = 1 \quad \text{and that } \sum n_r \frac{E'(N_r)}{N} = a/N \,.$$

This maximization problem is extremely classical; solved with the help of Lagrange multipliers, it yields:

$$\frac{E'(N_r)}{N} = G^{-1}(\beta) \exp(-\beta n_r) \,.$$

$G(\beta)$ is determined by the requirement that $\sum E'(N_r)/N = 1$; hence

$$G(\beta) = \sum_{r=1}^{\infty} \exp(-\beta n_r) \,.$$

The number of words of n proper letters being M^n, one finds

$$G(\beta) = \sum_{n=1}^{\infty} M^n \exp(-\beta n) = \frac{1}{1 - M\exp(-\beta)} \,.$$

Then, β is determined by the requirement that $\sum n_r E'(N_r) = a/N$; hence

$$a/N = -\frac{d \log G(\beta)}{d\beta} = \frac{M\exp(-\beta)}{1 - M\exp(-\beta)}$$

or $M\exp(-\beta) = a/(a + N)$ as in § 3.2. Thus, the mean and the most likely word frequencies are identical. In fact, when a and N are very large, a very small percentage of sentences correspond to N_r/N differing non-negligibly from either their mean or their most probable values.

3.4. The set of word frequencies, which carry the greatest amount of Shannon information per word, under the conditions of § 3.2. In its second form (using the Stirling approximation) the maximization problem of §3.3 has another interpretation, most remarkable and sometimes ill-understood. This is due to the fact that the expression

$$-\sum_r p(r) \log p(r) \quad \text{(where } p(r) \text{ denotes } E'(N_r)/N)$$

is precisely what Shannon has called *information per word* in an independent random process where $p(r)$ are the probabilities of the words. Hence, the probabilities corresponding to a random sequence of letters, to the mean discourse or to the most likely discourse, also turn out to be those which carry the greatest amount of information (given the mean number of letters per word, available for transmission, *given the role played by the symbol "space"*, and given the assumption that the total number of possible different words is infinite).

Further, the rank-frequency law given by all these criteria depends only slightly (through B and a little bit more) on the coding alphabet used in the construction of a random sequence of letters or in the specifications of the most informative sentence or of the average sentence. As a result, optimality (as well as randomness) may be valid simultaneously for two speakers (an emitter and a receiver) using different coding alphabets for the same set of words.

Unfortunately, it is difficult ever to shed completely the "intuitive" connotations of the terms "information", as employed in ordinary usage. Hence, the mathematical equivalence of many consequences of randomness and of informational optimality has been the source of an unending number of various misunderstandings, centered around the relationships presumed to exist between meaning and frequency. Some commentators, impressed by the rigor implied by the definition of Shannon's information, seem to believe that the problem of meaning and frequency has been solved by our model. Others stress that Shannon's information is irrelevant to any semantic problem; "hence" (assuming meaning to be relevant to frequency) information cannot be relevant to word frequencies in natural language. Actually, it is meaning that is largely irrelevant to frequencies in natural language which, on the other hand, seem indeed to be closely connected with information.

This false problem has been further complicated by the relationships which exist between Shannon's concept of information and the physical concept of entropy. (We show in reference [6] that even closer relationships exist between the structure of the models of this section, and some models of statistical thermodynamics.) But, again, the meaning of the physical concept of entropy has turned out to be very ill-understood at large. It is well-known to the physicist that the state of maximum entropy is also the average state of a macroscopic physical system and is further the state which the system tends to reach as a result of a long interplay of random interactions. Therefore, there is a great difference between the maximization of entropy and, say, the minimization of "action" which is involved in the "principles of least action" of mechanics. It seems however that some commentators of our work have understood our criterion of maximization of information as being something akin to the minimization of mechanical "action". This misunderstanding has been reinforced by the fact that Zipf's 1949 book, from which our original data were taken, carries the title *Human behavior and the principle of least effort*. It seemed, quite incorrectly, that our work has simply given an accurate meaning to Zipf's completely loose idea of "effort", and that Zipf's naive teleological approach has been vindicated. That is, certain critics dismissed the approach based upon maximization as being teleological, while others blamed us for not adopting such an interpretation wholeheartedly; some have even claimed that this interpretation is their own improvement upon our models. Actually, it is obvious that there would be nothing teleological even in a minimization analogous to that occurring in the principle of least action of mechanics; there is even less of a problem in the maximization of the probability of a sentence (or of the entropy or information of a frequency distribution).

Let us hasten to add that the relationship between the results of the several criteria largely subsists in the case of more complicated coding alphabets. A random sequence of letters has the maximum information property relative to a certain set of "costs" of letters. Conversely, a sequence of letters having the maximum property is in most cases a random sequence of letters and spaces, with well-defined probabilities. But it is seen that, in this generalization, the criterion of maximization turns out to be the more powerful. It also turns out to be the only one capable of a generalization to the case where $B < 1$, and to the case of syntaxes other than the crudest "Maxwell-Boltzmann" syntax used so far (for which the permutations of words in a sentence lead to possible and new sentences).

3.5. The case where the number of different words, R, is finite and n is bounded by $\log_M R$. This case cannot possibly arise in the method based upon a random sequence of letters and spaces; but, in the other cases, it only requires a fairly simple modification of the theory valid if $R = \infty$.

First consider the most likely or most informative set of N_r. The theory is unchanged by the finiteness of R, up to the results that

$$E'(N_r) = G^{-1}(\beta) \exp(-\beta n_r) \text{ and } a/N = d \log G(\beta)/d\beta .$$

But the expression for $G(\beta)$ is changed, so that, as a/N increases, the value of β no longer remains larger than $\log M$; that is, B *may become less that* 1.

Unfortunately, the mean values $E(N_r)$ are no longer as simple as $E'(N_r)$. The boundedness of n implies that the number of sentences of N words and a proper letters is equal to M^a multiplied by a factor which is different from

$$\binom{N + a - 1}{a} .$$

However, one need not worry about these combinatorial complications; for long sentences, the mean value and the most probable are identical.

We have just shown that the theoretical foundations for the law (pr) with $B < 1$ have less variety than the foundations of that law for $B > 1$ and $R = \infty$.

4. On the proposals to apply the lognormal distribution to word frequencies. As we have already mentioned, for the sake of comparison, the law of income distribution of Pareto is formally very similar to the law of Estoup-Zipf. As a result, it is quite easy to justify the law of Pareto by a random walk argument, once the use of log (income) is justified (which is very difficult). On the other hand, many authors have claimed that the distribution of log (income) is well represented by the gaussian law. Actually, the evidence is very mediocre, except near the most probable income and the basic reasons for the widespread use of the lognormal law for income appear to be theoretical rather than empirical; the normal law is very simple to manipulate and it seems also to be justified by the vague feeling that log (income) is the sum of very many contributions and *hence* should be normally distributed. (In our own theory of income distribution [9], we have shown that the presumed link between addition of many contributions and the normal law is not necessary; it is possible to introduce a slight modification of the Pareto law, called by us the law of Pareto-Lévy, for which the *income itself* is the sum of very many components; the key to the seeming paradox is that, for $\frac{1}{2} < B < 1$, the variance of income is infinite.)

Whatever its motivation, the lognormal law is widely used in several fields and, on pp. 101–102 of reference [1], one finds the following statement: "A number of distributions (similar to Pareto's) are given by Zipf, who uses a mathematical description of his own manufacture on which he erects some extensive sociological theory; in fact, however, it is likely that many of these distributions can be regarded as lognormal, or truncated lognormal, with more prosaic foundations in normal probability theory."

It can only be regretted that the "extensive sociological theory" of Zipf has thrown doubt on his data and that the authors of [1] do not include any non-gaussian limit law in what they call the "normal(!) probability theory". Such laws have been found useful in both Willis' problem and in the problem of income distribution. Whichever the case, several authors have taken up the challenge of the above quotation and have tried to apply the lognormal law to word frequencies. They do not attempt to justify the use of logarithms and they presumably believe that no special theory is needed to explain the normal distribution. We disagree on both grounds. However, we do not imply that there are no ways of building models of the normal law in this context: Suppose for example that a word is always made up of a *fixed* number n of letters having *very unequal* additive costs; these costs may be expressions of the form $-\log p$(letter), supposing that the probability of a word is the product of the probabilities of the letters. Then the cost of the word will be given by a multinomial distribution, which can be approximated by a gaussian (the approximation improves as a $n \to \infty$, but the relative dispersion of the cost—i.e., the root mean square of the cost divided by its mean—tends to zero, which is probably not what one desires).

Further, just like the lognormal theory of income emphasizes the average incomes, the lognormal approach to word frequency distribution emphasizes the most frequent words and not the rare ones (as our theory does). However, the distribution of frequent words depends very much on the exact decision taken in defining a "word" and is notoriously variable from language to language.

Let us also note that, in final analysis, the justification of the gaussian law sometimes simply amounts to the fact that almost any log (density) considered near the most probable value, can usually be approximated by a parabola; at most, one may have to change the scale of the variable and to take logarithms.   Such an approximation appears of course also at the beginning of the usual proofs of the central limit theorem of Moivre-Laplace; however, the crucial step of this theorem is in the proof that the range over which the approximation is valid increases with the number of variables which one adds.   There is no such thing in the arguments in favor of the reasonableness of the lognormal law in this context.

Finally, the major drawback of this approach is that there is complete lack of evidence that the lognormal law applies to non-pathological human discourse (the only good fit is obtained with English function words, to which our theory has no reason to apply).   However, we would not like to leave the impression that the lognormal law never appears in word frequency studies. Some evidence, privately communicated to us, shows that when the degree of severity of aphasia increases beyond a certain point, the word frequency law of aphasics goes from the Estoup-Zipf's "log-exponential" to the lognormal distribution.   We hope to study someday this most interesting phenomenon.

5. On the scope of the term "linguistics".

Despite its development on all fronts during the present century, the definition of "linguistics" is not very much clearer now than it was at the time of F. de Saussure [15].[5] Accepted usage is even less of a guide than it was then, because usage was not the same in the many different groups which have converged into the present international community of linguists. *We think that it is very appropriate to take advantage of this remaining undeterminacy to carefully distinguish the scope of the term "linguistics" from the terms which designate more special parts of the science of language.*   We think in particular that taking "linguistics" and "grammar" to be synonymous terms has no advantage either for grammar itself or for the broader science of language.

In other words, we think that it is still time to avoid the embarrassing situation which results from the fact that the two terms "physics" and "physical science" have unequal generality.   "Linguistics" and "linguistic science" should

---

[5] Of course, Saussure is old-fashioned (it has also become very clear now that the posthumous text published in 1916 was a rather poor reflexion of the notes taken by the ten-odd students who ever took Saussure's lectures—not to speak of it as a reflexion of the lectures themselves—see: R. Godel, *Les sources manuscrites du cours de linguistique générale de Ferdinand de Saussure*, Geneva, Droz, 1957). But, unless one takes the narrowest view of linguistics as identical to introspective grammar, Saussure is again very much relevant to the issue raised by the relationships between the recently greatly increased number of branches of the theory of signs.   If a personal reminiscence is permitted here, we would like to recall our own delight when we stumbled across Saussure in 1950 after groping for some time for order between the various concepts involved in what at that time was a problem of application of information theory to the study of linguistic discourse.   To an extent unrivaled by other classics in the field, Saussure exhibited an "esprit géométrique" which was most welcome to a mathematician.

both remain synonymous with "science of language" and include any sufficiently general model of "language" and of "discourse", irrespectively of whether the model is or is not "grammatical". Similarly, we think that the situation which exists in "biology" (also called "biological science") is fortunate insofar as this science covers not only the study of the differences between different living systems, but also (and mainly, in recent decades) the study of the differences between living systems and other systems.

As to the distinction which we make between language and discourse, it is very widely but not universally accepted: "language" may be considered as being relative to the native speaker's introspection, in his role as emitter (this in particular includes his introspective idea of what is or is not "grammatical"); "discourse" will be relative to the same person's view of messages which he receives from other also presumably native speakers. One can take samples of discourse and let them be examined by different persons. One has no real check of somebody's claims about the grammaticalness or ungrammaticalness of such and such sentence, and one must compare different introspections which are presumed to be relative to the same dialect.

The difference between emitter and receiver is particularly striking in the case of homonymy, which is a meaningless problem for the emitter. The study of the articulation-phonology-acoustics complex of studies also raises a question from this viewpoint.

Similarly there may a priori exist an emitter's grammar and a receiver's grammar for every dialect. In actual studies, however careful, one cannot help but mix them, but a priori they are conceptually quite different things. Any statement to the contrary encounters the problem of "deviant" sentences and should be very seriously documented from the psychological viewpoint.

Now, we arrive to the core of our discussion. What about statistical properties? Such things as frequency relationships are rather foreign to the emitter's introspection, except when specially trained. Signs are believed to be far more conditioned by the corresponding meanings than by any stochastic schemes. But, for the receiver, the statistical properties of discourse are extremely real (and not only when the profession of the receiver is to retransmit messages on communication networks). Should one worry whether these properties belong to "linguistics" in some narrow sense, or to "the psychology of language"? In any case, speaking of discourse, we cannot follow E. Galanter and G. A. Miller [12] in the opposition which they establish between stochastic *models* and grammatical *explanations*. It is clear from their comment that they exhibit some impatience with the philosophy, which has underlain American psychology in this century, that one should study what people do and not what they think they plan to do. However, it seems that one domain in which this philosophy is strong is in the study of language communication.

Actually, for models as well as for explanations, the test of a scholar's "good taste" is to distinguish the potentially "structural" properties which fit with other properties of the system, from the isolated facts which cannot be expected to fill in any very special role in *any* kind of structure.

For example, to qualify as "linguistic", the statistical properties of the words of discourse must be systematic and general enough to be independent of what discourse is about. Further, because statistical and grammatical structures seem uncorrelated, in the first approximation, one might expect to encounter laws which are independent of the grammar of the language under consideration. Hence, from the viewpoint of significance (and also of the mathematical method) there would be an enormous difference between: *on the one hand*, the collection of data that are unlikely to exhibit any regularity other than the approximate stability of the relative frequencies, when different samples are compared; and, *on the other hand*, the study of laws that are valid for natural discourse but not for other organized systems of signs.

We shall not prolong this discussion, which can be found in [6] (Chapters 1 and 2). We have discussed there the relations which must exist between the statistical and the grammatical models. Strictly speaking, they are contradictory but this does not mean that either is wrong. The example of physical science shows rather, that when the descriptions of several sections of a broad scientific field have been sufficiently well formalized, they end up by relying upon flatly contradictory axiomatics. One must learn to let them live together by never applying either outside of its range of validity.

Enumerations similar to those of statistics play a quite different role in another problem, that of species and of genera; that is, of classification and of taxonomy. There the problem is not that of the frequencies of usage of the labels of certain "specific" categories, but that of the numbers of "specific" categories in the different "generic" categories. These relationships can be very easily observed on long samples of discourse and one may perphaps argue that they are not laws of language as an organized system, but laws of the outside world which discourse describes. But one may also argue that they are laws of the way in which the human mind classifies the objects of the outside world for the purposes of human communication. If so, they would be linguistic laws (definitely not grammatical laws, however). Actually, we have shown that the observed laws of classification could be explained either as laws of the outside world or as laws of language, so that the question cannot be settled this way, and this border, between what is linguistic and what is relative to the environment, remains unclear. (We regret that this aspect of our work has attracted less attention than that on word frequencies; see [5] and Chapter 3 of [6].)

We would like to terminate this section by a very personal comment. The statistical linguistic laws mentioned at the beginning of §0 are based upon limit theorems of probability; their use is motivated by reasons very similar to those upon which statistical thermodynamics is based. Some critics of the relevance of our models to linguistics claim that our results are therefore of interest only to "certain statisticians", and not to "linguists", in a very narrow view of that term. This attitude could be contrasted with that of some physicists who, on the contrary, resent any suggestion that the laws of thermodynamics are also a mathematically self-contained conceptual system, mostly independent of its physical substratum (such a suggestion is an extrapolation of the attitude held by Josiah Willard Gibbs around 1900, and we have devoted much thought to its elaboration). To such physicists, it is almost a crime to ever stop to disentangle the physics and the mathematics of thermodynamics. Both of the extreme attitudes which we have mentioned are, in our opinion, based upon incorrect interpretations of the relationship which ought to exist between a mathematical model and its object. To motivate this opinion and to help bring both parties to a common and reasonable middle ground we have been led to fight for seemingly contradictory issues in different fields of our activity.

APPENDIX A

SAMPLE DISTRIBUTIONS LINKED WITH THE POPULATION RANK-FREQUENCY LAW $p(r) = Pr^{-B}$, WHEN $B > 1$ AND $R = \infty$

(Although the calculations of this appendix are quite obvious, it was felt that it is useful to put them in the record once for all.)

1. The number-frequency relationship. This relationship is defined only for samples and not for populations. We shall derive it from the above law $p(r)$, which applies to populations but was of course inferred, by a somewhat loose argument, from data relative to finite samples. Our purpose is to justify this loose inference. For that, note that the probability of the event (r, k, i) that the word W_r come out i times in a sample of k words is:

$$\binom{i}{k} p(r)^i [1 - p(r)]^{k-i} .$$

The number of words which occur i times in a sample of k is therefore:

$$f(i, k) = \sum_r U(r, k, i)$$

where $U = 1$, if the event (r, k, i) occurs, and $U = 0$, otherwise. The events (r, k, i) for different r are not independent, but the mean values add, so that:

$$E[f(i, k)] = \sum_r E[U(r, k, i)] = \binom{i}{k} \sum_r p(r)^i [1 - p(r)]^{k-i} .$$

Write $p(r) = x$, and hence $r = (x/P)^{-A}$, where $A = 1/B$, and compare the last sum to the integral

$$\int_0^1 x^i (1 - x)^{k-i} dr(x) = AP^A \int_0^1 (1 - x)^{k-i} x^{i-1-A} dx .$$

For large k, the sum differs little from the sum restricted to some range such as $(10, \infty)$, and the integral differs little from the integral restricted to $(0, p(10))$; finally, the restricted sum and integral differ little, so that

$$E[f(i, k)] \sim AP^A \frac{\Gamma(k - i + 1)\Gamma(i - A)}{\Gamma(k + 1 - A)} \cdot \frac{k!}{i!(k - i)!}$$

$$= AP^A \cdot \frac{\Gamma(i - A)}{\Gamma(i + 1)} \cdot \frac{\Gamma(k + 1)}{\Gamma(k + 1 - A)}$$

k being large,

$$E[f(i, k)] \sim AP^A \cdot k^A \cdot \frac{\Gamma(i - A)}{\Gamma(i + 1)} \, .$$

If i is also large,

(nf) $$E[f(i, k)] \sim AP^A k^A i^{-(A+1)}$$

which is indeed the form of the number-frequency relationship which is found to be obeyed by the empirical data (and can also be obtained by shorter but looser arguments).

If i is not large, one obtains a modification of the (nf) law.[6] One may examine this modification for $i = 1$, $i = 2$, etc.

$i = 1$, $\Gamma(1 - A)/\Gamma(1 + 1) = \Gamma(1 - A)$, which is always greater than $1^{-(A+1)}$; the margin becomes small as $A \to 0$, but it tends to ∞, as $A \to 1$.

$i = 2$, $\Gamma(2 - A)/\Gamma(2 + 1) = (1/2)\Gamma(2 - A)$, which is always greater than $2^{-(A+1)} = (1/2)2^{-A}$; the ratio is close to 1 if $A \to 0$, it becomes larger and tending to 2 if $A \to 1$.

The approximate form of $E[f(i, k)]$, which was found above, applies to all values of i. One might want to use it to verify that $k = \sum_i if(i, k)$. But in fact, the second term is infinite, so that this formula for k cannot be used.

The present problem provides an excellent opportunity to try the Turing-Good correction. According to Good [Biometrika vol. 40 (1953)], when the values of $f(i, k)$ are given, the maximum likelihood estimate of the population value of the number of occurrences of a label *is not* i, but is instead:

$$i^0 = (i + 1)f(i + 1, k)/f(i, k) \, .$$

Starting from the above number-frequency relationship, one finds

$$i^0 = (i + 1)\frac{\Gamma(i + 1 - A)}{\Gamma(i + 2)} \frac{\Gamma(i + 1)}{\Gamma(i - A)} = (i + 1)\frac{i - A}{i + 1} = i - A \, .$$

The correction is indeed in the right direction.

2. The rank-frequency relationship. Let us now perform the passage from the population (rp) relation to the sample (rf) relation, through the (nf) relation just obtained. Neglecting the values of r which correspond to small i, note that

---

[6] This modification (analogous to one suggested by H. A. Simon [17]) may also be obtained by approximating the original binomial by a Poisson distribution

$$[kp(r)]^i \exp[-kp(r!)](i)^{-1} \, .$$

Hence:

$$E[f(i, k)] = \sum_r [kp(r)]^i \exp[-kp(r)](i!)^{-1} \sim \int_0^\infty y^i \exp(-y)dr(y)(i!)^{-1}$$

$$\sim Ak^A P^A \frac{\Gamma(i - A)}{\Gamma(i + 1)} \, .$$

In both cases, the slight complication due to the ratios of gamma functions is an effect of the integral character of i. This effect is not very important from a conceptual viewpoint, but it makes $f(1, k)$ a very unreliable basis for an estimation of A.

$$\sum_{j=i}^{\infty} E[f(j, k)] = \sum_{j=i}^{\infty} A P^A k^A j^{-(A+1)}$$

is, among the words of frequency i, the rank of the one which was arbitrarily placed last in the sample ranking; also, $-1 + \sum_{j=i+1}^{\infty} A P^A k^A j^{-(A+1)}$ is the rank of the word arbitrarily placed first. Now consider the integral, $\int_i^{\infty} A P^A k^A j^{-(A+1)} dj$. Its approximation by trapezes, based upon integral values of j, is precisely the arithmetic average of the ranks of the first and last of the words having occurred i times; hence it is the arithmetic average of the ranks of the words occurring i times; further, the operations of averaging of $E(f(i, k))$ and of averaging of ranks can be permuted, to give:

$$E[\text{sample mean of } r(i)] = \int_i^{\infty} A P^A k^A j^{-(A+1)} dj = P^A k^A i^{-A} .$$

Hence, if the sample (rf) relation, considered as a function r of i, is doubly averaged (with respect to all chance events and with respect to all ways of ranking words of same i) one falls back on the population (rp) relationship. That something of the type should happen is of course obvious; but, because of the unusual coordinates, it was less obvious that this should happen to $r(i)$ rather than to $i(r)$. Further, the result no longer holds for the range of very small i ($i = 1, i = 2$), where the sample $E[E(r)]$ is larger than the population rank.

Consider now the sample average of $\log(r)$; it is smaller than $\log$ (average of r), but the difference is applicable only for small i, and this decreases the excess between the sample EE and the population norm.

3. The type-token relationship. It is useful to derive the relation existing between the number k, and the number of different words in a sample of length k, which we shall designate by $d(k)$; in this context, k is called the token number and $d(k)$ is called the type number. One obtains this expression from the rank-frequency law by "integration"; the rank-frequency law itself is derived from the number-frequency by integration. Hence, the sample fluctuations due to chance decrease as one goes from (nf) to (rf) to $d(k)$, and the precision in the graphic estimation of B increases.

We suppose that k is very large, and note that $d(k)$ is a random variable, which can be written as

$$d(k) = \sum_r d^0(r, k)$$

where $d^0(r, k) = 1$, if the word W_r of rank r has appeared in the sample k and $d^0(r, k) = 0$, otherwise. The variables $d^0(r, k)$ are not independent, but the mean of the sum is still the sum of the means of the addends. That is,

$$E[d(k)] = \sum_r E(d^0(r, k))$$
$$= \sum_r \text{probability that } W_r \text{ has appeared in the sample } k.$$

If successive words are independent,

$$E[d(k)] = \sum_r \{1 - [1 - p(r)]^k\} .$$

This will be computed by the intermediate of

$$E[d(k + 1)] - E(d(k)) = \sum_1^\infty [1 - p(r)]^k p(r) .$$

(One notes that this expression is identical to $f(1, k)\Big/\binom{1}{k} = f(1, k)/k$, irrespectively of the form of the law $p(r)$. This result is due to Turing and Good, see Good, *op. cit.*) Write $p(r) = x$ and hence $r = (x/P)^{-A}$. Compare the last displayed expression and the integral

$$\int_0^1 (1 - x)^k x \, dr(x) = AP^A \int_0^1 (1 - x)^k x^{-A} dx .$$

For large k, the sum differs little from the sum restricted to some range such as $(10, \infty)$; similarly, the integral differs little from the integral restricted to the range $(0, p(10))$; finally, the restricted sum and the integral differ little, so that

$$E[d(k + 1)] - E[d(k)] \sim AP^A \int_0^1 (1 - x)^k x^{-A} dx = AP^A \frac{\Gamma(k + 1) \cdot \Gamma(1 - A)}{\Gamma(k + 1 + 1 - A)}$$

which, since k is large, further becomes:

$$E[d(k + 1)] - E[d(k)] \sim [AP^A \Gamma(1 - A)] k^{(A-1)} .$$

Finally,[7]

$$E(d(k)) \sim P^A \Gamma(1 - A) k^A .$$

One may note that $E[f(i, k)] = [A/\Gamma(1 - A)] i^{-(A+1)} E[d(k)]$.

Conversely, the (rp) relationship may be derived from this type-token law. Remark that, as A tends to 1, the coefficient $P^A \Gamma(1 - A)$ of $E[d(k)]$ tends towards 1, while P^A tends towards 0. It is obvious that 1 is the correct result, since all words then tend to be different.

Remark that, in a useful terminology due to economists, the constant A, which is the ratio of $\delta d(k)/d(k)$ to $\delta k/k$, may be called the "type-token elasticity".

---

[7] This value should be compared with the value of r corresponding to the intercept between the population (rp) curve and the ordinate $i = 1$, that is, $p = 1/k$. This procedure gives:

$$d'(k) = P^A k^A$$

which differs from $E(d(k))$ by the factor $\Gamma(1 - A)$, independent of k. That is, on bilogarithmic coordinates, there is a constant interval between the intercept of the (rp) curve and the abscissa of the last word; but one should not except to find this exactly justified in fact, because of the wide fluctuations in $d(k)$.

Another estimate of $d(k)$ may be based upon the expression $\sum_i f(i, k)$, in which $f(i, k)$ is replaced by its approximation $Ak^A P^A i^{-(A+1)}$. One then gets $k^A P^A$ as with the intercept.

The exact distribution of $d(k)$ would be easy to evaluate, if the $d^0(r, k)$ were independent random variables. This is not the case, but one may modify the generation of the sample to make it hold. This modification implies that the total number of words itself is made a random variable, K, having the expected value $E(K) = k$.

The logarithm of the characteristic function of $d'(k)$ is then:

$$\sum \log \left[Z(r, k) \exp\{-it[1 - Z(r, k)]\} + [1 - Z(r, k)] \exp[-itZ(r, k)] \right]$$

where $Z(r, k) = (1 - p_r)^k$. This c.f. is mostly made of contributions of ranks r such that $p_r k \sim 1$, so that $Z(r, k)$ may be approximated by $\exp(-p_r k)$. Further, the finite sum may be approximated by an integral. Take $y = p_r k = Pkr^{-B}$ as the free variable of integration so that $r = P^A k^A y^{-A}$; at this step, the $\log$ (c.f.) is approximated by

$$P^A k^A A \int_0^{kp(1)} \log \left[e^{-y}e^{-it(1-e^{-y})} + (1 - e^{-y})e^{ite^{-y}} \right] y^{-A-1} dy .$$

There is no convergence problem near $y = 0$, nor near $y = \infty$ (where the expression in square brackets remains finite). Finally, $d'(k)$ is the sum of k^A random variables having a finite variance and zero mean value, so that $k^{-A}d'(k)$ is a gaussian variable.

As to the random variable K-k, it is easily seen that it is the sum of independent Bernouilli variables, each giving the number of occurrences of some W_r. They all obviously have finite variance proportional to k and are such that the sum of the variances converges to a fixed multiple of k. Finally K-k differs little from a gaussian.

If $d(k)$ is plotted on bilogarithmic paper, one should not expect much deviation from the straight line representing $E[d(k)]$.

APPENDIX B

We have assumed all through that discourse is a stationary process approximable by a stochastic sequence of independently chosen words; this is what we have called the Maxwell-Boltzmann syntax. Actually, this hypothesis of independence is rather worse for very frequent and very rare words, than it is for others.

For example, given the frequency of the most probable word, which in English discourse is typically THE, it should often happen that two THE's follow each other; but this is never so. As a result, the number of possible positions for THE is smaller than the total number of words in a sample and the probability of THE is underestimated by its gross frequency.

On the other hand, there is very definite clustering for rare words: if they occur once, there is an increased probability of their occurring again sooner than predicted by chance. As a result, the frequencies of rare words may be overestimated; this effect would be added to Turing's correction mentioned in Appendix A.

It may be that the above two effects, combined, straighten out the graph of $\log p(r)$ for small r and increase its slope for large r, that is, increase the estimate of B.

REFERENCES

1. J. Aitchison and J. A. C. Brown, *The lognormal distribution*, London and New York, Cambridge University Press, 1957.

2. G. Champernowne, *A model of income distribution*, Economic Journal vol. 63 (1953) pp. 318 ff.

3. J. B. Estoup, *Gammes sténographiques*, 4th edition, Paris, 1916.

4. W. Feller, *Fluctuation theory of recurrent events*, Trans. Amer. Math. Soc. vol. 67 (1949) pp. 98–119.

5. B. Mandelbrot, *On the language of taxonomy (categories with Willis structure)*, Information theory, Third London Symposium (edited by C. Cherry), London, Butterworths, and New York, Academic Press, 1956; pp. 135–145.

6. ———, *Linguistique statistique macroscopique*, Logique, langage and théorie de l'information, by L. Apostel, B. Mandelbrot and A. Morf, Paris, Presses Universitaires de France, 1957; pp. 1–78.

7. ———, *Théorie mathématique de la loi d'Estoup-Zipf*, Paris, Institut de Statistique de l'Université, 1957.

8. ———, *A note on a class of skew distribution functions*, Information and Control vol. 2 (1959) pp. 90–99.

9. ———, *The Pareto-Lévy law and the distribution of income*, International Economic Review vol. 1 (1960) pp. 79–106.

10. ———, *Some Pareto-Lévy stochastic processes and the variation of income*, Yorktown, New York, I.B.M. Research. Report RC-222.

11. A. Markov, *Essai d'une recherche statistique sur le texte du roman "Eugène Onéguine"*, Bulletin de l'Académie Impériale des Sciences de Saint-Petersbourg vol. VII (1913).

12. E. Galanter and G. A. Miller, *Some comments on stochastic models and psychological theories*, Mathematical methods in the social sciences (edited by K. J. Arrow, S. Karlin and P. Suppes), Stanford, Stanford University Press, 1960; pp. 277–297.

13. G. A. Miller and E. Newman, *Tests of a statistical explanation of the rank-frequency relation for words in written English*, American Journal of Psychology vol. 71 (1958) pp. 209–218.

14. V. Pareto, *Cours d'économie politique*, Lausanne and Paris, Rouge & Co., 1897.

15. F. de Saussure, *Cours de linguistique générale*, Lausanne and Paris, Payot, 1916.

16. C. Shannon, *A mathematical theory of communication*, Bell System Technical Journal vol. 27 (1948) pp. 379–423, 623–656.

17. H. A. Simon, *On a class of skew probability distributions*, Biometrika vol. 42 (1955) pp. 425–440 (see also H. A. Simon, *Models of man*, New York, Wiley, 1957; pp. 145 ff.).

18. J. C. Willis, *Age and area*, London and New York, Cambridge University Press, 1922.

19. G. U. Yule, *A mathematical theory of evolution, based on the conclusions of Dr. J. C. Willis, F.R.S.*, Philosophical Transactions of the Royal Society of London vol. B 213 (1924) pp. 21 ff.

20. G. K. Zipf, *Human behavior and the principle of least effort*, Reading, Massachusetts, Addison-Wesley Press, 1949.

I. B. M. RESEARCH CENTER,
YORKTOWN HEIGHTS, NEW YORK

GRAMMAR FOR THE HEARER

BY

CHARLES F. HOCKETT

Introduction. This paper deals, in a preliminary way, with the problem of grammatical design from the vantage point of a hearer: that is, of a person who knows a language and who, for the moment, is silently listening to someone else speak.

Perhaps this angle of approach should be called a "disadvantage point" rather than a vantage point. The grammarian can view a sentence as an enduring structure, to be scanned at leisure and repeatedly, and as easily from right to left or upside-down or inside-out as from left to right. He can do this because he deals not directly with a sentence, but only with a representation thereof, spread out before him like a cadaver on a marble slab, to be dissected at his convenience. The hearer has none of these advantages. He is exposed to an utterance just once, and is forced to register its ingredients in just the temporal sequence in which they reach him.

The hearer cannot know for sure, part way through a sentence, just what is going to be said next; he can at most have an array of expectations derived from earlier experience (that is, from his knowledge of the language) and from what has been said so far this time (that is, from his partial knowledge of the current sentence). For the hearer, then, a grammatical system must be viewed as a stochastic process.

The simplest stochastic model worthy of consideration is a finite Markov chain. Such a model, regarded as a "generative grammar," is called a finite state grammar, and it generates a finite state "language." Chomsky has shown that, if we accept certain very reasonable empirical assumptions about English, then English is not a finite state language.[1] He has also claimed that no finite state approximation to English can match the known facts of the language closely enough to be of any interest. This second point is, I believe, false. It will be shown later in this paper that it is in theory possible to match the facts of English as closely as we wish with a finite Markov chain.

1. Empirical assumptions. For the present investigation we shall make certain customary assumptions and two special ones.

The customary assumptions include the following three:

(A1) The vocabulary of a language is finite.

(A2) Grammar and semantics are separable.

(A3) We can validly confine our attention to spans of finite length called SENTENCES (though these need not coincide exactly with any traditional definition of "sentence").

The customary assumptions also include the following two, which are

---

[1] The proof is given informally in Chomsky, 1957 [2, chapter 3]; formally in Chomsky, 1956 [1].

rarely stated explicitly:

(A4) We can distinguish between events in which a hearer is learning a language and those in which he is merely using it, and we can neglect events of the former sort.

(A5) The hearer always hears correctly: that is, he hears two words or sequences of words as different if and only if they are phonemically different.

Each of these five assumptions, save possibly the second, can be questioned on empirical grounds, but each can be imagined as ALMOST true, so that results based on the assumptions can constitute some reasonable approximation to the facts.

Our two special assumptions are as follows:

(A6) In order to understand what he hears, a hearer sometimes has to PARSE a sentence—that is, discover its grammatical organization—in much the same way a grammarian parses it.

(A7) Any fact about a sentence used by a hearer in parsing the sentence is itself a grammatical fact.

The point of assumption (A7) is to preclude the possibility that a hearer may sometimes first figure out what a sentence means and then, using that information about its meaning, infer its grammatical structure. In learning a language this must happen often. In merely using a language already known, we assume it does not, since the hearer's purpose is to understand what he hears: if he achieves this understanding without parsing the sentence in all detail, he no longer has any motivation for completing the parsing.

Assumption (A6) requires sharpening before we can use it. At one extreme, we might imagine that a hearer never parses a sentence until he has heard all of it. Apart from the fact that the subsequent parsing would have to be done very fast, this would put the hearer on a par with the grammarian, in the sense that the parsing done by either would be based on all the information the sentence contains: words received last would bear on the parsing of the first part of the sentence as much as vice versa. This version of the assumption is almost certainly false. Yet it is the sort of false-to-fact "stupidity assumption" often usefully made at certain stages in any field of investigation, and is, indeed, just the assumption that has underlain the procedures of marble-slab grammar from Dionysius Thrax and Panini to the present.

At the opposite extreme, we could pretend that a hearer does as much parsing as he can after he hears each successive linear ingredient of the sentence—after each new morph, let us say, or after each new word. This extreme version is doubtless equally false. It is more likely that the actual frequency of hearer-parsing varies from occasion to occasion, as do, also, its completeness, its accuracy, and the degree to which the hearer is aware of the process. Some of the sentences we hear are long "idioms" for which no parsing at all is necessary. They have, it is true, an internal organization that can be dissected by a grammarian, but the hearer, once he recognizes that such-and-such an idiom is being uttered, can treat it as a single stored lexical unit. Other sentences are de novo creations of the speaker in most of their detail. For these, the hearer perhaps parses at a larger number of successive points.

But since we cannot know, in the majority of actual instances, just how frequently or completely a hearer parses, it makes a kind of sense to deal with hearer-parsing in terms of a stupidity-assumption that is the converse of the usual one. That is, we shall pretend that a hearer parses as best he can after receiving each successive word of a sentence. Thus the mesh of our net, though perhaps finer than absolutely necessary, is at least smaller than the fish we want to catch. The hearer can hardly do MORE successive parsing than is provided for by our model.

2. Informal examples. Let us pretend that we are listening to a lecture, and that the first word we hear is *empathy*. We shall assume that this word is not accompanied by an "utterance-closing" intonation.

Now how can anyone, hearer or grammarian, parse a single unit? In one sense, he cannot. However, since the first word is not accompanied by an utterance-closing intonation, we expect more to follow, and we expect that whatever follows will stand in one or another grammatical relationship with the first word. It is therefore possible to tabulate the various grammatical relationships in which this first word could possibly stand with any continuation, as shown in Figure 1. The notation *"Na"* means that the word we heard

Figure 1   Figure 2

is a noun of a certain subclass. The marks—borrowed from the typography, but in no sense from the semantics, of symbolic logic and mathematics—have the following meanings: " > " means that the next thing spoken might be something to which the part already spoken is an attribute, as in *empathy methods* or the like. " < " means that the next to come might be a postposed attribute modifying *empathy*, as in *empathy in psychotherapy*. " + " means that the next to come might stand in a coordinate construction with what has already been said: *empathy or intuition*, or *empathy and all similar magic.* "≡" means that the next to come might stand in apposition with *empathy*: *empathy, a method used in modern psychotherapy*. Finally, "ε" means that *empathy* might turn out to be all of a subject, the next element in the sentence beginning a predicate: *empathy is a powerful tool*.

This is a wide range of grammatical possibilities. Perhaps some further possibilities have inadvertently been omitted. But some grammatical relationships that function in English MUST be omitted: for example, it is entirely precluded that the next element should be the object of *empathy*, in the sense in which *you* is object of *for* in *for you* or of *see* in *see you*, since *empathy* is not the sort of word that can occupy the first position in any such construction.

Let us now assume that the next word we actually hear is *as*. The sequence *empathy as* yields, of course, a very different sort of diagram, as shown in

Figure 3   Figure 4

Figure 2. Most of the possibilities left open by the uttering of *empathy* have now been eliminated. *As* begins a grammatical form that will stand as a postposed attribute to *empathy*.[2] This fixed fact is indicated by the mark " < " at the junction of the boxes in the diagram for *empathy* and for *as.... As* must itself be followed by something standing to it in the relation of object: this is the significance of the mark " → ". The other three marks have the same meanings as before; they are put in parentheses because they do not indicate what can happen IMMEDIATELY next. The possibility of a further postposed attribute, or of something in apposition, or the like, is temporarily in abeyance, until the materials demanded by *as* have been spoken. However, though postponed, these possibilities have not been cancelled: they will come actively into play later.

Figures 1 and 2 are achieved by what we shall call OPEN-ENDED PARSING, and represent the GRAMMATICAL STATES established, respectively, but the first

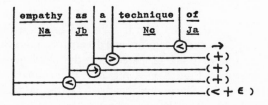

Figure 5

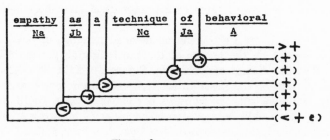

Figure 6

---

[2] The possibility of something like *Empathy, as you all know,...* is precluded by the assumed intonation.

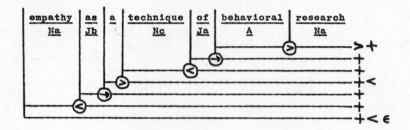

Figure 7

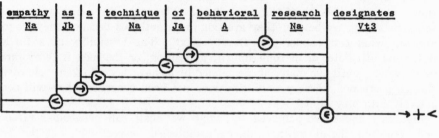

Figure 8

word and by the first two words heard. We can imagine that our idealized hearer does not register the incoming word *empathy* merely as a string of phonemes. Rather, the very act of perceiving the word generates in him all the information shown in Figure 1—a bit of it determinate, the rest merely a PATTERN OF EXPECTATION. Since our idealized hearer is faultless, each successive word actually fits into the proceding pattern of expectation in one or another of the ways for which the pattern provides, and replaces that pattern of expectation by a new one, at the same time adding to what is determinate. That is, each new word replaces a grammatical state by a new grammatical state.

Figures 3 through 8 show the open-ended parsings of our target sentence after the receipt by the hearer of the third through the eighth words.

Note that the receipt of *technique* (Figure 4) might be described as "opening up" certain of the possibilities that had been temporarily in abeyance. That is, while neither *empathy as* nor *empathy as a* could be followed by something that would be a postposed modifier of *empathy* or of some phrase centering on *empathy*, as soon as *technique* has been added this possibility is restored; hence the parentheses are deleted from around " > ".

Note also the sharp difference between the situation after *research* and that after *designates* (Figures 7 and 8). After *research* the grammatical possibilities are numerous—if the diagramming is accurate, there are eleven. After *designates* they are far fewer; all but one of the eleven after *research* have been eliminated, since one has been converted into a certainty. It is finally established that everything spoken so far, except *designates* itself, constitutes a unit (i. e., the subject of the sentence), and that anything further in the sentence will relate to that whole composite unit, not to any of its individual components. But it should also be noted that it is not the receipt of the last word of the subject that signals to the hearer the completion of the subject; rather, it is the receipt of the first word AFTER the completion of the subject.

3. Residual indeterminacy. In our first test sentence, as an examination of Figures 1–8 will show, the indeterminacies after the first n words all concern the grammatical relationship which will hold between something already spoken and something not yet said. But it is also possible for the parsing of words already heard to remain partly indeterminate until crucial later material has been added.

Suppose, for example, that a speaker begins with

(1)   *The old men and women.* . . .

Open-ended parsing of this initial fragment yields something like Figure 9. What can come next depends in part on whether *old* is construed with *men* or with *men and women*; but the hearer cannot tell which of these is the case until he has heard more. Even when the sentence has been completed, the ambiguity of parsing may remain: for example, if the rest of the sentence is

(2)   *. . . were all frightened.*

In any such case, we shall speak of a RESIDUAL AMBIGUITY. Residual ambiguity is the structural basis for one kind of verbal joke: the pun.

On the other hand, suppose that the continuation of the sentence were one of the following:

(3)   *. . . stayed at home while the young folks went off to the dance.*

(4)   *. . . stayed at home while the young men went off to the war.*

There seems to be little SEMANTIC ambiguity about *old men and women* by the end of either of these sentences (1–3 or 1–4). But before we can conclude that there is also no residual ambiguity of parsing, we must recall assumption (A7). If the hearer resolves the ambiguity of parsing of (1) by virtue of information conveyed later in the sentence, the information so used must itself be grammatical, not merely semantic. Considering the high degree of parallelism between (3) and (4), we should have to conclude that *folks* and *men*, or *dance* and *war*, or both of these pairs of words, are grammatically different rather than merely lexically distinct members of single form-classes. Similar consideration of other sentences soon shows that, for a hearer, the vocabulary of a language must fall into a vastly larger number of grammatically distinct classes than most grammarians have wanted to deal with.[3]

I can see nothing wrong with such a conclusion, but there is an alternative possibility to be considered. We might decide to say that no continuation removes the ambiguity of parsing of (1). But if no context can remove the

---

[3] Harris, 1946 [3], works with only about 18 form classes of words, and Harris, 1957 [4], with only 7; but in both cases the classes are *not* pairwise disjunct, as we require.

ambiguity, then it would be better to say that there is no GRAMMATICAL ambiguity about the phrase in the first place—any ambiguity is purely semantic. Our parsing machinery should then be revised in such a way as to provide the same grammatical description of *old men and women* regardless of the sentence context in which that phrase occurs. It is easy enough to do this: we merely recognize a four-part construction in which the first constituent must be a descriptive adjective, the second and fourth plural nouns, and the third the word *and*.

This second alternative might be attractive if we could carry it through so drastically as to achieve the following result: that at the end of a sentence there are never any residual ambiguities of parsing. I think it highly doubtful that any such result could be achieved, unless we were willing to transfer to the sphere of semantics an enormous number of distinctions that we have always thought were grammatical and without which our conception of grammar would be impoverished indeed. There are too many instances in which what strikes us intuitively as an indeterminacy of meaning seems to correlate with alternative interpretations of grammatical organization. We want to formalize the latter differences partly as a step towards the explication of the former. Therefore, whenever we seem to have some choice, we ought to accept a "richer" grammar rather than a poorer one. In the present connection, our empirical assumptions do not force either type of decision, but allow us to take our choice.[4] We shall choose a "richer" grammar—without necessarily implying that the particular examples displayed above must be among those for which the grammar provides, since they were meant merely to be suggestive. Our decision may be strengthened, perhaps, by a second example. Initial sequence (5) shows an ambiguity of parsing, unresolved by completion (6), resolved in one way—or at least pushed towards such resolution—by completion (7), and in a different way by (8):

(5)   *A man eating fish...*

(6)   *...has an unbalanced diet.*

(7)   *...called the piranha is found in the tropical waters of Brazil.*

(8)   *...on Friday is not necessarily a Catholic.*

Or, again (with credit to Noam Chomsky):

(9)   *Flying planes...*

(10)   *...can be dangerous.*

(11)   *...is dangerous.*

(12)   *...are dangerous.*

4. Garden-path jokes. Having concluded that an ambiguity of parsing can be removed by what follows the ambiguous phrase, we must now ask whether the reverse of this can happen. That is, can an unambiguous struc-

---

[4] A third alternative, of course, is to suspend Assumption (A7). But this would seem to threaten the highly-prized fundamental postulate of the separability of grammar and semantics (our assumption A2).

ture earlier in a sentence be rendered ambiguous by what comes later?

Something like this seems to happen in certain kinds of jokes. The jokester builds up in the hearer a conviction that a word or phrase is to be interpreted in a certain way, and then adds something that either renders the phrase ambiguous or forces a different unambiguous interpretation:

(13)   *He waxed wroth when I hit him, and Roth didn't like it a bit.* (Groucho Marx)

(14)   *We were going to take the plane to Chicago but it was too heavy.*

(14)   *Woman who cooks carrots and peas in same pot very unsanitary.* (Confucius)

However, in our model we are dealing with a faultless hearer who always does ALL the open-ended parsing he can after each successive word, regardless of the relative probabilities associated with the different possibilities. One residual fault of such a faultless hearer is that he can have no sense of humor. He cannot hear the difference between the adjective *wroth* and the surname *Roth* when he first hears the word, since they are homophones. Therefore his open-ended parsing of the initial sequence *He waxed wroth* must be ambiguous.

The impact on the hearer of a joke of this sort thus turns on the fact that real hearers are not faultless: they can be led up the garden path. They can be induced to neglect some of the grammatical possibilities and to expect others, and can thus be given a jolt by an unexpected though perfectly grammatical twist.

We conclude that, within our frame of reference, an initially unambiguous structure CANNOT be rendered ambiguous by what comes later. Whenever this seems to happen, the structure in question was actually ambiguous to start with.

5. End of sentence. We have been speaking freely of "end of sentence," but this, too, is a point about which a question must be asked: what signals "end of sentence" to a hearer?

Many of our co-workers on English would immediately say that end of sentence is signalled by the occurrence of a sentence-final intonation. There is doubtless a positive statistical correlation between so-called sentence-final intonations and grammatical ends of sentences, but the correlation is far from perfect. Thus someone might say (we use the Smith and Trager symbols for intonation):[5]

(16)   *I didn't want to go there at ³all¹#*

Open-ended parsing shows that this CAN be a whole sentence (at least by our everyday definition of "sentence"). A hearer, registering this possibility, might proceed to say something in reply. Or, if this does not happen, the speaker

---

[5] Only relevant parts of the intonation are marked. Pitch levels run from bottom to top, /¹/ through /⁴/; /|/, /||/, and /#/ represent terminals.

might continue—perhaps after a considerable pause—with

(17) $^3yesterday^2 ||, {}^2though\ to^3day^2 | {}^2I\ don't\ {}^3mind\ so\ much^1 \#$

Now (16) could be a whole sentence, as could also the sequence (16–17); but (17) alone could not. Therefore, if (16) is indeed followed by (17), it has turned out that (16) was not all of a sentence but only the beginning of one.

In general, the most that the hearer's open-ended parsing of an initial sequence can tell him—even if he takes into consideration, as he certainly does, the accompanying intonations—is whether or not that sequence CAN be a sentence. (16) is an instance of a sequence that can be; Figure 3 shows one that cannot be. If an initial sequence is fit to be a whole sentence, then the only reliable signal as to whether, in fact, it is one, is what is said next. If what is said next—by the same speaker or by some other, such as the erstwhile hearer—begins a new sentence, then the preceding sequence was a sentence; otherwise not.

This can be compared with the situation portrayed in Figures 7 and 8: *research* ends the subject, but the hearer cannot know this until he hears *designates*.

6. Constructional grammar. Our understanding of grammar for the hearer and our preference for one or another abstract ("marble slab") grammatical model are necessarily interrelated. Before we can continue with our exploration of the former, we must turn briefly to the latter.

For this, the diagrams shown in Figures 1–9 supply a good point of departure. They provide symbolization for four different sorts of things: (1) words; (2) the form classes to which words belong; (3) hierarchical organization or IC (immediate constituent) structure; and (4) construction types.

A construction type is a set of constructions that have some formal property in common: for instance, *black cat* and *ran quickly* are both built by constructions of a so-called "attributive" type, in that one of the constituents resembles the whole form more than does the other (*black cat* can be used much as *cat* can, but not as *black* can; *ran quickly* can be used much like *ran*, and not like *quickly*). In our diagrams, we symbolize construction types rather than individual constructions merely as a matter of convenience.

A CONSTRUCTION may be described as a way of putting forms together into larger forms — words into phrases, words and phrases into larger phrases. Abstractly, a construction is a relation: a class of ordered n-ads of forms, where n is always finite, usually small, often exactly 2, but never 1. A form "built by" a construction is necessarily COMPOSITE: that is, an atomic element (a word, in our current frame of reference) does not belong to a construction.

Two forms, simple or composite, belong to the same FORM CLASS if they have exactly identical privileges of occurrence: that is, if each occurs as the ith constituent in any construction in which the other occurs as the ith constituent. Two composite forms belong to the same construction if, for all relevant i, the ith constituent of each belongs to the same form class as the ith constituent of the other, and if the two composite forms belong to the same form-class. It follows that every member of a construction belongs to

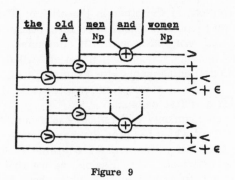

Figure 9

the same form class, but not necessarily vice versa.

The arrangement of constituents in a composite form is determined by the construction, and two constructions are different if the arrangement is different. Thus *John is here* and *Is John here?* both have ICs *John* and *is here*, put together by two different constructions of a single construction type: the first construction requires that *John* precede *is here*, while the second requires that *John* be inserted at a specifiable place within *is here*.

It is an empirical fact of English that in a great many instances the construction to which a composite form belongs is inferrable without residue from the identity of the constituents (and their arrangement). Thus *black cat* seems never to occur save in contexts in which the construction is a specific one of the type attribute-plus-noun-head. However, there are also ambiguous cases, and a great deal of the character of our abstract grammatical model depends on how we choose to deal with ambiguity.

Consider the two-word composite form *yellow clothes*. This can occur in sentence-contexts of either of the following varieties:

(18)   *Washing in strong soap will yellow clothes.*

(19)   *She likes to wear yellow clothes.*

In a CONSTRUCTIONAL GRAMMAR, we say that *yellow* is the same word in both, that *clothes* is the same word in both, but that the two words are put together by different constructions. The first construction is one of the type verb-plus-object, the second one of the type attribute-plus-noun-head. Along with this, we are able to say that two words are the same word if and only if they are phonemically identical (no homophones or zeros), and that no word belongs to more than one form class. Ambiguity is then handled wholly in terms either of constructions (*yellow clothes*) or of IC organization (*old men and women*).

An alternative method is to introduce inaudible differences among words in such a way that constructions are wholly eliminated as independent ingredients in the grammatical model. Thus, for example, we recognize two words, *yellow*₁ and *yellow*₂, the former belonging to some subclass of the class of verbs, the latter to some subclass of the class of adjectives. Sentence (18) contains the former, sentence (19) the latter. (Or, equally well, a single word *yellow* is assigned to two different form classes, and is said to be a member

of one in the one context, of the other in the other.) This alternative deals
with ambiguity in terms of homophony or of form classes (*yellow clothes*) and
of IC organization (*old men and women*). It eliminates constructions by reducing them all to a single "construction" often called COLLOCATION. With
certain further (optional) adjustments—for example, an insistence that forms
in collocation must always be adjacent, never separated—this procedure yields
what has been called a PHRASE GRAMMAR.[6]

Phrase grammar (as commonly understood) has a number of known weaknesses, the recognition of which has been the main motive behind the development of transform grammars. Constructional grammar does not share these
weaknesses. In the first place, it is possible (as we shall see presently) for
constructional grammar to handle quite simply those phenomena that any
reasonably manipulable phrase grammar best leaves for a transformational
overlay. In the second place, in constructional grammar it is possible to accept the intuitively desirable notion that some words, such as *and* or *or*, are not
constituents at all but rather MARKERS OF CONSTRUCTIONS (if there are no constructions, then obviously there is nothing for these elements to mark).
Finally, and specifically with reference to grammar for the hearer, the allo-
cation of ambiguity to IC organization and to constructions, and the elimination of homophony at the word level, seem to yield a kind of realism that a phrase
grammar, or a phrase-and-transform grammar, can deal with only in a more
indirect and complex way.

However, in order to use a constructional grammar as the basis for our
development of grammar for the hearer, it is apparently necessary to add one
further assumption to those given in § 1:

(A8) The number of constructions in a language is finite.

This is empirically as realistic (or unrealistic) as our earlier assumptions.
It has to be listed separately because it cannot be shown to follow from those
already listed. Thus, if we were to consider only those constructions in which
both (or all) of the constituents can be single words, then, because the vocabulary is finite by assumption (A1), we would clearly obtain at most a finite
number of distinct constructions. However, there is nothing in the earlier
assumptions to preclude any number of constructions in which the constituents
are themselves always composite forms.

Assumption (A8) asserts that, for some finite n, any composite form longer
than n words is built by a construction that also yields composite forms not
longer than n words. This can also be paraphrased in terms of form classes:
for some finite n, any composite form longer than n words belongs to a form
class that also includes forms not longer than n words (hence the number of
form classes in a language is itself finite).

Finally, the implications of (A8) can be stated in terms of CYCLIC ENDOCEN-
TRICITY. In the face of a finite number of constructions, if, as is obviously the
case, there is no limit on the length of grammatical forms, then there must
exist at least one finite set of constructions $C_1, C_2, \cdots, C_n$ with the following
property: for $1 \leq i < n, C_i$ builds forms that can be used as constituents in

---

[6] See Chomsky, 1956, 1957 [1; 2]. We shall not here constrain the term "phrase grammar"
to those in which constituents must be adjacent.

forms built by C_{i+1}; and C_n builds forms that can be used as constituents in forms built by C_1. (If $n = 1$, then the one construction C_1 is endocentric in the traditional sense.)

7. Reducibility of transformations. A grammar that makes use both of constructions and of not more than a finite number of transformations can be converted into a pure constructional grammar.

It will suffice to deal with the English passive transformation as representative of all optional transformations.[7] Suppose that an initial sequence is

(20) *The corpse of the seventh victim....*

Among the possibilities is that (20) will turn out to be all of a subject. Possible predicates would then include

(21) *...was lying behind some bushes.*

(22) *...was found by a troop of Boy Scouts.*

The open-ended parsing of (20) can provide for a distinction between these two types of possibility in the following way. We replace the single symbol "ε" by a pair, say "ε" to mean that what precedes may turn out to be a subject in an active clause, and "$\tilde{\varepsilon}$" to mean that what precedes, with what follows, may turn out to constitute a passive transform of an active clause in which what precedes would have been the object. As soon as the sentence has "grown" enough more to eliminate one of these possibilities, open-ended parsing will of course lack the symbol for that possibility.

We see, thus, that a constructional grammar provides for transformations by a proliferation of constructions. Since there are at most a finite number of distinct optional transformations, in addition to a finite number of constructions, this required proliferation will yield at most a finite number of constructions.

Conversion in the opposite direction is obviously also possible, provided that some of the constructions in a pure constructional grammar prove to be related in an appropriate way. For many purposes a mixed constructional and transform grammar has the advantage of compactness and the merit of highlighting certain relationships that might otherwise be missed. For grammar for the hearer, a pure constructional grammar seems somewhat preferable.

8. Reducibility of constructions. To reinterpret transformations as constructions achieves a more "homogeneous" abstract grammar, in that there is a smaller variety of seemingly different kinds of things. A constructional grammar can, in turn, be rendered more homogeneous if we redefine constructions not as relations between constituents but as themselves constituents. A comparison of Figure 10 with Figure 8 shows how this can be done. In Figure 8, where constructions are regarded as relations, the construction in which two constituents stand is indicated roughly (via a symbol for construc-

---

[7] Obligatory transformations are a matter of morphophonemics and hence of no interest to us here.

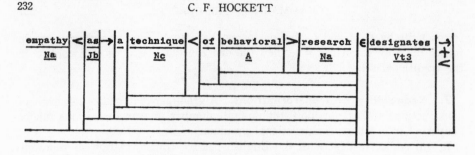

Figure 10

tion type) at the point of junction of the boxes for those constituents. In Figure 10, the same symbols are put in line with the words; the boxes now show nothing but the IC structure. (The latter fact is underscored even more by the redrawing in Figure 11, where the IC structure is represented by a "tree" in the way currently more popular.) The conversion involves a general recognition of composite forms with three rather than two immediate constituents, but this is clearly trivial.

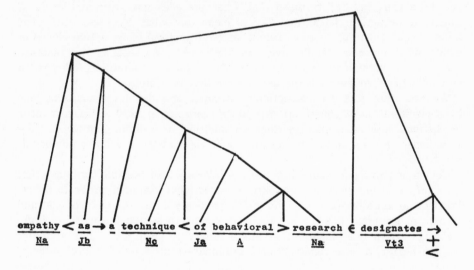

Figure 11

Seemingly less trivial is that the change forces a recognition of two kinds of basic elements in the vocabulary: elements that the hearer can hear (words), and those (constructions) that the hearer cannot hear but can only infer. For abstract grammar this does not matter—as long as the required inferences are of the sort that can be made, and this is a topic that has already been discussed. In any case, the dichotomy is not an entirely clearcut one. In our earlier view, certain "words" were taken not as constituents but as markers of constructions. By the earlier view, *men and women* would be diagrammed as shown in the upper half of Figure 9: here *and* and the sign "+" actually give the same information. By the new view, the diagram would be as shown in Figure 12, where the redundant sign "+" is omitted. The logical status of the audible form *and* is the same as that of the inaudible elements written on the line in Figures 10 and 11. Similarly, the handling of *a* and of *of* in Figures 10 and 11 is based on the notion that some CONSTITUENTS may stand in one-to-one correlation with certain constructions, so that both need not be recognized.

We see, thus that a constructional grammar can be converted to a phrase grammar; in the light of § 7, it also follows that a transform grammar can be converted to a phrase grammar. However, this reducibility entails a (finite) expansion of the basic vocabulary. If we insist that the basic vocabulary must be invariant from one tentative abstract grammar to another, the reductions are not possible.

In the sections that follow, it will be more convenient to speak of constructions as relations, but what will be said will apply with equal validity to the sort of phrase grammar achieved by the reduction described above.

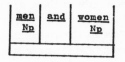

Figure 12

9. The formal respectability of grammatical states. We have imagined a faultless hearer who always does all the open-ended parsing he can. But just how much does this amount to? If the powers ascribed to the ideal hearer differ too drastically from those of real hearers—and of grammarians—then the paradigm is of no help to us.

Now the grammarian, in seeking to discover and describe the grammatical state established by an initial sequence of words, proceeds by testing various continuations of the sequence and determining how each possible continuation would fit grammatically into the initial sequence. Unless he goes about this systematically, he can easily miss some of the possibilities. Even if he precedes systematically, he will still miss some of the possibilities unless they can all be discovered by a FINITE number of trial-and-error operations. This would seem to be a fitting limitation to imposed on the powers of our ideal hearer.

It is immediately obvious that the grammatical state established by a given initial sequence cannot be tied to the whole class of sentences that might begin with the initial sequence, since in the typical case that class of sentences is infinite. We should still have an infinite class to deal with were we to consider only one out of each set of grammatically identical sentences of the whole class, since two sentences are necessarily grammatically distinct if they are of different lengths, and there is no theoretical limit to the length of a sentence.

What we have to demonstrate, then, seems to be along the following lines: The sentences that begin with a given initial sequence fall into families. Two sentences belong to the same family if all constructions (unambiguous or am-

biguous) within the initial sequence are the same for both, and if all constructions (unambiguous or ambiguous) across the boundary between sequence
and continuation are the same for both. Many, perhaps all, of the families
include an infinite number of sentences, but there is a finite number of families.
If this last is true, then the grammatical state at the end of the initial sequence
can be discovered by a finite number of trial-and-error operations, since one
need consider only one sentence of each family.

But in this form the assumption is clearly true. Assume that we know
nothing about an initial sequence except that it consists of n words. Each of
the n words is a grammatical form. Each pair of words, adjacent or not,
might turn out to be a grammatical form; likewise each triad, each tetrad,
and so on up to the whole sequence. Therefore the actual number of grammatical forms in the initial sequence cannot exceed

$$\sum_{i=1}^{n} {}_nC_i \, ,$$

which is obviously finite. Now any of these grammatical forms either stands
in construction only with other grammatical forms within the initial sequence,
or else with grammatical forms in the continuation. Therefore there can be
only a finite number of grammatical forms with constituents on both sides of
the boundary between initial sequence and continuation. Further, by assumption (A8) each one of these latter can stand only in one or another of a finite
number of constructions. This proves that there is only a finite number of
families. The infinite membership of any one family stems from the absence
of any limit on the length of grammatical forms in possible continuations.

As a limiting case, consider the degenerate initial "sequence" of no words
at all. All possible "continuations" yield sentences of a single family.

10. Stochastic representation. The total number of grammatical states
provided for by a language is not finite. A glance at Figure 7 shows why.
There is no limit to the number of additional postposed modifiers that could
be added after *Empathy as a technique of behavioral research*, indefinitely postponing the beginning of the predicate. Each would complicate the diagram
by one more horizontal line pointing to the right; therefore each would yield
a new grammatical state, not a repetition of one already passed through.

A given grammatical state, however, can be immediately followed only by
one of a finite number of grammatical states. This follows from assumption
(A1): a given initial sequence can be extended by one additional word only in
a finite number of ways.

These two facts about states suggest that grammar for the hearer might
be treated as an infinite-state Markov process. To construct the matrix, we
order the infinite set of states as follows: First comes that which pertains
when nothing has been said; then all those (a finite number) that can be established by an initial sequence of one word. After that, we order the rest
in such a way that, for some finite n, and for all $m > n$, the ABSOLUTE probability (or frequency of occurrence) of the $(m + 1)$th state is not greater than
that of the mth state.

Row sums of transition probabilities are unity because the probability that a grammatical state will be followed by SOME next grammatical state is unity. In any row, there will be some finite n such that all entries after the nth are zero. The non-zero entries will appear only in two loci: in a strip of columns on the extreme left, and in a strip of diagonals. The first locus for non-zero entries is because there are some relatively common states (those established by no word or by a single initial word) that can occur after a great many different states. The second locus is because any really rare state has a chance to occur only after some state that is almost as rare.

It follows from this stochastic representation that the grammar of a language can be APPROXIMATED AS ACCURATELY AS ONE WISHES by a finite state Markov process: from the infinite matrix for the infinite state process we delete all rows and columns after the nth, for some suitably large n, and make arbitrary small adjustments in the non-zero entries to preserve row sums.

11. Grammar for hearer and for speaker. There is a large and important class of phenomena in the actual use of English for which no existing abstract grammatical theory—nor, indeed, this grammar for the hearer—makes provision. Any honest examination of running conversational English shows that the neat, complete, "grammatical" sentence is something of a rarity (and this seems to be true regardless of our choice of definition of "sentence," unless we select a definition so weak as to be useless). We do find some, of course; but we also find a high incidence of false starts, of parenthetical insertions, of ungrammatical pseudo-sentences, and so on. Grammarians have for decades almost studiously ignored these phenomena. But speakers and hearers do not ignore them—they carry a sizable share of the communicative load.

This suggests that we may have to reexamine our basic premises, and perhaps overhaul them rather completely and make a new start. Before we undertake any such drastic move, however, we should consider certain ways in which we might be able to make empirically profitable use of the results of abstract grammatical theory.

It can be argued that grammar for the hearer, as discussed in this paper, has a certain kind of priority over grammar for the speaker. A speaker sometimes knows what he is going to say next; a hearer cannot know for sure until he has heard it. Yet the contrast between the terms "hearer" and "speaker" is misleading. One may at moments function purely as a hearer. The alternative to this is not to function purely as a speaker, but to function as BOTH speaker AND hearer—since anyone hears his own speech. The planning-ahead, in which a speaker obviously indulges sometimes, can be viewed as a rapid scanning of the alternatives allowed grammatically by what he has said up to a given point, and a selecting of one of them. These alternatives are public property, as available to the audience as to the speaker himself. Hearing thus involves no operations not involved in speaking; but speaking involves all the operations involved in hearing, plus the logistic operation of scanning ahead and making choices.

The logistics of speaking is something like that of playing very amateurish chess, in which one is allowed to take moves back and in which one may overlook part of the situation on the board (even to failing to notice that a king is in check!). However, taking moves back does not erase the sound waves that were produced: the audience has heard them and has drawn its own conclusions. Thus:

(23)   *I felt like kiss—like shaking his hand.*

A direction of development can be abandoned because of changes in the external circumstances:

(24)   *I felt like—Get out of here, Joe!*

An abandonment may be temporary (and its resumption may or may not entail recapitulation):

(25)   *I felt like—Get out of here, Joe!—like shaking his hand.*

A speaker may "lose the thread," and produce an "imparsible" sentence that is nevertheless understood its context:

(26) *Empathy as a technique of behavioral research developed originally in psychiatry, but later taken over by anthropologists, and some of the latter have put it to work in ways the psychiatrists never dreamed of.*

Along such lines as these, we can perhaps begin to understand the difference between a language as an abstract system and the way real human beings use the system.

One common phenomenon, however, resists this approach: the blend. I once intended to say *people born and raised in a culture* but came out with *people braised in a culture.* Everyone understood both the actuality and the intention. I do not know how to parse this phrase in a way that gives overt recognition to the blend. Until we can, our grammatical theories are and will remain inadequate.

Bibliography

1. Noam Chomsky, *Three models for the description of language,* IRE Transactions on Information Theory vol. IT-2 (1956) pp. 113-124.
2. ———, *Syntactic structures,* Mouton & Co., 's-Gravenhage, 1957.
3. Zellig Harris, *From morpheme to utterance,* Language vol. 22 (1946) pp. 161-183.
4. ———, *Co-occurrence and transformation in linguistic structure,* Language vol. 33 (1957) pp. 283-340.

Cornell University,
  Ithaca, New York

A MEASURE OF SUBJECTIVE INFORMATION[1]

BY

RULON WELLS

1. Aim of paper. Information theory may be expected to have three branches, if Charles Morris' division of semiotic is applicable to it. The syntactical part will deal with signs (symbols) considered in abstraction from their meaning; the semantical part must deal with signs *qua* meaningful, but in a way that abstracts from (takes no account of) the persons or beings who use these signs; and the pragmatical part, at last, takes account of the users as well as of the sign-vehicles and their meanings, and thereby completes the work of semiotic.

Most previous information theory has been syntactical. While noting that "frequently...messages have meaning", Shannon[2] goes on to observe that "these semantic aspects of communication are irrelevant to the engineering problem." The principal contribution to semantical information theory has been that of Carnap and Bar-Hillel,[3] which applies Carnap's logic, including his treatment of probability, to information theory. The pragmatical part has been little cultivated; in information theory as hitherto developed, "we make no distinction between useful and useless information.... The idea of 'value' refers to the possible use by a living observer. This is beyond the reach of our theory."[4] Certain treatments by economists belong here, however.[5]

The present paper outlines two contributions, the first to pragmatics, the second to semantics. The pragmatical part discusses 'subjective information', whereby one sentence, even one logically true sentence, may be subjectively more informative (important, valuable, revealing) than another; the semantical part deals with a function of sentences called 'informativeness'.

Inasmuch as the resources of syntactics are in a way meagerer and more parsimonious than those of semantics, and those of semantics than those of pragmatics, one wonders how far the third can be represented by the second,

[1] Research supported by the Office of Naval Research, Contract No. SAR/Nonr-609(16); (Problem Solving and Social Interaction).

[2] In Claude E. Shannon and Warren Weaver, *The mathematical theory of communication*, Urbana, University of Illinois Press, 1949, p. 3.

[3] Rudolf Carnap and Yehoshua Bar-Hillel, *An outline of a theory of semantic information*, Massachusetts Institute of Technology, Research Laboratory of Electronics, Technical Report No. 247, October 27, 1952. See also Y. Bar-Hillel, *Semantic information and its measures, Cybernetics—Circular causal and feedback mechanisms in biological and social systems.* Transactions of the Tenth Conference [April 22, 23, and 24, 1953] New York, The Josiah Macy, Jr. Foundation, 1955, pp. 33–48.

[4] Leon Brillouin, *Science and information theory*, New York, Academic Press, 1956, pp. 9–10.

[5] Jacob Marschak, *Towards an economic theory of information and organization*, "Decision processes" ed. by R. M. Thrall, C. H. Coombs, and R. L. Davis, New York, Wiley, 1954, pp. 187–220.

and the second by the first. The present paper bears on this question. Informativeness serves as a semantical model or representation of subjective
information. The reason is that the canonical form of a pragmatical statement
about subjective information is 'A judges that sentence S_1 is more informative
than sentence S_2', and that by simply dropping the phrase 'A judges that',
one obtains a semantical statement. The resulting semantical statement will,
if true, be true a priori.

2. The Carnap—Bar-Hillel approach. The *fundamental* idea of information theory has been to treat the amount of information of a message as a
function of the number of possible alternative messages. The fundamental idea
of Carnap and Bar-Hillel has been to work with a semantical analogue to this,
namely information as a function of the number of possible conditions under
which the message would be true.

To implement this fundamental idea they explicate 'possible conditions' in
terms of state-descriptions, a notion proposed by Wittgenstein and made by
Carnap the basis of his recent logical work. The number as well as the
descriptive richness of a set of state-descriptions depends upon the language
in which these descriptions are expressed. Certain theoretical difficulties that
arise for all but extremely simple languages will not concern us here—Kemeny[6]
has indicated a solution for some of them—because we shall find that for our
purpose the state-description approach is *radically* faulty.

The state-description approach (i.e., what is common to all varieties of state-
description models) formalizes certain philosophical ideas of Wittgenstein's
Tractatus logico-philosophicus: (1) All necessary truth is logical, and all contingent truth is empirical. (2) The logical truths may be regarded as those
that hold in all possible states of affairs (or in all possible worlds). (3) "All
propositions of logic say the same thing. That is, nothing" (5.43; cf. 5.142
and 6.11). All three of these ideas are involved in those theorems (T4–2a,
T6–1b, T6–4b, T7–8b; cf. R5–2*) of Carnap and Bar-Hillel that set the numerical
value zero on *all* L-true sentences.

3. Need for an alternative to the state-description approach. Carnap[7]
lists three "requirements for an explicatum," of which the first is "similarity
to the explicandum". Mates[8] in effect makes this requirement more precise
by proposing to lay down adequacy-conditions which a successful explicatum
must satisfy. His proposal has the further use that it can help us to distinguish
distinct explicanda, in cases where special help is needed. For instance, Carnap's explications of probability are based on the hypothesis that there are
two distinct explicanda, confounded under the single name 'probability', to be
explicated, but Carnap has no developed methodology for supporting this hypo-

---

[6] John G. Kemeny, *A logical measure function*, Journal of Symbolic Logic vol. 18
(1953) pp. 289–308.

[7] Rudolf Carnap, *Logical foundations of probability*, Chicago, 1950, p. 5.

[8] Benson Mates, *Synonymity*, University of California Publications in Philosophy vol. 25
(1950) pp. 201–226, p. 209. But cf. Carnap (see footnote 7), pp. 430–435 § 80: *Requirements of adequacy*.

thesis, beyond the usual methods of testing hypotheses in general by their consequences. In the present paper, I advance the hypothesis that there are at least two distinct explicanda both called 'information'; but in addition to the usual methods of testing hypotheses I employ the method of adequacy-conditions by proposing the following:

There is a sense of 'amount of information' (and hence of 'information') such that not all logically true sentences bear the same amount of information.

This adequacy-condition serves as a touchstone to distinguish at least two senses, a sense which demands it and a sense which does not. Carnap and Bar-Hillel have explicated a sense of 'information' which does not demand it; I suggest that we call this 'factual (or 'contingent' or 'a posteriori') information'. The task of the present paper, on the other hand, is to prepare for the explication of a sense that *does* demand it.

In such a sense of 'information', there will be diversities in the a priori realm analogous to those in the realm of empirical fact. Just as empirical sentences may differ in information-content (IC), information-degree (ID), and information-amount (IA), so may sentences that are true or false a priori. Just as a probable consequence of sentence S may bear information beyond that of S, so may a necessary consequence. And just as (Carnap and Bar-Hillel, pp. 30–31, § 9) the conjunction of two factual sentences may yield far more information than either one taken separately, so with a priori sentences.

It is customary in expositions of information theory to associate information with surprisingness: the more informative a sentence is, the more surprising it is if the sentence is transmitted (in syntactical versions) or if the sentence is true (in semantical versions). The proposition, then, that if S is L-true then $IA(S)=0$ is quite in keeping with Wittgenstein's doctrine (6.1251 and 1261) that there are no surprises in logic, any more than there are mistakes (5.473) or experiments (6.2331). Wittgenstein may mean no more than Aristotle (Metaphysics A.3: 983a lines 12–21) with his example that although "it seems wonderful to all who have not yet seen the reason, that there is a thing which cannot be measured even by the smallest unit", yet "there is nothing which would surprise a geometer so much as if the diagonal turned out to be commensurable". But there is another kind of surprise that never fades or vanishes, or if not surprise then informativeness, import, significance, or something of that sort. For example, it is generally agreed that the Pythagorean theorem is a more informative sentence than '7+5=12', although both are L-true. Likewise with entire systems of sentences. A grammar of a language may be regarded a system of sentences; in order that a grammar be considered 'good' or 'satisfactory', it must according to many grammarians not only be empirically true but also 'revealing' and 'non-trivial'. And I for my part would say that the formal developments of Carnap and Bar-Hillel, though they could easily be expressed as L-truths in a formalized metalanguage, are informative to a considerable degree.

That a priori truths may differ in informativeness is implied by another fact, also. This fact is that we make judgments about discoveries and about discoverers, regarding some as major and others as minor. Now a major discovery in the a priori realm (Gödel's theorem, for instance) is the discovery of a major truth, i.e., the discovery that such and such an important sentence is true. And a genius, i.e., a major discoverer, is one who has discovered major discoveries, i.e., important (highly informative) true sentences.

Yet a third consideration proves our recognition of a variable informativeness in the a priori realm; this is, that it figures in the rationale of research. Peirce's mathematical treatment of rationale[9] takes two variables into account, cost and utility; a more elaborate treatment, and one that adequately explicates 'rationale' in the a priori as well as the a posteriori realm, will break utility up into components of which the likelihood of success will be one and the informativeness of the various possible outcomes will be another.

4. A measure of subjective information.

The claims made in the previous section are empirical claims about certain judgments expressed or implied by human beings. Such judgments could be collected and processed by familiar methods.[10] The structure would be serial (comparative), like that of comparative judgments about a posteriori probability[11]; on this serial structure a metric could be imposed, arbitrarily in any case and possibly on the basis of some suitable join-relation (Hempel, pp. 63–65) j such that $m(xjy)=m(x)+m(y)$. (The prima facie obvious candidate, logical conjunction, will not serve; we will want to assert that information-amount is non-additive relatively to logical conjunction. Additivity is defined in Hempel, p. 75.)

The principal interest in an empirical investigation of the above sort will lie in the extent of agreement between the different judges whose judgments are collected. One reason for imposing a metric, provided that it be imposed on the serial judgments of each judge *before* comparison with the judgments of other judges, is that it makes comparison of the comparisons possible and easy. A method such as Kendall's rank correlation coefficient,[12] which metrically compares merely serial comparisons, is possible but less easy. It is not known how much the measure of agreement would be affected by the selection of the judges themselves. It would be interesting to study the judgments of a group of judges who, once chosen, rated themselves and each other on their expertise and authoritativeness, so that in the final synthesis of the judgments different judges might have different weights attached to their judgments.

Many would agree with Hempel (p. 62) that "the use of human instruments of comparison has various disadvantages.... Interobserver agreement is often far from perfect...; besides, even one and the same observer may show inconsistent responses. In addition, it appears that most of the concepts defined by reference to the responses of human instruments are of very limited theoretical import—they do not give rise to precise and comprehensive generaliza-

[9] Charles S. Peirce, *Note on the theory of the economy of research*, originally published in 1879; reprinted in his Collected Papers vol. 7, ed. by Arthur W. Burks, Cambridge, Harvard University Press, 1958, §§ 139–157.

[10] Carl G. Hempel, *Fundamentals of concept formation in empirical science*, Chicago, 1952, passim; especially pp. 54–78.

[11] Carnap (see footnote 7), pp. viii–ix, 22–23, 219–226, 428–482.

[12] Maurice G. Kendall, *Rank correlation methods*, London, C. Griffin, 1948.

tions." However, several comments to this conclusion may be made. First, it may well happen that intra- and inter-observer agreement may be markedly improved by several precautions. (a) There is no reason why the judgments should be rendered hastily and in solitude, as is rather common in psychological experiments; no reason why the judges should not confer with each other and mull over their judgments—taking months or years to do so—before reporting them. (b) In particular, each judge might apply certain checks upon the consistency of his judgments, such as[13] making sure that they never violate the transitivity of the relation 'is more informative than'. Second, even if the judges do not all agree, it may be that they can be divided into a relatively small number of schools of thought, such that the members of each school substantially agree with each other. And in that case it may further happen that two schools differ not on the fundamental structure but only on the details of the ordering. Third, the collected and synthesized judgments can be put to more than one use. They can be regarded as having possible empirical significance. But also, they can be regarded as heuristically valuable data for the a priori theorist, who would aim at constructing a pure theory which admits of an empirical application (interpretation) that is sufficiently in agreement with these data.

A study of the sort sketched here deals with 'subjective information', i.e., with information as it appears to various subjects. Their judgments may or may not be subjective in the popular sense of being erratic, unreliable, and at odds with one another. Consequently, it might be less prejudicial to call our present subject-matter 'pragmatical information'. However, it is widely believed by philosophers and scientists that insofar as a judgment is not merely subjective in this pejorative sense, it can be replaced by a judgment that is not pragmatical either. To draw an instance from probability theory—a field closely related to our own—critics of the subjective theory of probability urge that probability should be defined or determined, not by the strength of belief that a person does have, but by what he ought to have.[14] The deontic force is sometimes incorporated in the notion of an 'ideal believer', defined as one whose beliefs have just the strength that they ought to have. But probability is really semantical; its appearance of being pragmatical (*via* its reference to an observer) is illusory, because the reference to an observer can be dropped without loss.

I turn then to delineating a purely semantical and a priori treatment of informativeness.

5. The purely semantical model: informativeness. Here follow some statements which it would seem reasonable to include in a rigorous system. $IA(S)$ is the (metrical) informativeness-amount of the sentence S; $IC(S)$ is the (qualitative) informativeness-content of S. The variables S (without or with subscripts) range over necessarily true sentences. The restriction to true

---

[13] Kenneth J. Arrow, *Mathematical models in the social sciences*, The Policy Sciences, ed. by D. Lerner and H. D. Lasswell, Stanford, Stanford University Press, 1951, pp. 129–154, pp. 135–136 and footnote 20.

[14] Carnap (see footnote 7), pp. 46. 50.

sentences is made to avoid the problem of meshing the IA's of false sentences (and especially of necessarily false sentences) with the IA's of true sentences, e.g. by assigning negative values to the former. The restriction to necessarily true sentences is made in order to avoid the problem of meshing the IA's of necessarily true sentences with those of contingently true sentences. It may be that in the end one will want to effect one or both meshings, or it may be that one will want to leave two or four 'spaces' unrelated to one another.

The following statements are not offered as an axiom set. They are at once too incomplete and too redundant to be satisfactory in that capacity. They are, rather, samples of what would be included among the theorems of an adequate formalized and axiomatized explication of informativeness.

1. $0 < IA(S) < \infty$.
2. $(\exists S_1, S_2)\ IA(S_1) < IA(S_2)$.
3. $(\exists S_1, S_2)\ IA(S_1\ \&\ S_2) > IA(S_1) + IA(S_2) - IA(S_1 \lor S_2)$.
4. $(\exists S_1, S_2)(S_1 \to S_2)\ \&\ IA(S_2) > IA(S_1)$.
5. $(S_1, S_2)\ IA(S_1\ \&\ S_2) \geqq IA(S_1) + IA(S_2) - IA(S_1 \lor S_2)$.
6. $(\exists S_1, S_2)\ IA(S_1 \lor \sim S_1) < IA(S_2 \lor \sim S_2)$.
7. $(\exists E_1, E_2)\ IA(E_1 = E_1) < IA(E_2 = E_2)$.
8. $(\exists S_1, S_2)\ IC(S_1) \subset IC(S_2)\ \&\ IA(S_1) > IA(S_2)$.
9. $(\exists S_1, S_2)\ S_1 \longleftrightarrow S_2\ \&\ IA(S_1) < IA(S_2)$.
10. $(\exists S_1, S_2)\ IC(S_1) \neq IC(S_2)\ \&\ IA(S_1) = IA(S_2)$.
11. $(\exists S_1, S_2, S_3)\ IC(S_1) \neq IC(S_2)\ \&\ IC(S_1) \neq IC(S_3)\ \&\ IC(S_2) \neq IC(S_3)$
    $\&\ IA(S_1) > IA(S_2) + IA(S_3)$.

COMMENTS. (1) confines the range of values of IA to the positive real (finite) numbers. (2) allows necessary truths to differ in amount of informativeness. (3) denies additivity relatively to logical conjunction. (4) allows a consequence of S to be more informative than S itself. (5) says that logical conjunction can never *diminish* amount of information. (6) and (7) will receive separate discussion in the next paragraph. (8) allows an intensionally weaker sentence to be more informative than a stronger one. (9) allows logical equivalents to differ in amount of informativeness. (10) allows sentences qualitatively different to be quantitatively the same in informativeness. (11) is an example of a statement that amplifies Number (2), by allowing fairly *wide* differences in amount of informativeness.

Numbers (6) and (7) call for especial comment. They make available, in a simple way, a very useful means to the student of heuristitics. We often wish to give credit to someone not for proving a new theorem but for introducing a new concept, or for posing a new question. This can be done with the help of statements (6) and (7). We may correlate questions one-to-one with disjunctions, so that e.g. the question 'Are all infinite series convergent?' is correlated with the disjunction 'Either all infinite series are convergent or not all infinite series are convergent'. Then the valuable contributions of those mathematicians who first seriously posed this question can be recognized by assigning a higher value to the IA of this disjunction than to the IA of, say, 'Two is odd or two is not odd'. This method works easily for questions that can be answered 'Yes' or 'No'. Other questions, such as 'Under what circumstances does an infinite series converge?' and 'How many prime numbers are there?' require reduction by one method or another to yes-or-no questions before the correlation with a disjunctive tautology can be effected (in a reasonable way). Similarly, Number (7) may be used to distinguish between concepts of different value by distinguishing the IA's of the identities in which they respectively (and vacuously) occur.

None of the above statements, samples of what a semantical theory of informativeness might include, assign definite values to IA's. The theory is thus capable of being interpreted empirically and pragmatically in a way that is consistent with whatever empirical values the empircal study outlined in §4 may disclose.

The denial of additivity, Number (3), deserves further comment.[15] It is proposed as a partial explication of what William Whewell called colligation.[16] Whewell's account is most widely known today through Charles Peirce's frequent references to it.[17] Colligation brings ideas or thoughts together and into relation to one another; and so far as ideas can be represented by sentences, the bringing together can be represented by the logical operation of conjunction. Now colligation—'putting two and two together', as it is popularly called —can constitute a very important scientific advance; and statement (3) affords a means of expressing this advance by assigning a much higher value to $IA(S_1 \& S_2)$ than to the corrected sum of the two IA's taken separately.

6. Two possible connections. Why can't the state-description model adequately explicate informativeness? One fundamental reason is that if S_1 L-implies S_2, the model requires S_1 to be at least as informative as S_2. On the other hand, as Carnap and Bar-Hillel point out (p. 12, discussion of R5–1*), this requirement does not in turn require the state-description model. From this requirement, no matter whether it is treated as an axiom or as a derived theorem, there directly follow the theorems (a) that L-equivalent sentences are equally informative and (b) that L-true sentences are all minimally informative (and so have zero informativeness, if by convention the minimum be set at zero).

Clearly, this requirement is in conflict with intensionality. Intensionality has various aspects and some of these aspects admit of various degrees; but a number of logicians have aimed to construct systems so strongly intensional

---

[15] In the right-hand expression of Numbers (3) and (5), IA (S_1 & S_2) is subtracted in order not to count twice what is common to S_1, taken by itself, and S_2, taken by itself. Cf. Carnap and Bar-Hillel T6–1j, T6–4j, T7–8h.

[16] *Novum Organum Renovatum* (1858) II. iv. See the valuable exposition by C. J. Ducasse, *Whewell's philosophy of scientific discovery*, Philosophical Review vol. 60 (1951) pp. 56–69 and pp. 213-234. Page 213 quotes a passage that speaks of the two processes of explication, "by which conceptions are made more clear in themselves", and colligation, "by which the conceptions more strictly bind together the facts". Note the similarity between Whewell's use of the term 'explication' and Carnap's. Whewell is speaking with reference to a posteriori knowledge; I do not know whether he recognized the same two processes in a priori knowledge.

[17] The main passages are Collected Papers vol. 2, 1932, §§ 253, 442, 451, 469n2, and vol. 5, 1934, §§ 579, 581.

that they do not treat all L-equivalent predicates and all L-equivalent sentences as alike in the way that Carnap's logic in general, and the above
requirement in particular, do.

A recent and very promising system of this sort is that of Anderson and
Belnap.[18] Its strongly intensional relation of entailment is such that a logical truth is not entailed by every sentence, so that it cannot be proved that
all logical truths are equally and minimally informative.

A second approach to strong intensionality is that of Church.[19] The informativeness-content (IC) of statements (8), (10), and (11) above might be identified
with Fregean 'sense'. A present difficulty is that of the various explications
proposed so far, the most attractive one (Church's 'Alternative (0)') is inconsistent through contradicting Cantor's theorem.[20] But any modification that
avoided this and other inconsistencies would be worth considering as an explication of informativeness-content.

YALE UNIVERSITY,
NEW HAVEN, CONNECTICUT

---

[18] (1) A. R. Anderson and N. D. Belnap, Jr., *A modification of Ackermann's 'rigorous implication'* [*Abstract*], J. Symbolic Logic vol. 23 (1958), pp. 457–458; (2) A. R. Anderson, *Completeness theorems for the systems E of entailment and EQ of entailment with quantification*, Z. Math. Logik Grundlagen Math. vol. 6 no. 3 (1960); (3) N. D. Belnap, Jr., *The formalization of entailment*, Technical Report Number 7, Office of Naval Research, Contract SAR/Nonr–609(16), 1960.

[19] Alonzo Church, *A formulation of the logic of sense and denotation*, "Structure, method, and meaning", ed. by P. Henle, H. M. Kallen, and S. K. Langer, New York, Liberal Arts Press, 1951, pp. 3–24.

[20] John Myhill, *Problems arising in the formalization of intensional logic*, Logique et analyse, Nouvelle série, vol. 1, pp. 74–83 (1958), p. 82.

LINGUISTICS AND COMMUNICATION THEORY

BY

ROMAN JAKOBSON

Norbert Wiener refuses to admit "any fundamental opposition between the problems of our engineers in measuring communication and the problems of our philologists."[1] There appear indeed striking coincidences and convergences between the latest stages of linguistic analysis and the approach to language in the mathematical theory of communication. Since each of these two disciplines is concerned, although in different and quite autonomous ways, with the same domain of verbal communication, a close contact between them has proved to be of mutual use and undoubtedly will become ever more beneficial.

The stream of oral speech, physically continuous, originally confronted the mathematical theory of communication with a situation "considerably more involved" than in the case of a finite set of discrete constituents, as presented by written speech.[2] Linguistic analysis, however, came to resolve oral speech into a finite series of elementary informational units. These ultimate discrete units, the so-called 'distinctive features', are aligned into simultaneous bundles termed 'phonemes', which in turn are concatenated into sequences. Thus form in language has a manifestly granular structure and is subject to a quantal description.

The primary aim of information theory, as formulated for instance by D.M. MacKay, is "to isolate from their particular contexts those abstract features of representations which can remain invariant under reformulation."[3] The linguistic analogue to this problem is the phonemic search for relational invariants. The diverse possibilities for measurement of the amount of phonemic information, which are foreseen by the communication engineers (distinguishing between 'structural' and 'metrical' information content), may give both to synchronic and to historical linguistics precious data, particularly important for the typology of languages both in a purely phonological aspect and in the intersection of phonology with the lexicogrammatical level.

The dichotomous principle underlying the whole system of distinctive features in language was gradually disclosed by linguistics and found corroboration in the binary digits (or to use the popular portmanteau—*bits*) employed as a unit of measurement by the communication engineers. When they define the selective information of a message as the minimum number of binary decisions which enable the receiver to reconstruct what he needs to elicit from the message, on the basis of the data already available to him,[4] this realistic formula is perfectly applicable to the role of distinctive features in verbal com-

---

[1] Journal of the Acoustical Society of America vol. 22 (1950) p. 697.

[2] C. E. Shannon and W. Weaver, *The mathematical theory of communication*, Urbana, The University of Illinois Press, 1949, pp. 74ff., 112f.

[3] Cybernetics: Transactions of the Eighth Conference, New York, Josiah Macy, Jr. Foundation, 1952, p. 224.

[4] *Communication Theory*, ed. by W. Jackson, New York, Academic Press, 1953, p. 2.

245

munication. As soon as "the way of recognizing universals through their invariants" had been attempted and an overall classification of distinctive features was outlined according to these principles, then immediately the problem of translating the criteria proposed by linguists "into mathematical and instrumental language" was raised in D. Gabor's lectures on communication theory.[5] And recently there has appeared an instructive study by G. Ungeheuer offering a tentative mathematical interpretation of the distinctive features in their binary patterning.[6]

The notion of 'redundancy', taken over by communication theory from the rhetorical branch of linguistics, acquired an important place in the development of this theory, was challengingly redefined as "one minus the relative entropy" and under this new aspect has reentered present-day linguistics as one of its crucial topics. The necessity of a strict distinction between different types of redundancy is now realized in the theory of communication as well as in linguistics, where the concept of redundancy encompasses on the one hand pleonastic means as opposed to explicit conciseness (*brevitas* in the traditional nomenclature of rhetoric) and on the other hand explicitness in contradistinction to ellipsis. On the phonological level linguists have been accustomed to delimit phonemic, distinctive units from contextual, combinatory, allophonic variants, but the treatment of such interconnected problems as redundancy, predictability, and conditional probabilities in communication theory furthered a clarification of the relationship between the two basic linguistic classes of sound-properties — the distinctive features and the redundant features.

A phonemic analysis, when consistently purposing the elimination of redundancies, necessarily provides an optimal and unambiguous solution. The superstitious *belief* of some theoreticians unconversant with linguistics that "there remain no good reasons for the distinction between distinctive and redundant among the features"[7] is patently contradicted by innumerable linguistic data. If, for example, in Russian the difference between advanced vowels and their retracted counterparts is always accompanied by the difference between preceding consonants, which are palatalized before the advanced vowels and devoid of palatalization before the retracted vowels, and if on the other hand the difference between palatalized and non-palatalized consonants is not confined to a vocalic neighborhood, the linguist is obliged to conclude that in Russian the difference between the presence and lack of consonantal palatalization is a distictive feature, while the difference between the advanced and retracted vowels appears as merely redundant. The distinctiveness and redundancy, far from being arbitrary assumptions of the investigator are objectively present and delimited in language.

The prejudice treating the redundant features as irrelevant and the distinctive features as the only relevant ones is vanishing from linguistics, and it is again communication theory, particularly its treatment of transitional prob-

[5] *Lectures on communication theory*, Massachusetts Institute of Technology, Cambridge, Masachusetts 1951 p. 82.

[6] Studia Linguistica vol. 13 (1959) pp. 69–97.

[7] Word vol. 13 (1957) p. 328.

abilities, which helps linguists to overcome their biased attitude toward redundant and distinctive features as irrelevant and relevant respectively.

Preconceived possibilities, according to MacKay, "is the key phrase in communication theory," and a similar claim comes from linguistics. In neither
discipline has there been any doubt about the fundamental role of selective
operations in verbal activities. The engineer assumes a "filing system" of
prefabricated possibilities more or less common to the sender and receiver of
a verbal message, and Saussurian linguistics speaks correspondingly about
langue, which makes possible an exchange of *parole* between interlocutors.
Such an *"ensemble* of possibilities already foreseen and provided for"[8] implies
a code, conceived by communication theory as "an agreed transformation,—
usually one-to-one and reversible"[9]—by which one set of informational units
is converted into another set, for instance, a grammatical unit into a phonemic
sequence and vice versa. The code matches the *signans* with its *signatum*
and the *signatum* with its *signans*. Today, with respect to the treatment of
coding problems in communication theory, the Saussurian dichotomy *langue-
parole* can be restated much more precisely and acquires a new operational
value. Conversely, in modern linguistics communication theory may find illuminating information about the stratified structure of the intricate language
code in its various aspects.

Although the framework of the language code has been adequately outlined
in linguistics, it is still frequently overlooked that the finite ensemble of
"standard representations" is limited to lexical symbols, their grammatical
and phonological constituents, and to the grammatical and phonological rules
of combination. Only this portion of communication may be defined as a
mere "activity of replicating representations." On the other hand, it is still
opportune to recall that the code is not confined to what communication engineers call "the bare intelligence content of the speech," but likewise the
stylistic stratification of the lexical symbols and the allegedly "free" variation
both in their constitution and in their combination rules, are "foreseen and
provided for" by the code.

In his program for the future science of signs (semiotics) Charles Peirce
stated: "A Legisign is a law that is a Sign. This law is usually established
by men. Every conventional sign is a legisign."[10] Verbal symbols are cited
as a salient example of legisigns. The interlocutors belonging to one given
speech community may be defined as actual users of one and the same language code encompassing the same legisigns. A common code is their communication tool, which actually underlies and makes possible the exchange of
messages. Here is the essential difference between linguistics and the physical sciences, and this difference has been distinctly and repeatedly singled
out in the theory of communication, especially by its English school, which
insists on a clear-cut line of demarcation between the theory of communica-

---

[8] Cybernetics: Transactions of the Eighth Conference, New York, The Technology Press
of Massachusetts Institute of Technology, 1952, p. 183.

[9] C. Cherry, *On human communication*, New York-London, 1957 p. 7.

[10] *Collected papers*, vol. 2, Cambridge, Massachusetts, Harvard University Press, 1932,
p. 142f.

tion and of information. Nevertheless, this delimitation, strange as it seems, is sometimes disregarded by linguists. "The stimuli received from Nature," as Colin Cherry wisely stresses, "are not pictures of reality but are the evidence from which we build our personal models." [11] While the physicist creates his theoretical construct, imposing his own hypothetical system of new symbols upon the extracted *indices*, the linguist only recodes, translates into symbols of a metalanguage those extant *symbols* which are used in the language of the given speech community.

The constituents of the code, for instance, the distinctive features, literally occur and really function in speech communication. Both for the receiver and for the transmitter, as R. M. Fano points out, the operation of selection forms the basis of "information-conveying processes." [12] The set of yes-or-no choices underlying any bundle of these discrete features is not an arbitrary concoction of the linguist but is actually made by the addressee of the message, insofar as the need of their recognition is not cancelled by the prompting of the verbal or non-verbalized context.

Both on the grammatical and on the phonological level, not only the addressee in decoding the message, but also the encoder may practice ellipsis; in particular the encoder omits some of the features, or even some of their bundles and sequences. But ellipsis, too, is governed by codified rules. Language is never monolithic; its overall code includes a set of subcodes, and such questions as that of the rules of transformation of the optimal, explicit kernel code into the various degrees of elliptic subcodes and their comparison as to the amount of information requires both a linguistic and an engineering examination. The *convertible code* of language, with all its fluctuations from subcode to subcode and with all the current progressing changes, which this code is undergoing, is to be jointly and comprehensively described by the means of linguistics and communication theory. An insight into the dynamic synchrony of language, involving the space-time coordinates, must replace the traditional pattern of arbitrarily restricted *static* descriptions.

The linguistic observer who possesses or acquires a command of the language he is observing is or gradually becomes a potential or actual partner in the exchange of verbal messages among the members of the speech community, its passive or even active fellow member. The communication engineer is right when defending against "some philologists" the absolutely dominant "need to bring the Observer onto the scene" and when holding with Cherry that "the participant-observer's description will be the more complete." [13] The antipode to the participant, the most detached and external onlooker, acts as a cryptanalyst, who is a recipient of messages without being their addressee and without knowledge of their code. [14] He attempts to break the code through

[11] Op. cit., p. 62. Cf. W. Meyer-Eppler, *Grundlagen und Anwendungen der Informationstheorie*, Berlin-Göttingen-Heidelberg, Springer-Verlag, 1959, p. 250ff.

[12] *The transmission of information*, Massachusetts Institute of Technology, Research Laboratory of Electronics, Technical Report No. 65 (1949) p. 3f.

[13] *For Roman Jakobson*, The Hague, Mouton & Co., 1956, p. 61f.

[14] Cf. R. Jakobson and M. Halle, *Fundamentals of language*, The Hague, Mouton & Co., 1956, pp. 17-19.

a scrutiny of the messages. As far as possible, this level of linguistic investigation must be merely a preliminary stage toward an internal approach
to the language studied, when the observer becomes adjusted to the native
speakers and decodes the messages in their mother-tongue through the medium
of its code.

As long as the investigator knows no *signatum* of a given language, and
has access to nothing but *signans* he willy nilly has to strain his detective
capacities and obtain any possible information about the structure of this
language from the external evidences. The present state of Etruscology is a
good example of such a technique. But if the linguist is familiar with the
code and namely masters the agreed transformation by which a set of *signantia*
is converted into a set of *signata*, then it becomes superfluous for him to play
Sherlock Holmes, unless he aspires to finding out how wide and reliable data
could be obtained by such a mock scrutiny. It is difficult, however, to simulate
the ignorance of a familiar code: smuggled meanings distort one's allegedly
cryptanalytic approach.

Obviously "the inseparability of objective content and observing subject",
singled out by Niels Bohr as a premise of all well-defined knowledge,[15] must
be definitely taken into account also in linguistics, and the position of the observer in relation to the language observed and described must be exactly
identified. First, as formulated by Jurgen Ruesch, the information an observer
can collect depends upon his location within or outside the system.[16] Furthermore, if the observer is located *within* the communication system, language
presents two considerably different aspects when seen from the two ends of
the communication channel. Roughly, the encoding process goes from meaning
to sound and from the lexicogrammatical to the phonological level, whereas
the decoding process displays the opposite direction—from sound to meaning
and from features to symbols. While a set (*Einstellung*) toward immediate
constituents takes precedence in speech production, for speech perception
the message is *first* a stochastic process. The probabilistic aspect of speech
finds a conspicuous expression in the approach of the listener to homonyms,
whereas for the speaker homonymy does not exist. When saying $/s \wedge n/$, he
knows beforehand whether 'sun' or 'son' is meant, while the listener depends on the conditional probabilities of the context.[17] For the receiver the
message presents many ambiguities which were unequivocal for the sender.
The ambiguities of pun and poetry utilize this input property for the output.

No doubt there is a feedback between speaking and hearing, but the hierarchy of the two processes is opposite for the encoder and decoder. These two
distinct aspects of language are irreducible to each other; both are equally
essential and must be regarded as *complementary* in Niels Bohr's sense of
this work. The relative autonomy of the input pattern is documented by the
widespread temporal priority of a passive acquisition of a language both by
infants and adults. L. Shcherba's request for a delimitation and elaboration

[15] *Atomic physics and human knowledge*, New York, John Wiley & Sons, 1958, p. 30.
[16] *Toward a unified theory of human behavior*, ed. by R. R. Grinker, New York,
Basic Books, 1956, p. 54.
[17] See International Journal of Slavic Linguistics and Poetics vols. 1-2 (1959) p. 286f.

of two grammars — 'active' and 'passive', recently reemphasized by young
Russian linguists, is equally important for linguistic theory, for teaching
languages, and for applied linguistics.[18]

When a linguist deals with one of the two aspects of language *à la Jourdain*,
namely without realizing whether his observations are devoted to output or
to input, it is still less dangerous than the arbitrary compromises frequently
made between the output and input analyses, for example, an output grammar
discussing the generating operations without appeal to meaning, despite the
necessary priority of meaning for the encoder. At present linguistics receives
from communication theory particularly valuable suggestions for the somewhat
neglected study of the verbal input.

MacKay warns against the confusion between the exchange of verbal messages and the extraction of information from the physical world, both abusively
unified under the label 'communication'; this word has for him an inevitably
anthropomorphic connotation "which bedevils discussion."[19] There is a similar
danger when interpreting human inter-communication in terms of physical
information. Attempts to construct a model of language without any relation
either to the speaker or to the hearer and thus to hypostasize a code detached
from actual communication threaten to make a scholastic fiction from language.

Beside the encoding and decoding, also the procedure of recoding, code
switching, briefly the various faces of translation, grow to be one of the focal
concerns both of linguistics and of communication theory here and in Western
and Eastern Europe. Only now do such fascinating problems as those of ways
and degrees of mutual understanding among speakers of some closely cognate
languages, as for instance Danish, Norwegian and Swedish, begin to attract
the attention of linguists[20] and promise to give a lucid insight into the phenomenon known in communication theory under the label "semantic noise"
and into the theoretically and pedagogically important problem of overcoming
it.

Incidentally, both linguistics and communication theory for a certain period
were tempted to treat any concern with meaning as a kind of semantic noise
and to exclude semantics from the study of verbal messages. At present,
however, linguists display a tendency to reintroduce meaning while utilizing
the very instructive experience of this temporary ostracism. Also in communication theory a similar trend may be observed. According to Weaver,
the analysis of communication "has so penetratingly cleared the air that one
is now, perhaps for the first time, ready for a real theory of meaning," and
especially for handling "one of the most significant but difficult aspects of
meaning, namely the influence of context."[21] Linguists are gradually finding
the way of tackling meaning and in particular the relation between general

---

[18] See I. Revzin, *Tezisy Konferencii po mashinnomu perevodu*, Moscow, Pervyj Moskov.
Gos. Ped. Inst. Inostrannyx Jazykov, 1958, pp. 23–25.

[19] Cybernetics: Transactions of the Eighth Conference, New York, 1952, p. 221.

[20] See particularly E. Haugen, Nordisk Tidskr. vol. 29 (1953) pp. 225–249.

[21] Shannon and Weaver, op. cit., p. 116. Cf. D. M. MacKay, *The place of 'meaning' in
the theory of information*, Information Theory, ed. by C. Cherry, New York, Basic
Books, 1956.

and contextual meanings as an intrinsic linguistic topic, distinctly separated from the ontological problems of reference.

Communication theory, after having mastered the level of phonemic information, may approach the task of measuring the amount of grammatical information, since the system of grammatical, particularly morphological categories, like the system of distincitive features, is ostensibly based on a scale of binary oppositions. Thus, for instance, 9 binary choices underlie over 100 simple and compound conjugational forms of an English verb which appear, for example, in combination with the pronoun *I*.[22] The amount of grammatical information carried by the English verb may be subsequently confronted with the corresponding data about the English noun or about the verb and noun of various languages; the relation between the morphological and syntactic information in English is to be compared with the equivalent relation in other languages, and all these comparative data will present important auxiliary material for a linguistic typology of languages and for the inquiry into the linguistic universals.

The amount of grammatical information which is potentially contained in the paradigms of a given language (statistics of the code) must be further confronted with a similar amount in the tokens, in the actual occurrences of the various grammatical forms within a corpus of messages. Any attempt to ignore this duality and to confine linguistic analysis and calculation only to the code or only to the corpus impoverishes the research. The crucial question of relationship between the patterning of the constituents of the verbal code and their relative frequency both in the code and in its use cannot be passed over.

The semiotic definition of a symbol's meaning as its translation into other symbols finds an effectual application in the linguistic testing of intra- and interlingual translation, and this approach to semantic information concurs with Shannon's proposal to define information as "that which is invariant under all reversible encoding or translating operations," briefly, as "the equivalence class of all such translations."[23]

When dealing with meanings whether grammatical or lexical we must be careful not to misuse the polar notions—'regularity' and 'deviation'. The idea of deviation frequently emerges from a disregard for the stratified, hierarchic structure of language. There is, however, a substantial difference between secondariness and deviation. We are not justified in envisaging as deviant either Kurylowicz' 'syntactic derivation' with regard to the 'primary function',[24] or Chomsky's 'transforms' *versus* 'kernels',[25] or Bloomfield's 'marginal' ('transferred') meanings in relation to the 'central' meaning of the word.[26]

---

[22] 1. Preterit (*vs.* non-preterit), 2. perfect, 3. progressive, 4. expective, 5. morally determined, 6. contingent, 7. potential, 8. assertorial, 9. passive. Cf. R. Jakobson, American Anthropologist vol. 61, no. 5, Part 2 (1959) pp. 139-141, and W. F. Twaddell, *The English verb auxiliaries*, Providence, Brown University Press, 1960.

[23] Cybernetics: Transactions of the Seventh Conference, New York, 1951, p. 157.

[24] Bulletin de la Société de Linguistique de Paris, no. 110 (1936), pp. 79-92.

[25] *Syntactic structures*, The Hague, Mouton & Co., 1957.

[26] *Language*, New York, Henry Holt & Co., 1933, p. 149.

Metaphoric creations are not deviations but regular processes of certain stylistic varieties, which are subcodes of an overall code, and within such a subcode there is nothing deviant in Marvell's figural assignment of a concrete epithet to an abstract noun (properly a 'hypallage')—"a green Thought in a green shade"—or in Shakespeare's metaphoric transposition of an inanimate noun into the feminine class—"the morning opes her golden gates"—or in the metonymic use of "sorrow" instead of "sorrowful while", which Putnam's paper excerpts from Dylan Thomas ("A grief ago I saw him there"). In contradistinction to the agrammatical constructions as "girls sleeps" the quoted phrases are meaningful, and any meaningful sentence may be submitted to a truth test exactly in the same way as the statement "Peter is an old fox" could lead to a reply "It's not true; Peter is not a fox but a swine, while John is a fox." Incidentally, neither ellipsis nor reticence or anacoluthon could be considered as deviant structures; they, and the slurred style of speech, a brachylogical subcode to which they belong, are merely lawful derivations from the kernel forms embedded in the explicit standard. Once again, this "code variability", which clarifies why the standard is not actualized in some overt behavior, was overlooked rather by linguists than by the less 'biased' communication engineers.

To sum up there exists a wide range of questions calling for cooperation of the two different and independent disciplines we are discussing. The first steps in that direction were actually lucky. May I finish by quoting an example of the longest and, until recently, perhaps the most spectacular tie between linguistics, in particular the study of poetic language, on the one hand, and the mathematical analysis of stochastic processes on the other. The Russian school of metrics owes some of its internationally echoed achievements to the fact that some forty years ago such students as B. Tomashevskij, expert both in mathematics and in philology, skillfully used Markov chains for the statistical investigation of verse; these data, supplemented by a linguistic analysis of the verse structure, gave in the early twenties a theory of verse based on the calculus of its conditional probabilities and of the tensions between anticipation and unexpectedness as the measurable rhythmical values, and the computation of these tensions, which we have labeled 'frustrated expectations', gave surprising clues for descriptive, historical, comparative, and general metrics on a scientific basis.[27]

I am convinced that methods newly developed in structural linguistics and in communication theory, when applied to verse analysis, and to so many other provinces of language, are capable of opening up wide perspectives for further coordinated efforts of both disciplines. Let us anticipate that our expectations will not be frustrated.[28]

HARVARD UNIVERSITY AND
    MASSACHUSETTS INSTITUTE OF TECHNOLOGY
    CAMBRIDGE, MASSACHUSETTS

---

[27] Cf. B. Tomashevskij, *O stixe*, Leningrad, 1929; R. Jakobson, *O cheshskom stixe*, Berlin-Moscow, 1923, and *Linguistics and poetics*, "Style in Language," New York, The Technology Press of Massachusetts Institute of Technology, 1960.

[28] I should like to dedicate this paper to the memory of the engineer O. A. Jakobson.

MINUTES OF THE SYMPOSIUM ON THE STRUCTURE OF LANGUAGE AND ITS MATHEMATICAL ASPECTS

NEW YORK CITY, APRIL 14–15th, 1960

SPONSORS: American Mathematical Society
Association for Symbolic Logic
Linguistic Society of America

PROGRAM COMMITTEE: Noam Chomsky   Roman Jakobson (Chairman)
                         H. B. Curry   Hilary Putnam
                         Henry Hiż   W. V. Quine

SECRETARY OF THE SYMPOSIUM: E. S. Klima, Massachusetts Institute of Technology

FIRST SESSION: Morning, April 14th.

CHAIRMAN: Roman Jakobson, Harvard University and Massachusetts Institute of Technology

W. V. Quine, Harvard University
Noam Chomsky, Massachusetts Institute of Technology
Hilary Putnam, Princeton University
Henry Hiż, University of Pennsylvania
Nelson Goodman, University of Pennsylvania
H. B. Curry, Pennsylvania State University

DISCUSSION LEADER: Max Black, Cornell University

PARTICIPANTS IN THE DISCUSSION:

L. M. Court, Diamond Ordnance Fuze Laboratories, Washington 25, D.C.
Frank Harary, University of Michigan
Henry Hiż, University of Pennsylvania
Roman Jakobson, Harvard University and Massachusetts Institute of Technology
Russell Kirsch, National Bureau of Standards, Washington, D.C.
William P. Livant, University of Michigan
Irina Lynch, Wellesley College and Harvard University
Murray S. Miron, University of Illinois
Leonard Newmark, Ohio State University, Columbus, Ohio
Hilary Putnam, Princeton University
Arthur Sard, Queens College, Flushing, New York
R. J. Solomonoff, Zator Company, Cambridge, Massachusetts

INTRODUCTORY REMARKS

BY

MAX BLACK

The summaries we have heard provide tantalising glimpses of ideas that deserve careful examination and are bound to provoke fruitful discussion. I am sorry to have had no chance to read the papers, and must confine myself to some general comments.

The topic of the symposium is, 'The structure of language and its mathematical aspects'. Three tasks are plainly involved: the elaboration of well-defined notions of 'linguistic structure', construction of appropriate mathematical systems, and provision of suitable 'co-ordinative definitions' as links between the abstract mathematics and the actual languages studied by linguists. My impression is that sufficient mathematical resources are already available —the theory of recursive functions, or, alternatively, the methods of combinatory logic (for which see Curry's paper) suggest themselves as promising arsenals. Modern algebra, mathematical logic, and possibly topology, may be expected to provide all the necessary mathematical tools.

However, severe conceptual difficulties remain to be resolved in identifying the 'linguistic structure' that is to receive mathematical analysis. The basic distinction between a 'grammatical' and a 'non-grammatical' sentence is still somewhat problematic, as Putnam's comments illustrate. Chomsky's proof of the limitations of the model of 'constituent analysis' that has so long controlled the work of linguists is a striking example of how mathematical analysis can foster the enlargement of the imagination by forcing the empirical scientist to review fundamental presuppositions of method.

Of course, there is the usual risk of excessive distance between the mathematical model and its intended application. Quine has presented a persuasive case for the value to linguists of the distinctions emphasised in mathematical logic. But that subject was invented in the service of the adequate analysis of mathematical discourse and deliberately neglects for its own good purposes much plainly visible linguistic structure (e.g. as shown in the so-called 'token-reflexive words' distinctions of tense and mood, etc.). There is danger here (as possibly also in the results reported by Goodman and Hiż) of the mathematics being pursued for its own sake, with little profit for the linguist. Contrast, for instance, Quine's remarks about the analysis of the phrase, 'The lady I saw you with' with what is implied in such a fragment of familiar speech as the wisecrack, 'That's no lady—that's my wife'. If language has a rigid skeleton, speech remains so flexible—so much a matter of invention and creation—that the communication of the speaker-in-the-street may tax the resources of the most refined grammar to explain. A valuable outcome of the studies that have been reported to us is the healthy tension between linguists and mathematicians they are likely to generate.

COMMENTS

ON QUINE'S PAPER

IRINA LYNCH: If, as Quine states, pronouns may stand for definite participants only, how can one explain the presence of the pronoun "they" in, for example, "They say that the lady I saw you with is somebody else's wife"? Should the 'impersonal' use of pronouns be exempt from Quine's definition, we still could find a number of contexts where a pronoun, be it personal, interrogative, or relative, stands for an indefinite noun. To give just a few examples:

(1)   *Who* is at the door?—*A* man, I saw *him.*—*Whom* did you see?—A man.

(2)   This morning I gave a book to a student.   *He* thanked me.—*Who* thanked you?   A student.   *What* did you give *him?*   A book.

(3)   An apple that falls from a tree is called a "windfall".   *What* is a "windfall"?—An apple *that* falls from a tree.

W. V. QUINE: In supposing that her examples conflict with my remarks, Mrs. Lynch is assigning to my words 'stand for' a meaning abruptly at variance with the meaning which I specified and illustrated in the questioned passage.   In that passage (the sixth from last paragraph of my paper) I used 'stand for' to mean 'be replaceable by', and contrasted it with the relation of grammatical antecedent.   I asserted that pronouns, even when their grammatical antecedents are indefinite singular terms, can be replaced only by definite singular terms.   Thus consider her examples.   Her first 'him' is replaceable only by 'the man', 'he' by 'the student', and the second 'him' likewise.   She is put off by the fact that the grammatical antecedents of these pronouns are the indefinite singular terms 'a man' and 'a student'; but this contrast was my very point.

Mrs. Lynch's last 'that', being a relative pronoun, needs for present purposes to be expanded into 'such that it' (in conformity with my seventh from last paragraph) if we are to isolate its role in cross-reference.   This done, we find that 'it' has 'an apple' as antecedent but only 'the apple' as appropriate replacement, true to form.

Mrs. Lynch's 'who', 'whom', and 'what', finally, are interrogative pronouns. These, like the 'they' of her first example, are irrelevant to the contrast I was concerned to draw, for they have no grammatical antecedents at all.

ON CHOMSKY'S PAPER

ARTHUR SARD: What is the motivation of considering many grammars simultaneously?

NOAM CHOMSKY: Consideration of a variety of grammars is motivated by an interest in linguistic universals (i.e., general features of linguistic structure) and in justification of grammars, a task which can be undertaken in a serious way only in terms of a presupposed general theory of linguistic structure (cf. in this connection my *Syntactic structures*, chapter 6; M. Halle, *On the role of simplicity in linguistic descriptions*, this volume).

W. P. LIVANT: I speak as a psychologist interested in trying to validate Chomsky's grammar with human speakers.   If one were instructed directly to convert one sentence string into another, would the considerations which lead to putting some strings in the kernel and others in the transform grammar, lead to an inequality in the time taken to expand a kernel, or to collapse the transformed string into the very same kernel?   Would the time taken to expand a declarative active into an interrogative passive be longer than the recursive operation?

NOAM CHOMSKY: I am hesitant about commenting on this particular suggestion without further details. In general, I think that the problem to which this question is directed, that of determining the "psychological reality" of linguistic constructs, is as difficult as it is important.

A. G. OETTINGER: If I understood him correctly, the speaker said that the grammars were constructed to apply indifferently to the speaker's or the hearer's point of view. Since the hearer is more concerned with the analysis of sentences than with their synthesis, does this not imply that he must first have a phrase structure analysis of given sentence, then also a means for discovering inverse transformations required to the phrase structure to that of a kernel? Is there in your system any means of obtaining a phrase structure analysis for a given sentence, and then finding the inverse transformation, other than generating all sentences until you obtain one that matches the given one?

NOAM CHOMSKY: A grammar, in the sense in which I have been using the term, specifies the structural description of each grammatical sentence. It is thus neutral as between speaker and hearer, in the sense that it says nothing specific about how either actually operates.

The hearer can be represented (in part) as a device that takes a sentence as input and gives as output the structural description assigned to the sentence by the grammar that the speaker has internalized. One can speculate about various specific mechanisms by which this process could be carried out. For example, the hearer may scan the sentence for hints as to which rules of the grammar are used to generate it, generate a sentence by a route compatible with this initial specification, compare the result with the original, repeating the process, etc., approaching the correct analysis by some sort of successive approximation. And there are many other possibilities, such as that suggested in the question, that should also be seriously considered.

There are no doubt many ways of constructing recognition procedures that can be made to work, to some degree of adequacy. The task of real scientific importance, however, is clearly that of developing a procedure that avoids ad hoc and arbitrary rules, and that makes use of the generalizations about sentence structure provided by a well-constructed grammar to simplify the procedure of analysis.

L. M. COURT: Chomsky arranges his three types of grammars (languages) in a descending sequence, each member of the hierarchy including its successors. Finite sources (even counter devices) are too feeble to generate his Types I and II, whereas automata of this kind suffice for his Type III languages. The extra power of a Type II over a Type III language appears to inhere in the self-embedding character of the former. ("Self-embedding" in the vernacular means that fresh phrases from a selected list can *repeatedly* be introduced to modify existing words.)

One feels intuitively that a self-embedding language is a far richer instrument for conveying ideas. *Infinity*, especially in its mathematical usages, is an advanced concept, and the very finiteness (in the sketched sense) of a Type

III language should militate against the emergence of such notations in civilizations in which this type of language is the medium of discourse. The calculus, which rests firmly on the application of the infinitely small, was crystallized in Renaissance Europe (Chomsky observes that English seems to approximate a Type II language, and probably this is also true of French and German), whereas nothing corresponding to the calculus or the even subtler notion of transfinite numbers can be found in Polynesian cultures.

It may prove profitable, in the light of these remarks, to devise an empirical program to simultaneously compare various languages for the closeness with which they approximate Chomsky's second and third types and the maturity or immaturity of their concepts of infinity. There are other avenues besides the linguistic, e.g., visual and aural experiences, through which these notions enter our consciousness, and their involvement will undoubtedly complicate the relation we are seeking to establish. The physical environment also plays an important role, and the age of a civilization usually qualifies the ripeness of its intellectual pursuits. Despite these obstacles, a program of the sort we are envisioning should throw some light on the influence of language on a people's thought processes.

SECOND SESSION: Afternoon, April 14th.
CHAIRMAN: H. B. Curry, Pennsylvania State University
Y. R. Chao, University of California, Berkeley
Murray Eden, Massachusetts Institute of Technology
Morris Halle, Massachusetts Institute of Technology
Robert Abernathy, Massachusetts Institute of Technology
Hans Herzberger, University of Pennsylvania
A. G. Oettinger, Harvard University
V. H. Yngve, Massachusetts Institute of Technology
DISCUSSION LEADER: Joshua Whatmough, Harvard University
PARTICIPANTS IN THE DISCUSSION:
Andras Balint, Teacher's College, Columbia University
William Fourst, Harvard University
Dennis Fry, University College, London
Saul Gorn, University of Pennsylvania
J. A. Greenwood, Princeton University
V. E. Giuliano, Arthur D. Little, Inc., Cambridge, Massachusetts
C. F. Hockett, Cornell University
Henry Hiż, University of Pennsylvania
Russell Kirsch, National Bureau of Standards, Washington, D.C.
John G. Mackinney, General Kinetics, Arlington, Virginia
Don Mittleman, National Bureau of Standards, Washington, D.C.
Murray S. Miron, University of Illinois
George W. Patterson, University of Pennsylvania

INTRODUCTORY REMARKS

BY

JOSHUA WHATMOUGH

There is, I think, no need for apology for insisting, as I think I was the first to do (fully ten years ago) upon the importance of the Mathematical Theory of Communication for Linguistics, and of Linguistics for Communication Engineering; nor apology for the phrase Mathematical Linguistics, which is precisely what it is called, namely Linguistics studied mathematically, both as theory (what some are now calling type-token mathematics) and practice (which includes automatic translation and various other applications).

In passing I should point out that my theory of Selective Variation in Language, which says

a linguistic status is produced and maintained by consistent selection
which preserves the system from gross inconsistency of variation

was framed even earlier but not published (1951) until I was sure that descriptive and historical (and comparative) linguistics, upon which the theory was first based, had a firm mathematical foundation, which Communication Theory furnished. There is, in fact, a convergence of all these three approaches to the study of language. Philologists had always supposed that language could not be reduced to laws capable of mathematical statement. Attempts to find articulate laws, even on such a trifling matter as tense and aspect a recent writer declares to have occupied him seventeen years, and reaches the conclusion that linguistics must undertake to perform transformations that make it obvious that the theory and practice of descriptive linguistics are not (as at present) incompatible. This can be done only by means of logic and mathematics.

It is perhaps invidious to single out certain papers for comment. I cannot, however, refrain from calling attention especially to those of Chao, with its courageous attempt to obtain some agreement in terminology in our convergent disciplines; of Eden, which is, I think, very promising in the field of bringing writing and speech still closer together in their already close relationship (not always realized to be as close as it is); and of Oettinger, with its fascinating attack that now has been going on for nearly a year, upon problems of syntax, which turn out not to be so terrifying after all once we get away from subjective (descriptive) grammar to the laws of probability.

It would be easy, and I find it tempting, to comment upon these and all the other papers at length. I must await some other occasion. But a general remark may be appended.

Communication theory is not incompatible with linguistics—only with nearly all current structural theory. Structuralism has had its place: for over thirty years I have insisted that its place is neither so important nor so vast as its advocates have urged. But if there can be, as now seems likely, a meeting of minds—the minds of linguists, and of communication engineers, not only will this apparent contradiction be resolved: there will also be discoveries in store, formulated (I hope and believe) in elegant and economical theorems (instead of in rambling and impenetrable tomes), discoveries of great power and practical application in human communication, and, therefore, in all human affairs, and hence in the development (if not evolution) of man for decades, and perhaps centuries, to come.

COMMENTS

ON HALLE'S PAPER

H. Hiż: The notions of simplicity and of economy may be very misleading and call for much clarifications. One can write any text using only two different symbols. It would be a great economy in the kind of symbols used but not very simple to decode. In practice one has to take into account very many factors and aspects. The notion of simplicity is, thus, close to the concept of tact and good scientific taste.

Morris Halle: It was one of the aims of my paper to give a meaning to the notion "simplicity of phonological descriptions" that would not suffer from the same vagueness and subjectivity as the notions "good taste" and "scientific tact," and that at the same time would also guide us in making the appropriate choice among competing descriptions. This can be done only if one severely restricts the number of descriptions that would be considered adequate. I required, therefore, that admissible phonological descriptions be framed in terms of a fixed set of properties, the distinctive features, which, being linguistic universals like the phoneme or the morpheme, are to be applied in the description of every language and cannot be changed to suit special situations. To choose among the relatively small number of phonological descriptions satisfying this rather severe requirement I suggested the mechanical criterion of counting the number of distinctive features mentioned in the description. Finally, I attempted to show that in specific instances the criterion led us to choose descriptions of greater generality, in the usual sense of that term.

ON HERZBERGER'S PAPER

V. Giuliano: To what extent are the rules for string generation and adjoining independent, in the sense that changing one rule need not result in the necessity of examining and possibly revising several other rules? This question appears to be of particular importance when one is concerned with analysis of unrestricted technical English, when it will be necessary for some time to come to make refinements and revisions in yet imperfect rules.

H. G. Herzberger: The rules would not in general be independent in that sense. The center strings are the generators of the language only with respect to some given adjunction (and replacement) operations. A change at any point in the system requires corresponding changes elsewhere, if the set of sentences is to be held constant. The grammatical rules that are associated with elementary strings introduce the points of adjunction as well as the adjuncts; and other rules co-ordinate the two. Evidently there will be many interconnections between the two types of rules.

ON OETTINGER'S PAPER

D. MITTLEMAN: What is the relation of the syntactic analysis as presented here to the predictive syntactic of Mrs. Rhodes?

J. G. MACKINNEY: The oral presentation of this paper left the impression that there is only *one* conceptually simple algorithm for converting ordinary algebraic formulae to the Łukasiewicz notation. In a note of limited distribution entitled *An application of sorting to the translation of algebraic coding to machine coding*, A. E. Roberts, Jr. has shown an equally simple algorithm for the assignment of weights to consecutive symbols as a formula in full-parenthetic notation is scanned from left to right. When the symbols are then sorted by weight, the result is in effect a parenthesis-free, prefixed-operator formula. Ill-formedness of the original *may* by detected during scanning or sorting, but a full examination probably can not be made until the parenthesis-free formula is created. Oettinger is of course correct in rejecting methods involving sorting on the grounds of inefficiency as compared with the push-down store.

A. G. OETTINGER: Our experimental approach to the syntactic analysis of Russian and English owes its inspiration to the method of Mrs. Rhodes. The theoretical studies described in my paper were, in turn, inspired by the experimental work.

There is certainly no claim of uniqueness, but Mackinney is correct in contrasting the efficiency of sorting and of pushdown store techniques. Moreover, as I indicate in the paper, the pushdown store technique has the merit of tying together hitherto unconnected experimental observations and theoretical analyses.

THIRD SESSION: Morning, April 15th.
CHAIRMAN: W. V. Quine, Harvard University
      Frank Harary and G. E. Peterson, University of Michigan
      Joachim Lambek, McGill University and Institute for Advanced Study
      H. A. Gleason, Jr., Hartford Seminary Foundation
      Benoit Mandelbrot, International Business Machine Corporation
      C. F. Hockett, Cornell University
      R. S. Wells, Yale University
      Roman Jakobson, Harvard University and Massachusetts Institute of Technology
DISCUSSION LEADER: R. M. Fano, Massachusetts Institute of Technology

PARTICIPANTS IN THE DISCUSSION:
Andras Balint, Teacher's College, Columbia University
L. M. Court, Diamond Ordnance Fuze Laboratories, Washington 25, D.C.
Henry Hiż, University of Pennsylvania
Roman Jakobson, Harvard University and Massachusetts Institute of Technology
Russell Kirsch, National Bureau of Standards, Washington, D.C.
R. B. Lees, International Business Machines, Yorktown Heights, New York
Irina Lynch, Wellesley College and Harvard University
A. G. Oettinger, Harvard University
W. V. Quine, Harvard University
J. D. Sable, Radio Corporation of America, Princeton, New Jersey
Mortimer Taube, Documentation, Incorporated

INTRODUCTORY REMARKS

BY

R. M. FANO

It has been pointed out by a number of speakers, and particularly emphasized by Jakobson, that the process of understanding speech or written languages involves sequential decisions made on a probabilistic basis, and that language constraints play a key role in these sequential decisions. I wish to expand further this point by mentioning certain fundamental results of information theory concerning the problem of communicating accurately and efficiently in the presence of random disturbances.

Random disturbances arising from various sources, and of varying degree of severity are always present in the communication process between individuals, regardless of whether spoken or written language is used. The sources of these random disturbances are not necessarily external to the individuals concerned; for instance, the random variations of the physical appearance of the various phonemes in speech and of the various letters in handwriting act as disturbances in the communication process, just as the noise arising from the environment in which individuals communicate.

It is well known that our ability to understand spoken or written language in the presence of random disturbances stems from the redundancy present in the language. Redundancy may be defined, at least for our present purposes, as the fraction of the letters in a written text, or the fraction of the phonemes in a spoken utterance that could be eliminated if no random disturbances were present. For instance, it has been estimated from experiments performed by C. E. Shannon [1] some years ago that at least four out of five letters in printed English are redundant. Of course, I don't mean by this that four out of five letters could be eliminated out-right, but rather that the same text could be recoded, at least in principle, into one-fifth as many letters.

Redundancy is present in linguistic communication in the form of constraints (mostly deterministic) between successive linguistic events. These constraints, known to the listener or the reader, allow him to resolve ambiguities resulting from random disturbances, or as a matter of fact, from homonyms. One of the most important results of information theory is that the span of these constraints in addition to the redundancy resulting from them, is a key factor in overcoming random disturbances. More precisely, it is possible to design artificial codes that insure as accurate a reception as desired by making the span of the constraints sufficiently long while keeping constant the associated redundancy. It is only necessary for this purpose that the redundancy be greater than a certain minimum value which depends on the characteristics of the disturbances that must be overcome.

The net result is that, once the redundancy has been made greater than this minimum amount, the accuracy of reception can be improved by either further increasing the redundancy or by increasing the span of the constraints while keeping the redundancy fixed. A further increase of redundancy implies a further reduction of the rate at which information is transmitted. This is evident when the redundancy is increased, let us say, by repeating each successive element of the message. Increasing the span of the constraint implies increasing the complexity of the encoding and decoding operations, and therefore of the equipment required to perform them. Thus, for a fixed reception accuracy, a greater rate of transmission of information can be obtained at the expense of greater equipment complexity, and vice versa.

Since my knowledge of linguistics is rather limited, I will not explore in any detail the linguistic implications of these theoretical results. However, I will express my belief that the structure of languages, (presumably resulting from evolution) must have been greatly affected by the fact that they must enable individuals to communicate accurately and efficiently in the presence of random disturbances. For this reason, I would expect languages to exhibit structural characteristics similar to those of artificial codes designed to meet the same communication requirements. The point that I want to stress in particular is that, while the encoding operation performed, let us say, by the speaker may well be based entirely on deterministic (as opposed to probabilistic) rules, the rules themselves must reflect the needs of the listener who must make accurate estimates about what the speaker is saying on the basis of probabilistic considerations.

It turns out that the equipment required to generate efficient codes with long constraint spans is only moderately complex. The decoding equipment is inherently much more complex. A decoding procedure that does not require prohibitively complex equipment was suggested three years ago by J. M. Wozencraft [2]. The reason for my mentioning this procedure is that it presupposes a form of sequential encoding with a tree structure somewhat similar to that postulated for languages in some of the papers presented in this session. Roughly speaking, the message transmitted can be regarded as the set of instructions for climbing the tree from node to node. The decoding procedure consists of deciding at each node which branch is most likely to have been followed by the encoder. Each successive decision is made only after exploring some distance ahead the parts of the tree connected to the different branches involved in the decision.   I wish to stress that this procedure is strikingly similar to what I think I do when I am listening to a conversation in a particularly noisy environment, or when I am reading some very poor handwriting.   The amount of work that the equipment has actually to do according to the decoding procedures suggested by Wozencraft increases with the severity of the random disturbances.   This fact reminds me, of course, of the greater mental effort required in listening or reading under adverse environmental conditions.   The moral of my remarks, if there is one, is that linguistics and information theory have still much to offer to each other. Unfortunately, in order to take full advantage of this mutual interaction information theorists have to learn more about languages, and linguists have to learn more about information theory.   This is where interdisciplinary cooperation begins to hurt.

REFERENCES

1. C. E. Shannon, *Prediction and entropy of printed English*, Bell System Technical Journal vol. 30 (1951) p. 50.

2. J. M. Wozencraft, *Sequential decoding for reliable communication*, Technical Report 325, Research Laboratory of Electronics. Massachusetts Institute of Technology, August 9, 1957.

COMMENTS

ON HARARY'S PAPER

W. V. QUINE: Harary's quotation from Russell, "Mathematics is that subject in which one does not know what one is talking about nor whether what one says is true," dates from an essay of 1901 (reprinted 1918 in *Mysticism and Logic*). It represents an attitude in which, happily, Russell did not long persist. Already by the time of *Principia Mathematica* his view had changed to one which is well represented by an equally quotable passage in a later book of Russell's, perhaps *Introduction to Mathematical Philosophy*: "The axiomatic method has certain advantages over logical construction, which are precisely the advantages of theft over honest toil."

F. HARARY: In this context, the following quotation from the book *Introduction to the Foundations of Mathematics* by R. L. Wilder, 1952, is appropriate:
"Axioms are statements about some concept with which we already have some familiarity.   Thus, if we are already familiar with arithmetic, we might begin to set down axioms for arithmetic.   Of course the method is not restricted to mathematics.   If we are familar with some field such as physics, philosophy, chemistry, zoology, economics, for instance, we might choose to set down some axioms for it, or a portion of it, and see what theorems we might logically deduce from them.   We may say, then, that an axiom, as

used in the modern way, is a statement which seems to hold for an under-lying concept, an axiom system being a collection of such statements about the concept. Thus, in practice, the concept comes first, the axioms later."

ON LAMBEK'S PAPER

L. M. COURT: At the start Lambek stresses the analogy between the syntactic algebra and dimension theory in physics. But dimensional analysis is largely sterile; it provides a preliminary (superficial) check on the soundness of a physical equation but does not assess the underlying causes. It is only in certain applications, where we possess sufficient insight into a physical situation, but do not comprehend it fully, that it can be applied fruitfully; such is the case when we invoke one of Buckingham's theorems to obtain an expression for the dimensionless Reynold's number from a knowledge of the *complete* list of the physical variables (density, viscosity, etc.) on which the drag (a force) depends, even though we are ignorant of the precise form of the dependence. (See *Exterior ballistics* by McShane, etc., Denver University Press.)

The sentence (s) and the name or "proper" noun (n) are the fundamental entities in the syntactic algebra, corresponding to time, mass and distance in physics; every other word or phrase in the sentence is expressed by this algebra in terms of n and s. Besides the observation that the *same* word in the *same* sentence can have two (or more) distinct expressions in this algebra, which Lambek proceeds to identify, there is little ground for believing that two words in separate sentences, having *identical* formal expressions (in n and s), necessarily exercise similar grammatical functions. Syntactic algebra is therefore unlikely to be an apt instrument for comparing one sentence with another and even less so for shedding light on the logical or semantic validity of a sentence.

J. LAMBEK: The sterility of dimensional analysis in classical physics does not weaken my comparison. After all, grammatical analysis is also sterile, in the sense that the grammatical correctness of a sentence does not guarantee its validity. A similar comparison could have been drawn between gram-matical sentences in English and covariant equations in relativity theory. The second part of Court's comment seems to be based on a misunderstand-ing. It has nowhere been claimed that the words or phrases of a language can be expressed in terms of n and s (and other primitive types), only that their grammatical types (adjective, adverb, conjunction, etc.) may be so ex-pressed. Surely, if the word "sound" occurs as an adjective in two different sentences then it exercises a similar grammatical function in those two sentences, even though it may occur as a noun or verb elsewhere.

H. HIŻ: The paper is a substantial improvement in the line of thought that originated with Husserl (informally) and Leśniewski and was later popularized by Ajdukiewicz. One essential extention done by Lambek consists in considering also functors that have their arguments to the left rather than to the right. One, of course, could extend Lambek's techniques to the cases when there are several arguments to the left and several arguments to the right.

In many cases in order to decide what are the arguments of a functor one has to examine more of the text than just these arguments; one has to see how the expressions are situated in the entire sentence.

It is often assumed that a modifier of an expression occurs adjacent to the expression it modifies. The analysis presented in Lambek's work is based on this kind of assumption. An expression acts on another expression from the left, or from the right, but always in juxtaposed role. This is a proper grammatical analysis for languages in which concatenation plays a fundamental grammatical role like it does in English. But there are non-concatenative languages, e.g., Latin. In a Latin sentence a masculine noun can be modified by an adjective in the masculine form nearly in any place of the sentence, provided that other nouns in the sentence are feminine or neuter. Incidentally, for non-concatenative languages the tree analysis, like that presented by Yngve, will not be suitable either.

J. Lambek: As to the first point of Hiż's comments, one can ascribe types of functors of several arguments without having to extend the techniques already described. Thus "likes" in "John likes Jane" has type $(n \backslash s)/n$. Similarly $((x \backslash s)/y)/z$ would be the type of a functor having one argument of type x on the left and two arguments of types z and y on the right.

His remaining comments do bring out an essential limitation of phrase structure and type theory grammars. Deviations from some idealized word order may be easily described by transformation rules, but only with great difficulty or not at all by type assignments.

ON GLEASON'S PAPER

R. Jakobson: The question of genetic kinship between roots or affixes of different languages cannot be handled without an elucidation of their semantic relationship. Problems of lexical and grammatical meanings, to the same extent as the examination of external form, require a thoroughly critical approach and methodological skill from any comparativist.

ON MANDELBROT'S PAPER

L. M. Court: That there is a common core to all languages, and that it, at least initially, should be the focal point of linguistic studies, is the burden of Mandelbrot's paper. Since man is a biological species and since human psychology in its fundamentals (when the frills are stripped away) is everywhere alike, the thesis is more than warrantable. Every language has terms corresponding to nouns or the names of things and to verbs or words implying action. Modifiers of these two basic types (adjectives and adverbs) probably also occur in all languages, although the forms which they assume may vary. Without exception every culture must somehow take account of number, time and personal and social relationships, and in one way or another these concepts or interconnections are embodied in all languages. The paramount question is exactly how any one of these physically or biologically real entities and relationships is communicated in a particular language, i.e., what device or grammatical structure is employed. We may find, for example, that two real-world distinct relationships receive identical grammatical treatment in one group of languages, whereas in another they are managed by unmistakably different devices. The writer believes that such a correlation between real entities and their grammatical instrumentations should be the heart of language structure study, at least in its embryonic phases.

B. MANDELBROT: I do not assert that there is a common core to all languages from the grammatical viewpoint. There is likely to be one, but I am not concerned with it. I think that there are ways in which the structure of natural language or rather discourse differs from that of artificial sign systems, but I have concentrated on *non*-grammatical features of similarity between different discourses and of dissimilarity between natural and artificial discourse. My study of the species-genera relationship is perhaps closest to the problem raised by the speaker.

ON HOCKETT'S PAPER

R. B. LEES: During the previous session Yngve advanced the hypothesis that if sentences are produced by speakers in the manner of a certain simple finite-state device, and if these sentences are assumed to have the usual immediate-constituent phrase-structure (parenthesized phrases of words), then the length of left-branched constituent-tree paths would have to be limited to some small number of nodes lest the amount of temporary storage, or memory, exceed reasonable limits, and that the principle syntactic devices in the grammar serve primarity to ensure this asymmetric limitation on "depth". Professor Hockett announced his approval of Yngve's hypothesis. But today he has described a reasonable model of behavior of the *hearer* in which constituent structure is assigned to successive element of an incoming sentence in such a way that for an increasing number of nodes on a *right*-hand branch of the constituent tree the amount of temporary storage required by the hearer would increase. Thus if Hockett's model for the hearer is correct, and it seems quite plausible, then Yngve's hypothesis, which he recommended so positively, could *not* be, despite *its* superficial plausibility. There are also certain other arguments against Yngve's hypothesis, such as the following: (1) There are predominantly *left*-hand branching languages, such as Turkish or Japanese, in which the favorite constituent structure pattern is a *regressive* construction. (2) In ordinary speech, in both right- and left-branched languages, one never observes node-chains longer than some small number, whether to the left *or* to the right. (3) Those left-branched constructions which *are* widely used in English such as strings of attributive adverbials (as in: Any of those not too overwhelmingly grandiose structures ⋯), are not any more difficult to understand or produce than are the more frequently used right-branched constructions; and exactly the same is true in the other order for left-branching languages such as Turkish.

V. H. YNGVE: Lees' comment appears to be directed more to my paper than to that of Hockett. It is my understanding that Hockett's approval extended only to the fact that I had proposed an hypothesis that could be tested, and not necessarily to the predictions of the hypothesis itself, since he has not put the hypothesis to a careful test. It is not necessarily true that a model from the point of view of the hearer must be the reverse of a model from the point of view of the speaker, and that a past-to-future asymmetry in the one model must become a future-to-past asymmetry in the other. In point of fact, I am not aware that Hockett's model contradicts mine in any way. As to Dr. Lees' other comments:

1. Even if the "favorite constituent structure patterns" of Turkish and Japanese are regressive constructions, this need not necessarily contradict the depth hypothesis. I have a few preliminary indications that depth phenomena consistent with the hypothesis may be found in Arabic, Chinese, Hidatsa, Japanese, Shilha, Toba-Batak and Turkish. We will not be sure, however, until careful and thorough investigations have been carried out by experts in these languages.

2. Ordinary speech in English frequently involves node chains that extend many more than seven steps in the right-hand or progressive direction, but not in the regressive direction, as I pointed out in my paper.

3. The quoted English construction has a depth of four. The fact that it is easy to understand and to produce is in perfect harmony with the hypothesis.

A. G. OETTINGER: There is a strong kinship among the hypotheses advanced by Yngve, the theory and practice of predictive analysis as described in my paper and the proposals of Hockett. The behavior of the prediction pool (approximately a pushdown store) corroborates, at least qualitatively, the nesting and depth analysis of Yngve. Most of Hockett's proposals seem to be already embodied in the predictive analysis system, where the use of the so-called hindsight provides a systematic means of detecting the presence of more than one alternative structure for a sentence.

ON WELLS' PAPER

J. D. SABLE: I take the phrase "necessarily true propositions" to mean analytic statements. Can the "Informativeness" measure be extended to synthetic statements? If so, will it then be equivalent to the "Content" measure of Carnap and Bar-Hillel on synthetic statement and hence be a generalization of "Content"? What relation does "Informativeness" have with the notion of "quantitative credibility and confirmation" of Hemphill and others?

R. WELLS: The informativeness of necessarily true sentences may as well be kept entirely separate from that of contingent truths. For if their respective degrees are placed in the same one-dimensional series, we would still want to keep them separate by picking an arbitrary number such that all degrees of contingent informativeness are less, and all degrees of necessary informativeness more, than this number—or else vice versa. We would then also want to say that only contingent informativeness depends on serial degree or metrical amount of confirmation as explicated by Hempel, Carnap, etc.

INDEX